Three Centuries of
East Herefordshire Farms and Families

1700 until now

Jean Ila Currie

Jean Ila Currie

Published by Owlstone Press, for Owlstone Developments Ltd
33 Owlstone Road, Cambridge CB3 9JH
United Kingdom
www.eastherefordshirefarmsandfamilies.co.uk
history@farmsandfamiles.co.uk

First published 2018.
Printed in the United Kingdom by Severn, Gloucester.
Design/typography by Rob Norridge, norridgewalker.com
A catalogue record for this book is available from the British Library.

ISBN: 978-0-9564455-2-0

This book is dedicated to Jane and Honor Yeomans and to their brothers, Haywood and Walter, both tragically killed in the First World War.

Jane and Honor knew and loved the farms of Herefordshire – their history, beauty and the families who farmed and worked there. They surmounted the tragedy of the loss of their brothers and the men they would have married. They supported the young people around them, often transforming their lives.

The Hereford Cathedral First World War Poppies:
Weeping Window display April 2018.
Haywood and Walter Yeomans attended the Cathedral School shown in the background.

They shall not grow old, as we that are left grow old

Contents

Acknowledgements xii
Overview and introduction xv

PART I

1 **THE LONG 18th CENTURY: 1700–1792** 2

Landownership 2

The Church 2

The Dean and Chapter of Hereford Cathedral 2

The Bishop of Hereford 3

St Katherine's Hospital, Ledbury 3

Established landowning families 3

New landowners 3

The Foley family 4

The Cocks family 5

The Hankins and Hammond families 6

The Philipps family and their successors, the Stocks family 6

Other smaller new landowners 7

Farmers' rents, land tax and tithes 7

Problems of communication 8

Water transport 8

Road transport 9

Crops and livestock 10

Cider 10

Hops 13

Wheat 14

Cattle 16

Sheep 17

Horses 17

New crops, land managements and equipment 18

2 **THE FRENCH REVOLUTIONARY AND NAPOLEONIC WARS TO THE COMING OF THE RAILWAYS: 1793–1852** 21

Farming during the French Revolutionary and Napoleonic Wars 1793–1815 21

Rise in consumer prices 22

Some increase in agricultural wages 23

The importance of wheat 24
Apple and pear orchards 25
Growing demand for cattle 26
Ineffective efforts to introduce new crops 27
Farming after the Napoleonic Wars 27
Investment in hops 29
The specialised breeding of Hereford cattle 30
Sheep normally kept 32
Growing demand for farm horses 32
New agricultural societies 33
Investment in new equipment 34
Improvements in communication 35
The Great Irish famine 35
The abolition of the Corn Laws 36

3 **PROSPERITY, DEPRESSION, STABILISATION: 1853–1913** 39
Transformation with the start of the railway age 39
Prosperity and high farming: 1853–1874 40
The Foley estate: Lady Emily Foley 40
The Eastnor estate 42
The Hopton estate of Canon Frome 42
Pedigree Hereford cattle 42
Sheep and other livestock 43
Control of common livestock ailments 44
Boom in hop growing 44
Decline in cider production 50
Depression: 1875–1899 50
Stabilisation: 1900–1913 51
Export of pedigree Hereford cattle highly profitable 51
Reduced demand for hops 52
Profitability of fruit 52
Low farmworkers' wages 53
Farming on the eve of the First World War 54

4 **WAR, DEPRESSION, WAR AND IMMEDIATE POST-WAR: 1914–1949** 55
The First World War: 1914–1918 55
Britain dependent on imports of food 55

High prices and food shortages. 56
Shortage of agricultural labour. 57
Further rises in prices. 58
Changes in agricultural production 58
Major sale of tenant farms 1916–1919 58
Eastnor estate sale. 58
Stoke Edith estate sale 59
The interwar period: depression. 60
The 1920s 60
Depressed price for cereals. 60
Increased dependence on livestock and orchards 61
Difficult times for hop growers 62
The hard years of the 1930s: further depression 62
Fall in livestock prices for pedigree cattle 63
Establishment of the Hop Marketing Board in 1932 63
Establishment of the Milk Marketing Board in 1933. 64
Orchards 64
Farmers' recollections 64
Government subsidies and advisory facilities. 65
An entertaining incident with a prize-winning Hereford bull in 1939. 67
The Second World War: 1939–1945 67
A second Domesday Book: the National Farm Survey of 1941–1943 and the annual Agricultural Census of June 1941. 68
Lack of electricity. 70
Drainage, ditches, hedges and farm buildings. 71
Tractors versus horses 71
Farmworkers. 71
Further changes during the Second World War 71
The human cost 74
Immediate post-war: 1945–1949. 74

5 FARMING AS A SUPPORTED INDUSTRY: 1950–1999. 77
Guaranteed prices, capital subsidies, marketing boards: 1950–1972. 78
Traditional farming 78
Hereford cattle. 79
Dairy cattle 80
Hop production. 81

Orchards 81
Potatoes 81
New machinery and equipment 82
New types of farming. 83
Intensive poultry, pig and milk production. 83
Instant trees 83
The Common Agricultural Policy: 1973–1999 84
Arable farming prospers 85
Problems with hop production. 86
Soft fruit 87
Hereford pedigree cattle 87
Increased competition 87
Spread of BSE 88
Dairy farmers 88
Sale of land with farmhouses and buildings converted to residential use. 89
Exit from European Exchange Rate Mechanism 90

6 FARMING IN THE EARLY 21st CENTURY. 93
Changes in farms and farming 93
Further sales of farms. 93
Foot-and-mouth strikes again. 94
Changes in EU support 94
Some revival in farming. 94
Wheat and rapeseed 95
Potatoes 96
Cider, perry and single variety apple juices 97
Soft fruit production of national importance 98
Rising popularity of Herefordshire beef 99
Hops still grown. 101

PART II
7 SOME FARMING FAMILIES. 103
Farming families with associations of almost 100 years or more. 104
The Bowcotts of Felton Court. 104
The Bradstocks of Freetown, Ashperton, the Dents of Withington Court and Perton Court, Stoke Edith and the Leakes of Stone House Farm, Withington . . 104

The Cryer/Davies family of Bent Orchards, the Sayce family of Yare Farm and the Williams family of Overbury Farm, Woolhope . . . 105
The Hawkins of Thinghill Court, Withington and the Thompsons of Pixley Court . . 105
The Skittery family of Lillands, Little Marcle . . . 105
The Watkins family of Park Farm and Court Farm, Woolhope . . . 106
Farming families with associations of over 200 years . . . 106
The Davies dynasty . . . 106
The three Godsall dynasties . . . 107
Showle Court, Yarkhill and Park Farm, Woolhope . . . 107
Eastwood Farm, Tarrington . . . 107
Weston Corner Farm, Withington and Hynett Farm, Lugwardine . . . 107
The Powells of Laddin Farm, Little Marcle . . . 108
Farming families of the 18th and 19th centuries . . . 109
The Apperley dynasty of Stone House Farm, Withington . . . 109
The Bosleys of Baregains Farm and Lower House Farm, Little Marcle . . . 109
The Hoopers of Beans Butts and the Mailes of The Hyde, Woolhope . . . 110
The Pitt family of Walsopthorne Farm and Freetown, Ashperton . . . 110
The Vevers family of Yarkhill Court and Dormington Court . . . 111
A unique farming family . . . 111
The Yeomans family of Thinghill Court and Stone House Farm, Withington . . 111

8 GLIMPSES OF FARMING LIVES . . . 113
The 18th century . . . 113
Superstitions . . . 113
Education . . . 114
Outside contact . . . 114
The first half of the 19th century . . . 117
Social life . . . 117
Hunting with privately-owned hounds and steeplechasing . . . 119
The game laws . . . 119
The condition of farmworkers . . . 120
Lady Emily Foley: 1805–1900 . . . 122
Some farmworkers . . . 126
William Field: 1826–1890 . . . 126
The Farley farmworker dynasty of Little Marcle: late 18th–early 20th centuries . . 126
Women farmers . . . 127
The second half of the 19th century . . . 129

More reliable records . . . 129
The coming of the railways . . . 130
The role of religion. . . . 131
Early deaths. . . . 134
The South and North Herefordshire hunts . . . 135
Agricultural shows . . . 135
Growing political importance of farmers . . . 135
The 20th century . . . 136
Support for farmworkers and living standards . . . 136
Community activities. . . . 137
The early 21st century. . . . 139

PART III
JOURNEY 1: WITHINGTON AND FELTON PARISHES. . . . 142
Withington parish. . . . 143
Stone House Farm . . . 145
Thinghill Court . . . 151
Weston Corner Farm . . . 156
Withington Court. . . . 161
Felton parish . . . 167
Felton Court . . . 168
JOURNEY 2: WESTON BEGGARD AND YARKHILL PARISHES . . . 176
Weston Beggard parish. . . . 177
Moorend Farm . . . 178
Yarkhill parish . . . 185
Garford Farm . . . 187
Showle Court . . . 192
The Grove Farm . . . 198
Yarkhill Court. . . . 202
JOURNEY 3: LUGWARDINE, DORMINGTON, STOKE EDITH, TARRINGTON AND ASHPERTON PARISHES . . . 210
Lugwardine parish . . . 211
Hynett Farm . . . 215
Old Court . . . 219
Dormington parish. . . . 227
Claston Farm . . . 228
Dormington Court. . . . 237

Stoke Edith parish 243
Perton Court 245
Tarrington parish 251
Eastwood Farm 253
Hazel Court 257
Ashperton parish 261
Freetown 263
Walsopthorne Farm 269
JOURNEY 4: PIXLEY, AYLTON, LITTLE MARCLE AND WOOLHOPE PARISHES . . 280
Pixley parish 281
Pixley Court 282
Aylton parish 293
Aylton Court 295
Court Farm 300
Little Marcle parish 309
Baregains Farm 311
Brook Farm 314
Laddin Farm 319
Lillands 322
Little Marcle Court 328
Lower House Farm 332
Woolhope parish 337
Beans Butts 339
Bent Orchards 343
Canwood Farm 347
Court Farm 352
Overbury Farm 356
Park Farm 360
The Hyde 363
Yare Farm 370

EPILOGUE: THE WAY FORWARD 379

Selected bibliography 382
General index 388
Names index (selected) 394

Acknowledgements

This book covering so many centuries would not have been produced without the collaboration of many people. I am most grateful to Elizabeth Semper O'Keefe, formerly Collections and Archive Manager at the Herefordshire Archive and Records Centre, Rhys Griffith, Senior Archivist and all the staff at the Herefordshire Archive and Records Centre for their meticulous help and support over the years, without which this book could not have been written. I would similarly like to express my deep gratitude for the help I have received from Rosemary Firman, Librarian, Bethany Hamblen, Archivist, James North, Library and Archives Assistant and staff at the Hereford Cathedral Library. I also deeply appreciate the help of the staff at the Hereford Museum Resource and Learning Centre, particularly Catherine Willson, Collections Officer: Fine and Decorative Art. The staff at the Rare Books section of Cambridge University Library, The National Archives and Gloucestershire Archives have invariably been most helpful.

I am specially grateful to the support over years given to me by David Prothero, Secretary of the Hereford Cattle Society for so many years. My special thanks goes out to David Deakin who provided me with photos and important archive material as well as permitting me to use his office to consult copies of the *Hereford Herd Book.*

I would like to thank the two young illustrators for their dedicated work. Heather Colbert (www.heather-colbert.com) produced no fewer than 17 different maps. Included in the 13 parish maps are charming little illustrations of the Hereford bull and Hereford farmhouses. Amanda Summers (amandasummersillustration.co.uk) was meticulous in devising and producing the two cartoons "Road rage 18th-century style" and "I should have had the First Prize!". I would like to thank Nick Newton Design for producing four graphs and to Bill Clark, Technical Director of NIAB, for permitting me to use the graph showing NIAB's wheat calculations.

I would like to express my heartfelt thanks to all those who generously gave up time to talk about their individual farms and often to check what I had written. They included amongst others Robert Barnes, Keith Bayliss, Reginald Bayliss, Anne Blandford, Tania Blonder and her mother, Jane Pasquill, Richard and Margaret Bradstock, Jemima Bristow, Penelope Cunningham, Tom and Harvey Clay, Stephen Dale, Edward Davies, Susan Davies, Fiona Day, Elizabeth and John Dent, Joy Edwards, Richard and Clare Edwards, Geoffrey Gibbs, James Hawkins, Sheila Hawkins, Jenny Jackson, Ian Jones, Rachel Leake, Michael and Gilla Leigh, Lillian Moss, Penny Oliver, James and Helen Parker, Elaine Pudge, Desmond and Marion Samuel, Barbara Sayce, Cheryl Shearer, James and Jane Skittery, Michael and Lesley Skittery, Irene Skelton, Norman and Annie Stanier, Edward Thompson, Andrew Williams, Gwyneth Williams, James and Diana Williams, Norman Williams, Valerie and Vivien Williams, John and Mary Windham.

I deeply appreciate the kindness of the many people who allowed me to use their photos, or to take photos of documents in their possession. They are acknowledged in the footnote attached to each of the photos provided. Amongst others Reginald Bayliss provided a photo of a YFC meeting and gave me permission to photograph the Moorend farm book, Anne Blandford of Underhill Farm provided photos of the Laddin, Margaret Bradstock the photo of Freetown farmhouse, Tony Bradstock the photo of Free Town Decree and Tania Blonder the photos of Weston Corner Farm. Penelope Cunningham (née Davies), who grew up at Aylton Court, was a fount of information on family history, as well as providing some remarkable historical photos. Susan Davies and her sister-in-law, Lillian Moss, provided the historic pictures of Bent Orchards. Fiona Day provided the photo of Yarkhill Court alpacas. John Dent, whose family have played a major role in the development of Hereford cattle, provided pictures of the famous prize-winning Hereford bulls belonging to his grandfather as well as fascinating documents on the landownership of Withington Court in the 19th century. Joy Edwards gave permission for me to photograph the Little Yarkhill Farm prize certificate. Melissa Hawker provided a photo of Little Marcle Court, Rachel Leake photos of Stone House Farm pedigree Hereford cattle and a Ryeland lamb, and David Lovelace a photo of Walsopthorne hop kiln. Barbara Sayce provided some of the farm accounts of the Yare Farm in the early post-war period. Edward Thompson gave permission for me to photograph the picture of Pixley Court and the certificate marking his father's appointment as a Chevalier of the Order of the Hop as well as the cartoon lamenting the demise of the Hop Marketing Board. Alison Wilcox provided a photo of Court Farm, Woolhope, Gwyneth Williams provided a photo of Hazel Court Friesian cows, Norman Williams provided early post-war receipts for Overbury Farm and John and Mary Windham photos of the sales particulars of The Hyde.

The work could not have been completed in its present form without access to important documents, often unpublished. I am grateful to Richard Bradstock for providing me with the unpublished reminiscences of his father, Tom Bradstock, describing life at Freetown in the 1920s and 1930s, as well as a scrapbook of the same period. I would like to thank Edward Davies for welcoming me over the years to the beautiful Tudor farmhouse of Walsopthorne, as well as providing me with the Walsopthorne farm accounts of the early 1920s. Similarly I would like to express my very special thanks to Ian and Rebecca Jones for providing me with the detailed and meticulous study they commissioned as part of the application for DEFRA Higher Level Stewardship funding for Aylton Tithe barn from PJM Associates Ltd. of Much Marcle entitled *Aylton Court Farm Landscape and Historical Analysis.* I would also like to thank David Lovelace for transcribing the 1668 letters to Hugh Philipps from Roger Farley. My old friends Tom and Ann Nellist, both coming from local farming families, have answered numerable queries on many topics over the years. Ann has provided important historic photos and documents from the farms associated with her parents, Jack and Hilda Price, as well as providing information on family members. Tom has been the knowledgeable source on farming issues, provided introductions to individual farmers and lent me documents and books. I am especially indebted to him for access to the rare biography of the farmworker Union leader Sidney Box and for showing me the *Hereford Journal* document *The farmers and millers guide at the markets etc. 1853* which gave, amongst other useful information, an insight into treatment of livestock ailments at this time. In addition to informative conversations, David Powell kindly provided me with the comprehensive family history researched by Theodora Reeves in 1974 and entitled *The Powell, Stedman, Sparkman Family History.*

In our digital age a book no longer involves just research and writing but an ability to communicate with computers and their software, and to surmount the many hazards they conjure up. I am deeply grateful to Jonathan Simpson (jsimpson@jpspc-repair.co.uk) for his outstanding skill, calmness and support without which this book would never have seen the light of day.

Lastly I would like to thank Ruth Atkinson, my editor, for her dedication, meticulous editing, for her many insightful suggestions and for drawing my attention to important internet sources. I am deeply grateful for her unswerving encouragement and support throughout this time. She is now enthusiastic about East Herefordshire, its beauty and history.

Fig. 1 Study: Towards the Malverns by Brian Hatton, 1910, © Hereford Museum Service

A tragic casualty of the First World War, Brian Hatton (1887–1916) was an extraordinarily talented Hereford artist. Many of the paintings in his short life were of Hereford country and farming scenes, some of which were painted when he was only a young boy. Two Horses Ploughing reproduced in Chapter 3 was submitted with other paintings and drawings to the Royal Drawing Society in 1899 at the age of 11, when he won the Gold Star as the best exhibitor. The collection of his works is one of the treasures of Hereford Museum & Art Gallery. I am extremely grateful to them for permitting me to use three of Brian Hatton's lovely pictures in this book.

OVERVIEW AND INTRODUCTION

Herefordshire with its exceptionally beautiful and fertile countryside escaped the industrial revolution. The farms were not swept away by factories and factory workers. Access was not easy. A common theme throughout the three centuries under consideration was the poor quality of the roads and the lack of other communications – even the railways came late.

One happy result was that the farms, the fields around and the families that farmed the land had a remarkable continuity, lacking elsewhere. The farmhouses themselves often date back to the 17th century and are on sites that are even older. In the last quarter of the 20th century the farmworkers left, replaced by machinery, with the cottages transformed into residences for prosperous professionals normally unassociated with agriculture. Increasingly in the 21st century, the lovely farmsteads themselves, often with hop kilns and extensive farm buildings, are now being sold off. However many of the farms and their farming families still remain and intend to remain. They are often the descendants of those who farmed this land for many years and sometimes for centuries. The purpose of this book is to highlight the history of these farms and families, so that they can be treasured for what they are, a remarkable British heritage, and continue, though in modern guise, in the years to come.

The book is divided into three parts. Part I with its six chapters describes the very varied history of farming in East Herefordshire over more than three centuries. Part II with two chapters describes some of the farming dynasties and provides glimpses of their lives. Parts I and II both draw on Part III, which gives the individual history over this period of 36 East Herefordshire farms situated in 13 different parishes.

There are some features associated with individual parishes. Consequently the farms in Part III are grouped by parish with a sketch map of the approximate location of each farm. Parishes close to each other can also share characteristics. The parishes are therefore divided by 'journeys' rather than alphabetically. Journey 1 covers the farms in Withington and Felton parishes; Journey 2 Weston Beggard and Yarkhill parishes; Journey 3 Lugwardine, Dormington, Stoke Edith, Tarrington and Ashperton parishes; Journey 4 Pixley, Aylton, Little Marcle and Woolhope parishes. A map showing the principal roads and the approximate location of the parishes is attached to each journey.

THE LONG 18TH CENTURY: 1700–1792

Fig. 1.1 The orchards of Herefordshire: "... on the other side is Herefordshire which appears like a Country of Gardens and Orchards the whole Country being very full of fruit trees etc. it looks like nothing else-the apple and pear trees etc. are so thick even in their Corn fields and hedgerows." [1]

Celia Fiennes writing in the late 17th century was not alone in her view of the county as a "Country of Gardens and Orchards". Herefordshire was renowned in the 18th century, as indeed it is now, for its beauty. It was also well known for its cider, hops and wheat. In his poem Cyder published in 1708 the poet John Philips extols all three.

Although there was often continuity throughout the 18th century in the farming families as well as in the methods of production and in the crops, there were however some considerable changes in landowners at this time. Celia Fiennes herself was visiting a cousin, a former Commonwealth officer, who had recently bought New House Farm in Stretton Grandisson.

Landownership

The Church

Although the dissolution of the monasteries in the 16th century had resulted in land being purchased by lay families, the Church remained a substantial landowner with no fewer than three different entities of the established church owning the freehold of land in East Herefordshire throughout the 18th century.

The Dean and Chapter of Hereford Cathedral

The Dean and Chapter of Hereford Cathedral owned the largest acreage. A most important possession of the Dean and Chapter in the 18th century and one from which they received a considerable return was the manor of Woolhope which had been bequeathed to the Cathedral by Lady Godiva and her sister Wulviva before the Norman Conquest. Throughout the 18th century the farms were leased to tenants on copyhold terms. Under this arrangement the land was rented out for a modest annual payment for a number of years. This was often a period of 21 years, although it could be for up to three nominated 'lives' (the farmer, his wife and a descendant). In addition a periodic capital sum or 'fine' was imposed. This could be at the end of the lease or when a son or other member of the family was registered as the new copyhold tenant. In Woolhope it seems to have been the usual practice to impose this capital sum every seven or eight years and to leave the annual payments unchanged during the normal lease period. Generations of the same family held their farms in Woolhope under this system. Bean Butts was farmed by the Hooper family from about 1731, The Hyde by the Mailes from about 1738, and Bent Orchards by the Winniatts from about 1752. The Gregory family of Hill House, Woolhope (later known as Wessington Court), intent on building a landed estate from their copyhold possessions, secured the copyhold for a number of farms from the late 17th century onwards, including Court Farm, Woolhope. The Foley family similarly secured and renewed their copyhold on some Woolhope farms close to Stoke Edith and Tarrington parishes, including Canwood Farm and Park Farm. The Dean and Chapter also owned the medieval manor of Overbury which had been absorbed into Woolhope parish. The copyhold tenant of Overbury varied throughout the 18th century, but the farm seems to have been farmed normally by subtenants. The Yare Farm, Woolhope was unusual in being a freehold property certainly from the late 18th century.

The Dean and five specified Prebendaries of Hereford Cathedral each owned the freehold of one of six out of the eight manors in Withington parish at the beginning of the 18th century, as indeed they had done for centuries before. Stone House Farm,

Withington was originally part of Withington Parva manor, but there are no extant records of annual payments nor periodic fees and the 18th-century Apperleys who lived and farmed there were effectively treated by Duncumb in his *General View of the Agriculture of the County of Hereford* in 1805 as if they were the freehold owners. Withington Court comprised the larger part of the manor of Church Withington and was similarly in the hands of the long-established Philips family[2] until 1763 and then their relatives the Broomes. From the 1780s the copyhold was held by Mr Griffiths of New Court, Lugwardine. Throughout this long period there are few extant records of annual payments or periodic fees. The modest land attached to Weston Corner Farm seems to have been freehold by the latter 18th century, possibly spun off from the manor of Church Withington at some earlier period.

The Bishop of Hereford

In addition to tithe land in each of the parishes, the land tax records show that the Bishop of Hereford owned Baregains Farm and part of Brook Farm in Little Marcle in the latter 18th and early 19th centuries. These were part of a major exchange of land with the Cocks family in 1785.

St Katherine's Hospital, Ledbury

St Katherine's Hospital, Ledbury, founded in 1232 and not dissolved at the time of the Reformation, continued to own land in Little Marcle, Yarkhill and Weston Beggard parishes throughout the 18th century, including The Grove Farm, Yarkhill.

Established landowning families

A few long-established landowning families, such as the Hoptons of the Canon Frome estate, an estate which included land in the parishes of Ashperton, Stretton Grandison and Castle Frome, had survived the 17th century upheavals virtually unscathed. The Ravenhills, a Woolhope family traceable back to medieval times, continued to own Hazel Court on the borders of Tarrington and Woolhope until towards the end of the 18th century, albeit with a remarkably shrunken acreage, and Old Court, Lugwardine was owned by the branch of the old-established Walwyn family who lived at Longworth, Lugwardine until the beginning of the 19th century.

New landowners

However although some of the landowning families from earlier times remained, many of the East Herefordshire gentry had supported the royalist cause in the Civil Wars of

1642–1651. After the restoration of the monarchy in 1660, there was never enough money to compensate those who had suffered in the wars and their aftermath as a result of fines paid to keep or regain possession of their estates. Throughout Britain the commercial classes were gaining in wealth, opportunities for investment were limited and land was an essential prerequisite for political power.

Two families who came to prominence in the 18th century were the Foleys of Stoke Edith parish and the Cocks family of Eastnor parish some four miles east of Ledbury. Charles Cocks was ennobled in 1784 as Baron Somers and his son, John Somers Cocks, was later made Earl Somers in 1821.

The Foley family

The Lingen family, the largest landowners in the East Herefordshire parishes of Stoke Edith and Tarrington in the 17th century, had been especially affected by the Civil Wars as Sir Henry Lingen had been one of the leading Cavaliers. In the Commonwealth period he had been crippled by fines amounting to the astonishing amount of £6,342 and died in 1662 shortly after the restoration of Charles II. The estate had reverted back to Henry's near bankrupt widowed mother following the death of both Henry's

Fig. 1.2 The South and East sides of Stoke Edith House in 1872[3]: Paul Foley began to rebuild the house in 1695 and it was substantially complete by 1698

sons without issue and in 1670 the estate had been purchased by Thomas Foley, the son of a wealthy nonconformist ironmaster on behalf of his second son, Paul Foley, later Speaker of the House of Commons 1695–1698. Farms which formed part of this initial Foley estate included Freetown (from 1886 part of Ashperton parish) and Showle Court (from 1886 part of Yarkhill parish). Both farms were curiously included in the parish of Stoke Edith at this time and they contain the remnants of medieval moats indicating their earlier importance. Perton Court in Stoke Edith parish, Claston Farm in Dormington parish and land in Weston Beggard parish, including the land later attached to Moorend Farm, were also probably part of the initial estate.

Ambitious and wealthy, Paul Foley rebuilt himself a fine new house and Celia Fiennes in her visits to Herefordshire described the progress of the construction of Stoke Edith House over the last few years of the 17th century.

The Foleys expanded their estate throughout the 18th century. The important farms of Garford Farm and Yarkhill Court in Yarkhill parish, known to have still been owned by the Royalist and Catholic Bodenham family of Rotherwas in the early 18th century, were recorded as part of the Foley estate in the land tax records of the latter 18th century. The Lordship of Dormington parish, which included Dormington Court, seems to have been purchased by the Foley estate from the bankrupt Wallwyn Shepheard in 1795. It is also probable that the Foley landholdings were increased following the Enclosure Act of 1798 for Yarkhill, Dormington, and Weston Beggard parishes.

The Cocks family

Like the Foley family, the Cocks family, resident in Eastnor parish, were expanding their landholdings at this time. As part of this expansion Charles Cocks purchased the Little Marcle estate from Velters Cornewall of Moccas Court in 1750. The Bodenham family of Rotherwas had owned the Little Marcle estate, including the Little Marcle parish farms of Brook Farm, Laddin Farm and Lillands as well as Little Marcle Court, but had probably been involved in heavy expenses to retain their land following the Civil War. A Parliamentary Commission in 1651 speaks of an Act for the sale, forfeited for treason, of several lands and estates belonging to the family. The estate had then been sold in 1670 to Thomas Hanbury. Velters Cornewall's wife, Catherine, née Hanbury, Thomas Hanbury's granddaughter, had become a coheir with her three sisters on the death of her father, William Hanbury in 1737.

Part of the Cocks land in Little Marcle parish formed part of the major exchange of land with the Bishop of Hereford later in the 18th century mentioned above, a transaction also described in Part III, Little Marcle, which does not appear to have constituted a good bargain for the bishopric. 147 acres were received by the Bishop, partly poorish land, and just over 221 acres were received by the Cocks family.[4] Castleditch, one of the two manors in Eastnor parish, had belonged to the Bishops of Hereford since at least early medieval times. The Bishop of Hereford agreed to relinquish ownership of this entire manor in exchange for some land in Little Marcle. The land tax records for Little Marcle in the late 18th century show the Bishop as owning Baregains Farm with 137 acres but only part of Brook Farm as in 1789 William Drew, the tenant of Brook Farm, was paying £6 5s for land belonging to the Bishop of Hereford but was also paying £13 10s to Lord Somers who must therefore have been the owner of much the larger part of the land. The Bishop seems to have held only a copyhold title for the smaller part of Brook Farm as the freehold ownership was transferred by Act of Parliament to the Eastnor estate in 1835.

The Hankins and Hammond families

It was not only the Foley and Cocks families with their large landholdings who were determined to rise further in the world. Other farms at this time came into the ownership of those aspiring to rise, albeit only to the status of minor gentry.

Court Farm and Aylton Court, both in Aylton parish, occupied land which had belonged to the medieval manor of Aylton. This land had been purchased in the 16th century by the Warncombe family, sometime mayors of Hereford, and then through marriage bequeathed to the important Harley family of Brampton Bryan. The Hankins were at first copyhold tenants of the Harleys but rose by the 18th century to own the freehold of Court Farm and its land of over 100 acres, which included the remains of the medieval manor house and farm buildings. The Hankins were to farm there until the late 18th century and their descendants (by then absentee landowners) continued to own the farm until the 20th century. The remaining larger portion of the previous medieval manor of Aylton came into the possession of the Hammond family. They built a late Georgian gentry house, confusingly called Aylton Court, and were farming around 200 acres during the last quarter of the 18th century.

The Philipps family and their successors, the Stocks family

The most remarkable example of a farm that had been purchased to improve the status of the owner is Walsopthorne Farm, Ashperton. In 1066 Walsopthorne was a manor in its own right. The remains of a moat hark back to the early medieval occupants, the Criketots. The unfortunate Roger Farley sold the Elizabethan manor house with 234 acres to Hugh Philipps in 1669 for £1,219 3s, which was the minimum price required by Roger Farley's creditors to permit his release from a debtor's prison. Hugh Philipps' family had quite probably acquired money from illegal development north of Lincoln's Inn Fields. The Philipps family and their successors, the Stocks family of Putley Court[5], owned Walsopthorne throughout the 18th century until 1823 when it passed to the Hopton estate of Canon Frome following an exchange of properties.

Other smaller new landowners

Other smaller new landowners came into possession of farms in the 18th century. Both Thinghill Court in Withington and the small parish of Felton, including Felton Court, had originally belonged to St Guthlac's Priory before coming into the hands of lay families following its dissolution in 1539. In 1700 Thinghill Court was purchased by General Cornewall and then left to a female relative who married William Moore. Parish records show that Thinghill Court was owned by William Moore and then by his son until early 1799. Initially the Moores farmed the land, but in the last quarter of the 18th century Thinghill Court became a tenanted farm. In the 1780s Felton Court and Green Farm, Felton were purchased by Mr Griffiths of New Court, Lugwardine. Around the same time Mr Griffiths became the copyhold owner of Withington Court as well as another farm in Withington, Eau Withington Court. After his death the estate was left to John Lilly, also of New Court, Lugwardine. The freehold title of the Withington farms remained with the Dean and Chapter of Hereford Cathedral.

Farmers' rents, land tax and tithes

The tenant farmers of the East Herefordshire's 18th-century landowners had to find quite substantial cash outgoings each year.

Apart from farmworkers' wages, the major cost was rent, which varied according to the classification of the land. An idea of early 18th-century tenants' costs can be obtained from the details given by Roger Farley in 1669 of the payments due from the tenant of Walsopthorne Farm, Ashperton two years previously.

The whole estate together both mine and the other lands containing		
134 acres of arable which but at 5 shilling an acre		*£33 10s*
66½ acres of pasture which but at 10 shilling per acre		*£33 5s*
33½ acres of meadow which but at 15s an acre		*£24 7s*
The coppice and choise (sic)-rents which but at		*£10 0s*
Sydar & other commodities which comunibus anis but at		*£20 0s*
besides houses, buildings, gardens, etc.	*Sum*	*£121 2s* [6]

The figures show that pastureland was worth twice as much as arable, and that meadowland, hopefully nourished by winter floods, was even more highly valued as it was critical for the production of hay for animals. Most equipment and buildings made use of timber so coppices were important. However, times had not been good and the payment received had actually been less. Farley states that the tenant "gave £90 for all except the coppice worth £10 per annum for diverse yeares together till these late cheape years come which was the only cause Mr Dowdeswell abated him £10 a yeare since".

Information on 18th century rents is meagre. Writing in 1728 Mr Gregory of Hill Court, Woolhope suggested an appropriate rent for Court Farm, Woolhope with its 100 acres would be £40 per year, so payments for different types of land would probably not have been much more than at Walsopthorne. During the last quarter of the 18th century however the periodic 'fines' for the Woolhope farms, though not the annual payments, start to rise sharply. This suggests that rents were rising even before the start of the Napoleonic Wars, reflecting perhaps the nationwide increase in population. Tithes, officially one tenth of the value of annual output, were second in importance only to the rent.

Land tax was a further expense and remained in the order of £5 for a 100-acre farm throughout the second half of the 18th century. Farmers also contributed to the parish expenditure on the poor.

Problems of communication

Although Celia Fiennes encapsulated the fertility of Herefordshire as well as its great beauty in her letters, her writing also emphasised the county's appalling communications of which as a traveller she could not but be acutely aware. This constrained the potential market for crops and reduced the prices received by the farmer.

Celia was travelling in August, surely the easiest time of the year, but she had this to say of the seven miles from the Worcester border to Stretton Grandisson:

> *This is the worst way I ever went in Worcester or Herifordshire its alwayes a deep sand and soe in the winter and with muck is bad way, but this being in August it was strange and being so stony made it more difficult to travel.*[7]

Water transport

As newly established landowners of an important estate, with the added sophistication provided through their national and commercial, rather than rural, background, the

Foley family were at the forefront of efforts to improve communications. Water was usually the cheapest form of transport. Paul Foley had initiated the Act of Parliament of 1695–1696 for 'making navigable the Rivers of Wye and Lugg in the County of Hereford', including prohibiting weirs. The Wye, the only significant river in the county, connecting Hereford with Gloucester and the Severn estuary, and with it access to vitally important coastal as well as export trade does not flow through East Herefordshire, but the Wye's tributary, the River Lugg, the River Wye's tributary, runs through the East Hereford parishes of Lugwardine and Withington and the little River Frome runs through Yarkhill and Dormington parishes before joining the River Lugg. However, despite Paul Foley's efforts, not all the weirs were removed from the Wye or the Lugg and the fast-flowing River Wye did not always lend itself to transport in winter, whilst in summer months the flow could be too low.

Road transport

In an effort to improve the condition of the roads which had deteriorated even further as a result of the widespread introduction of wheeled traffic in the late 17th century, it is not surprising that the local gentry appear as subscribers to the toll roads nor that these came to Herefordshire quite early. The toll road between Ledbury and Hereford was established by an Act of Parliament of 1720. The Gloucester–Leominster road which goes through Little Marcle, Pixley, Aylton and Ashperton parishes was also an early toll road and followed for much of its way the old Roman Road. However, not everyone approved of these roads and for small farmers, it made driving their animals and produce to Ledbury, Hereford or Bromyard markets very expensive. Dislike of the tolls became such that it ended in riots in Ledbury in 1734 and 1735 which actually culminated in the execution of one of the ringleaders, shamefully made lawful by an Act of Parliament passed shortly after the riots had taken place.

Regrettably the Herefordshire roads continued, more often than not, to be badly maintained throughout the 18th century despite the best efforts of the local gentry. William Marshall, a well-informed contemporary commentator, had this to say in his account of Herefordshire farming published in 1789: "The roads of Herefordshire may well be proverbial, in England: they are such as one might expect to meet with, in the marshes of Holland, or the mountains of Switzerland." Of the principal thoroughfare from Mayhill to Ross which he expected to be the best of the roads he found "in many places it is impossible for two carriages to pass each other; while in some, the bared rock, worn into inequalities, by heavy rains, and by being travelled upon century after century, is the present turnpike road!"[8]

Fig. 1.3 Road rage 18th-century style: cartoon by Amanda Summers

Crops and livestock

Despite the difficulties of communication, Herefordshire was celebrated from the late 17th century onwards for its cider, hops, wheat, cattle and sheep, and horses were important, too. Oak and woodland products were also exceptionally valuable but were retained as the domain principally of landowners rather than that of the tenant farmers.

Cider

Daniel Defoe's *A Tour Through the Whole Island of Great Britain* published in three volumes between 1724 and 1727 speaks of the importance of cider in Herefordshire:

> *And as for cyder, here it was that several times for 20 miles together, we could get no beer or a ale in their public houses, only cyder; and that so very good, so fine and so*

cheap, that we never found fault with the exchange; great quantities of this cyder are sent to London, even by land carriage, though so very remote, which is an evidence for the goodness of it, beyond contradiction.[9]

Virtually all 18th-century farms had their orchards of cider and perry trees. Right until well into the 20th century farmworkers normally received cider as well as their pay and farms would produce their own cider for this purpose. Cider was clearly also important as a cash crop in East Herefordshire from at least the second half of the 17th century. The unfortunate Roger Farley, the owner at that time of Walsopthorne Farm, writing from his debtor's prison, tells of the income received by the tenant:

Consider I pray you Sir that the tenant by everyone's relation hath made already this yeare at least £50 in sydar and fruit at very low rates 12 or 13 or 15 shillings at most from the mill a hogload besides what he keepes for himself. [10]

At the beginning of the 18th century John Philips in his poem *Cyder* wrote of the wide mix of varieties needed:

From different Mixtures, Woodcock, Pippin, Moyle
Rough Elliot, sweet Permain, the blended Streams.[11]

At Baregains Farm in 1767 of 129 acres, 37 acres, 30% of the total, were orchards. According to a marriage settlement map of 1766 Court Farm in Aylton parish had 22 acres, 19% of the total 115 acres, under orchards. When Aylton Court with its 190 acres was advertised to let in January 1783, the orcharding was described as being "in high perfection, and capable of producing a high quality of cider of the best sorts of fruit."

Despite the high transport costs Herefordshire cider did indeed have a national market. *The Ipswich Journal* of 22 June 1765 for instance advertised "Fine old Herefordshire Cyder now fit for bottling at Three Guineas per Hogshead … It is of Vintage 1762 very strong and of an exceedingly good flavour". There has always been a rumour in Herefordshire that the Scottish soldiers had acquired a special and longstanding liking for Herefordshire cider in the Civil Wars. Perhaps this had a basis of truth. The Aberdeen Journal of 2 September 1767 advertised "A Parcel of the best HEREFORDSHIRE CYDER to be sold on the most reasonable Terms, by the Puncheon, Hogshead, Half hogshead or in Bottles".

William Marshall devoted no fewer than 159 pages[12] of Volume II of *The Rural Economy of Gloucestershire; Including its Dairy: Together with the Dairy Management of North Wiltshire; and the Management of Orchards and Fruit Liquor, in Herefordshire* to Herefordshire cider production. Marshall thoroughly disapproved of the fact that much of the cider from orchards, the rough cider, was made on the farm and consumed by the farmer and farmworkers: "The primary object of farmers, in general, has been that of supplying their own immoderate consumption." Fruit trees were sometimes grown from seed and then used as grafting stock. On occasion the harvest could actually be from trees grown from seed: "Consequently, each tree is a separate variety: bearing the name, perhaps, of its planter, or of the field it grows in." Marshall discusses the relative merits of planting orchards on arable or on grass. He generally comes down in favour of young orchards being under arable but he cautions on the need to protect "against sheep; which in winter, especially while snow is upon the ground, will peel off the bark of the young trees; and, in a few hours, destroy the whole plantation." He criticises poor pruning: "A redundancy of wood is the cause of numerous evils." and describes different methods of cultivation. Trees were sometimes planted very close, some 40 trees per acre, which prevented the trees coming into their full potential, but

Fig. 1.4 Aylhill cider mill still in place

by the time Marshall was writing, it had become more common to plant 10 trees per acre which could of course further facilitate the dual use of land as arable or grazing.

Marshall describes the high cost of a cider mill and records that the millstone was normally obtained from the Forest of Dean. A small mill could cost £10–£12 and a more substantial mill £20–£25. The cost was normally borne by the landlord.

According to Marshall the cider crop intended for the national market was purchased mainly by local dealers, principally based in Upton-Upon-Severn and Ledbury, but also in Hereford and Bromyard. The dealers preferred to purchase from the farm cider press and to undertake the fermentation and bottling themselves as the national market preferred a sweeter cider to the local rough cider. The price could vary greatly between years depending on the quality of the rough cider. The dealers' price of liquor from the press was five guineas a hogshead in 1786 and a mere 16 shillings in 1787. The harvest was also very variable and generally the trees produced a good crop only once every three years. At a very maximum it was conceivable for an orchard planted with 40 trees per acre to produce 20 hogsheads (1,260 gallons) per acre.

Hops

Daniel Defoe also remarked on the Herefordshire hops in 1724, making it clear that in the early 18th century hops were an important, if risky crop:

As for hops, they plant abundance indeed all over this county, and they are very good.

Hops were subject to an excise duty from 1707. In 1823, the earliest date providing a breakdown of the national figures by district level, Hereford district with 10,631 acres was second in importance only to Rochester with its 10,668 acres. Although some caution is required here as the Hereford figures might well have been in the local traditional acres which were smaller than the national ones, there is no doubt that Herefordshire was an important hop producer and that at least some East Herefordshire farms in Part III were clearly growing hops in the 18th century, some as early as the first half of the century. Peter Davies believed that the round hop kiln at Claston Farm, Dormington dated back to 1740–1750.[13] Laddin Farm has a very early hop kiln and Baregains Farm, both in Little Marcle, had an acre given over to hops in 1767 and a further acre described as a hop field. Court Farm, Aylton is specified as having one acre of hops in a 1766 marriage settlement. When Aylton Court was advertised to let in 1783 the advertisement specifically stated that hops were grown. In Ashperton, Freetown also has an old hop kiln, as has Walsopthorne.

Fig. 1.5 Walsopthorne hop kiln[14]

Hops could be very profitable and weighed little compared with the price, a major consideration with such heavy transport costs. However the crop is expensive to produce in terms of equipment needed (the hop poles, the fuel for drying, fertiliser) as well as the high labour cost and the excise duty which also had to be paid. Hops are very susceptible to weather conditions and the crop could totally fail, resulting in heavy financial loss. No figures are available for East Herefordshire, but a detailed analysis of Tatlingbury Farm in Kent in 1746–1756 showed a significant overall profitability with a substantial loss made in five of the 10 years recorded.[15] It is notable that Baregains Farm and Court Farm, Aylton allocated only a small acreage to hops in the 18th century, so reducing the risk.

Wheat

Despite the importance of cider and hops it was wheat grown under rotation that formed the most important cash crop in the 18th century, especially on the rich heavy soils in the Lugg and the Frome valleys. As William Marshall stated in 1789: "The present productions of Herefordshire are uncommonly various: in a general view, however, it falls under the idea of a corn country." Marshall, the confident farmer, in his inimitable fashion, pointed to the financial cost born by the farmers in consequence of the appalling roads: "At present, six or seven horses are necessary to drag a load of corn to market."[16]

An inventory prepared following the death of Walter Godsall of Showle Court (see Fig. 1.6) in 1705 and an inventory following the death of John Drew of Brook Farm (see Fig. 1.7) in 1741 provide an insight into the farming in the first half of the 18th century. The wheat on the farm at Showle Court was listed as being worth the extraordinarily high sum of £90 and beans, peas, etc. worth an additional £39 10s. John Drew's inventory included wheat, barley and other grains of all sorts worth £78 10s.

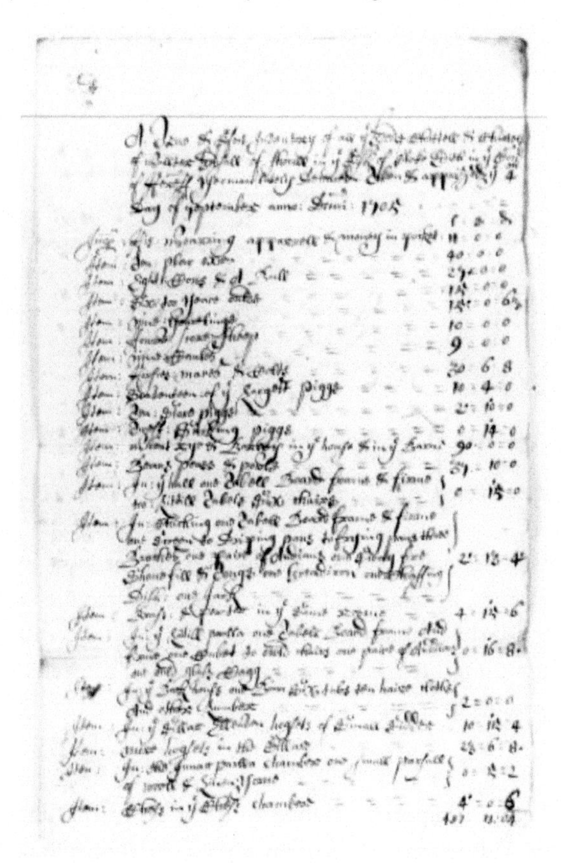

Fig. 1.6 Inventory following the death of Walter Godsall of Showle Court in 1705

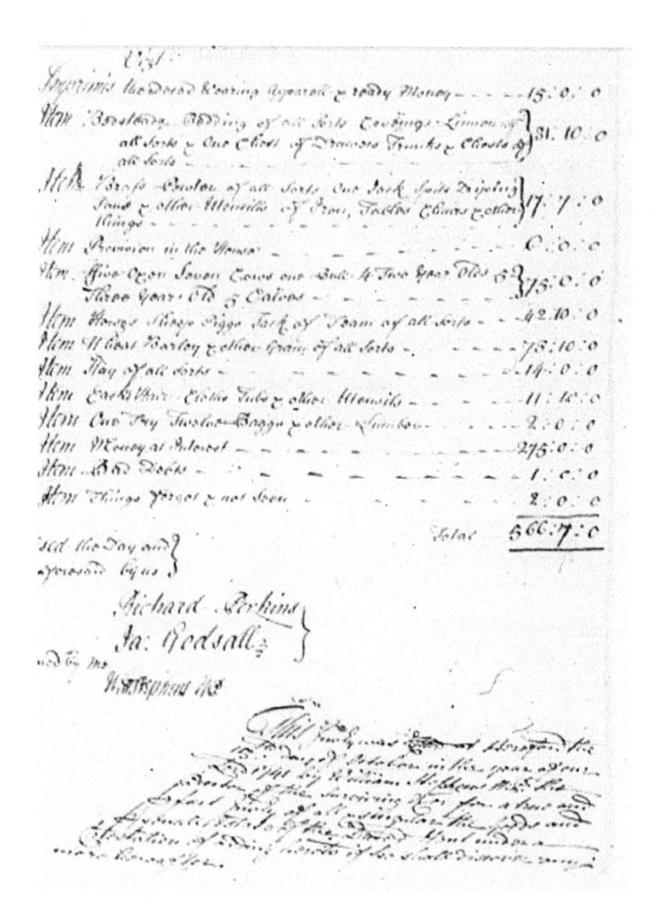
Imprimis the Deceased Wearing Apparel & ready Money ... 15:0:0
Item Bedsteads Bedding of all sorts Coverings Linnen of all sorts & One Chest of Drawers Trunks & Chests of all sorts ... 31:10:0
Item Brass Pewter of all sorts One Jack Spits Dripping Pans & other Utensils of Iron, Tables Chairs & other things ... 17:7:0
Item Provision in the House ... 6:0:0
Item Five Oxen Seven Cows one Bull 4 Two Year Olds & Three Year Olds 5 Calves ... 75:0:0
Item Horses Sheep Pigs [illegible] of Team of all sorts ... 42:10:0
Item Wheat Barley & other Grain of all sorts ... 75:10:0
Item Hay of all sorts ... 14:0:0
Item Earthenware Cider Tubs & other Utensils ... 11:10:0
Item [illegible] Timber [illegible] & other Lumber ... 2:0:0
Item Money at Interest ... 275:0:0
Item Bad Debts ... 1:0:0
Item Things forgot & not seen ... 2:0:0
Total 566:7:0

Richard Perkins
Ja: Godsall

[illegible]

Fig. 1.7 Inventory following the death of John Drew of Brook Farm, Little Marcle in 1741

Ploughing was done mainly or exclusively by oxen, seed was broadcast by hand and the wheat harvested by hand-held sickle. The harvest required additional labour and William Marshall stated that men were paid one shilling per day at harvest plus full board of cold meat at breakfast, bread and cheese in the field, with six or eight quarts of beverage and a hot supper at night.

Cattle

Cattle had long been an important feature of the great Michaelmas market held at Hereford each year with graziers from other counties attending to purchase Hereford as well as Welsh cattle for fattening for the London market. They presented a significant source of income for East Herefordshire farmers throughout the 18th century with the main focus on draught and beef animals. Thinghill Court in Withington was already breeding improved cattle in the latter part of the century.

Marshall mentioned that there was some cheese-making in Herefordshire farms bordering on Gloucestershire but it was oxen that played such a key role in the cultivation of the sticky heavy clays of East Herefordshire. Both Walter Godsall and John Drew clearly relied on oxen for ploughing and other farm work. Walter Godsall's 10 oxen were worth a total of £40 and he also owned eight cows, a bull and six two-year-old and nine one-year-old animals, presumably cattle. John Drew's five oxen, seven cows, a bull and five calves were valued at £75, which would suggest that the prices had not altered very much between 1706 and 1741. William Marshall in 1789 commented:

> *In Herefordshire, working oxen are the principal object of breeding. Great numbers of cattle are here in use, as beasts of draught. Half the plow teams appear to be of oxen; which are, likewise, often used in carriages: The ox cart – provincially 'wain' – is here a common implement. They are still, in general, worked double, in yoke; even in the deep-soiled parts of the district; with, however, some few exceptions. ... So lately as fifty years ago, the wain was the only farm carriage of the district: there being many men, now living, who remember the first introduction of waggons.*[17]

Sheep

The local breed of sheep, the Ryeland, was associated more with the lighter soils around Ross-on-Wye than East Herefordshire, although the inventory of 1706 for Showle Court lists a flock of 80 sheep and sheep are also mentioned in the 1741 inventory for Brook Farm. Marshall thought well of them:

> *The Ryeland sheep are remarkable for the sweetness of their mutton; but still more for the fineness of their wool. ... Instead of folding them in the open field, agreeably to the practice of other districts, they are generally shut up, during the night, in a building, which is provincially termed a 'cot,' – and the practice termed cotting. ... In 1793, Ryeland wool was sold for two shillings a pound, when the ordinary wool of the kingdom was not worth more than fourpence a pound.*[18]

Horses

In 1669 Roger Farley had stated that Walsopthorne Farm kept three ploughing teams, two of oxen and one of horses, and use was clearly made of horses to work the land throughout the 18th century. Walter Godsall's inventory of 1705 included an unspecified number of horses, mares and colts worth in total the substantial sum of £38 and John Drew's inventory also mentions horses and tack.

New crops, land management and equipment

It is not easy to document improvements in productivity over this long period, but changes were probably mainly associated with the introduction of new crops and the better preparation of land.

The farming community would have known about the new crops and new growing practices being introduced in the vicinity. Clover had been introduced into Herefordshire from the 17th century and the Hopton family accounts show that the improved Dutch clover was being used in Canon Frome in 1780; Canon Frome Court is a mere mile from Walsopthorne Farm. Dutch clover as well as swedes, the new form of turnip, were being used in 1795 by Mr Wallwyn of Hellens in nearby Much Marcle. Cabbages and turnips were being sown as a rapidly growing cash crop between the rows in hop yards.

The farms in Withington and Lugwardine benefited from the natural flooding of the River Lugg and some of the bigger farms in Yarkhill close to the River Frome, such as Yarkhill Court, may have benefited from artificial flooding of water meadows, increasingly common elsewhere in Herefordshire. There may have been some experiments by landed gentry with new equipment, but there seems to have been very little change generally in farming equipment over the 18th century.

Notes

[1] Fiennes, Celia. (1947). *The Journeys of Celia Fiennes*. Ed. Morris, Christopher. The Cresset Press. p. 233. Photo kindly provided by Amos Locke

[2] This family is not to be confused with the Philipps family of Putley.

[3] Robinson, Rev. Charles J. (1872). *A History of the Mansions and Manors of Herefordshire.* Longman and Co. p. 257.

[4] Herefordshire Archive Service (HAS) BG 26/7 and AA 59/50/7/1.

[5] Currie, Jean Ila. (2009). *Three Centuries of a Herefordshire Village.* Owlstone Press.

[6] Herefordshire Archive Service (HAS) E 3/24; transcript kindly provided by David Lovelace.

[7] Fiennes, Celia. *op. cit.* p. 233.

[8] Marshall, William. (1809). *The Rural Economy of Gloucestershire; Including its Dairy: Together with the Dairy Management of North Wiltshire; and the Management of Orchards and Fruit Liquor, in Herefordshire*, Vol. II. p. 223.

[9] Defoe, Daniel. (1927). *A Tour Through England and Wales*, Volume II. J. M. Dent & Sons Ltd. p. 49.

[10] Herefordshire Archive Service (HAS) E 3/24; transcript kindly provided by David Lovelace.
[11] Philips, John. (2001) *Cyder: A Poem in Two Books*. Eds. Goodridge, John & Pellicer, J. C. The Cyder Press. Book 2, lines 288–289.
[12] Marshall, William. *op. cit.* pp. 221–401.
[13] Davies, Peter. (2007). *A Herefordshire Tale: Claston, Hops and the Davies Family*. Peter Davies. p. 7.
[14] By kind permission of David Lovelace.
[15] Cordle, Celia. (2011). *Out of the Hay and into the Hops*. University of Hertfordshire Press. Appendix 6.
[16] Marshall, William. *op. cit.* p. 224.
[17] Marshall, William. *op. cit.* p. 230.
[18] Marshall, William. *op. cit.* p. 233.

THE FRENCH REVOLUTIONARY AND NAPOLEONIC WARS TO THE COMING OF THE RAILWAYS: 1793–1852

Fig. 2.1 Rare late 18th-century wagon, © The Museum of English Rural Life, University of Reading. Cambridge Wagon, 53/8

Farming during the French Revolutionary and Napoleonic Wars 1793–1815

Life in the East Herefordshire countryside changed from the start of the French Revolutionary and Napoleonic Wars in 1793. The population had been rising for the past half century in the country as a whole although the increase had been somewhat lower in Herefordshire. In most years the United Kingdom was now importing wheat. Recognising the need to feed a growing population at a time when supplies could be affected by war conditions, the government was concerned to increase agricultural output. In 1793 the Board of Agriculture was established and commissioned reports on the state of agriculture for each county. The Herefordshire report was written by John Duncumb, a local clergyman, and first published in 1805.

Rise in consumer prices

The first noticeable impact of the political situation in Europe was on prices, with farmworkers and other poorer groups adversely affected. Although wages did increase, consumer prices rose faster. Duncumb provides information on consumer prices in 1804 compared with 1691, 1740 and 1760 (see Fig. 2.1). Much of the increase in prices between 1760 and 1804 would have occurred in the 1790s. The consumer price of the all-important wheat in 1804 was a staggering three and a half times more expensive than in 1760. Butcher's meat was more than four and a half times more expensive and hardly ever, if ever, consumed by such groups.

	1691		1740		1760		1804		
	s.	*d.*	*s.*	*d.*	*s.*	*d.*	£.	*s.*	*d.*
Wheat, per bushel of ten gallons,	3	0	3	0	3	0	0	10	6
Rye, (very little sown of late years)	2	0	—		—			—	
Oats	0	10	0	11	1	0	0	4	0
White peas,	—		—		2	6	0	8	0
Barley,	—		—		3	6	0	6	0
Malt,	—		—		4	0	0	12	0
Butcher's meat per *lb.*	—		0	1½	0	1½	0	0	7
Pigs for bacon per *lb.*	—		—		0	4	0	0	6½
A goose,	—		0	10	1	0	0	4	0
A roasting pig,	—		—		0	10	0	3	6
A couple of fowls,	—		0	6	0	7	0	2	4
Pigeons per doz.	—		—		1	6	0	4	0
Fresh butter per *lb.*	—		—		0	4½	0	1	3
Best cheese,	—		—		0	3	0	0	9
Fresh salmon,	0	1	0	2	0	4½	0	1	3
Coals per ton,	—		11	0	14	0	1	4	0

Fig. 2.2 Changes in consumer prices 1691–1804 [1]

To alleviate the suffering of the poor in November 1800 some members of the Herefordshire Agricultural Society, including Mr Williams of Thinghill Court, agreed a rota to provide 30 bushels of wheat each week to be distributed in small quantities to the poor of Hereford.

Some increase in agricultural wages

Wage increases only partially compensated for the rise in consumer prices. Duncumb made the point clear:

> *The price of labour throughout the county, except during the period of harvest, averages six shillings per week in winter and seven shillings in summer, with liquor and two dinners. These prices are somewhat higher than those paid forty years ago; but in the opinion of the writer of this survey, the increase is not proportioned to the increase in provisions and every article of life since that date.*[2]

Harvest wages were higher. John Clark, a landowner from nearby Radnorshire, recorded in his account of farming in Herefordshire in 1794 that male labourers from Wales were paid 14 pence (one shilling two pence) a day at harvest plus meat and drink, while women received six pence a day with meat and grain – note the women were not offered the drink! These rates would probably have increased by 1804. It was common, until well into the second half of the 19th century, for many of the permanent Herefordshire farmworkers to be housed within the farmhouse. Duncumb provided figures on average wages for such employees – rare information for Herefordshire. This information is given in guineas (one guinea = one pound one shilling):

Waggoner	*10 to 12 guineas per annum.*
Bailiff or cattleman	*8 to 10 ditto.*
Dairy maid	*6 to 7 ditto.*
Under maid	*2 to 3 ditto.*[3]

Whilst the rising price of food caused great hardship to poorer families, farms, on the contrary, were largely self-sufficient in food and so were not affected. However, farmers did need to contend with some increases in their costs as landowners charged higher rents when leases came up for renewal. Increasing rents probably resulted in an increase in the assessment for tithes. According to Duncumb the charge for tithes when commuted to cash varied "from three shillings and sixpence, to four shillings for every pound of money paid in rent". Land tax remained unaltered, but farmers were obliged to pay more for the parish poor rates. Also incomes oscillated sharply in individual years depending on weather conditions and such extraneous factors as prevalence of disease. Yet for most farmers the period 1793–1815 as a whole was a time of general prosperity.

The importance of wheat

Duncumb recorded that:

> *A very considerable surplus of wheat is produced in the county, beyond the internal consumption, and admits of a large exportation every year to Bristol and other places. … Wheat is the grand dependence of the farmer, who is situated on the stiff clays, with which this county abounds.*[4]

He pointed out that wheat was particularly important in East Herefordshire: "The heaviest crops of wheat are produced in a clayey tract extending from Hereford towards Ledbury." In the later 1813 edition of his report, Duncumb noted that land in this area of the county was rented for between 18 and 20 shillings per statute acre, whereas the average rent for arable land in the whole of Herefordshire was not more than 10 shillings.

Duncumb gave a clear picture of the lengthy rotation of crops of the time, which started with a good fallow on a clover lee well worked, with lime and manure followed by wheat. The lime quarries associated with Dormington Court and the lime quarries in the parish of Woolhope would have been very useful in this instance. In the following spring the ground was sown with peas or sometimes beans after one ploughing and without manure. After two ploughings it was sown with wheat in the autumn. In the following spring it was sown with barley and clover after two ploughings but still without manure. The sheep were turned onto the young clover as soon the barley was removed. As Duncumb explained: "In this manner almost one-third of the arable land is constantly under the culture of wheat."

An article in the 1979 Transactions of the Woolhope Naturalists' Field Club entitled *Wheat Supplies and Prices in Herefordshire 1793–1815* described annual movements in prices in Herefordshire and in the country as a whole and comparing them with prices in 1792.[5] Despite being a major producer of wheat, Herefordshire was constrained by its notorious communication problems. Hence prices for wheat were usually only around 80% of the national average. Only in the good harvest year of 1798 did prices of wheat fall to a level similar to that pertaining before 1793. In 1801 prices were more than three times as high reflecting the poor harvest conditions in that year and the previous two years. Harvests in 1810 and 1811 were also poor and in 1812 imports were affected by the British blockade of French ports. For the country as a whole this was the peak year for prices and even in Herefordshire prices were virtually treble those of 1792.

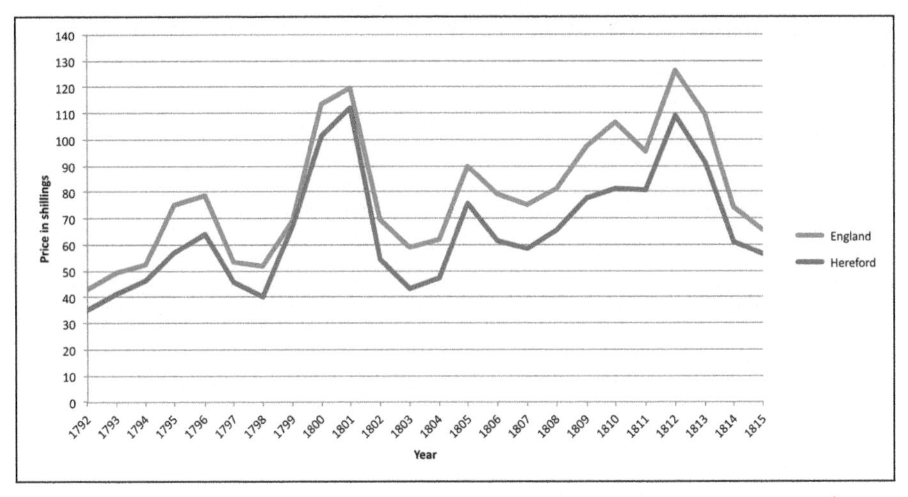

Fig. 2.3 Average wheat prices per quarter for Hereford and England: 1792–1815[6]

Although no firm evidence is available, there was almost certainly an increase in average wheat yields per acre as a result of a greater expenditure on fertilisers and lime, and with the purchase of more effective ploughing and other farm equipment. Although in 1794 John Clark commented that "the plough in general use is the long heavy one of the district. It contributes to the ease of the Ploughman and the burden of the cattle, by its great length", Duncumb reported that the Stoke Edith estate was already experimenting with new land drainage methods in the 1790s "the late Hon. Edward Foley drained a considerable extent of land at Stoke Edith, by means of a plough drawn by four or more horses, and having an iron cylinder pointed at the end, which was forced through the soil at a proper depth. This experiment appears to succeed on a clayey soil."[7] Three of the East Herefordshire parishes, Dormington, Yarkhill and Weston Beggard, were subject to a Parliamentary Enclosure Act in 1798. This would have resulted in more intensive use of land but would have involved considerable initial expenses. Part of the cost would have been born by the landowner, the Foley family of Stoke Edith, but this would then have been reflected in higher rents. (In Much Marcle, the cost of enclosure in 1797 averaged £4 per acre even before the hedging and ditching costs.[8])

Apple and pear orchards

In addition to wheat, fresh apples, cider and perry were in high demand especially from the growing industrial areas.[9] On a number of the East Herefordshire farms in Part III 20% or more of their acreage is known to have been devoted to orchards around this time, for example Court Farm in Aylton parish, and Bent Orchards and Yare Farm in Woolhope parish. Others could well have had a similar proportion.

Growing demand for cattle

There was also an increased demand for cattle with prices rising sharply. Although horses started to be used instead of oxen for ploughing in the late 18th century, oxen continued to be important until the early 19th century. It is through a book describing the different varieties of oxen produced by the meticulous painter, model maker, sculptor, engraver and printmaker, George Garrard, under the patronage of the Board of Agriculture in 1800 that we have an accurate contemporary description of the traditional use for Hereford cattle at this period.[10] According to Garrard:

> *It is allowed, when worked singly that four or five oxen will plough as much ground, day by day, as the same number of horses, of about 15 hands high. Against a steep bank the oxen seem to suffer less than the horses, and excepting the hot summer months, they are the most desirable stock to cultivate the land with; working them double is the best mode during the hot months, as they are apt to be unruly on account of the flies.*

Garrard thought highly of Hereford cattle, many of which would have been in East Herefordshire. As he said:

> *We are much indebted to the rich pasture by the Wye and the Lugg-side for that perfection which so eminently distinguishes the Herefordshire Cattle. These noble animals are found in the highest state of beauty and condition within about seven miles round the City of Hereford.*

Garrard was conscious of the sharp rise in the prices for livestock from Hereford that occurred between 1793 and 1800:

> *Seven or eight years back a good cow and calf were worth from 12 to 15 guineas, which at present would fetch from 18 to 25. A pair of steers, or young oxen, for work, then worth £28, now will fetch £38.*

As earlier in the 18th century, during the first few years of the Napoleonic Wars the principal interest of most farmers continued to be in oxen with the excess cows and calves sold off. There was a not a great deal of interest in dairying. Garrard states that although Herefordshire cattle were good milkers the farmers only produced sufficient butter and cheese for their household needs:

> *As breeding is the first object with the Herefordshire farmer, the dairy, of course, is not much considered, and the quantity of milk that an individual cow may give is not often ascertained. The calves are kept with the cows; and the farmer only attends to the dairy as a convenience for his own family; but it is said that the average of a good dairy (of which there are a few) is about 3 hundredweight of cheese in a year or 2 pounds of butter by the day.*

However there were changes afoot. Ian Jones points out that Hereford cattle were now providing meat for a mass urban market rather than just for London. Pioneers were becoming interested in breeding more for meat rather than primarily for quality working oxen. Benjamin Tomkins the younger (1745–1815) of King's Pyon continued the selective breeding of his father and grandfather. John Apperley of Stone House Farm, Withington and Henry Williams of Thinghill Court, Withington were founder members of the Herefordshire Agricultural Society which was established in 1797. During the first decade of the 19th century both received prizes for their Hereford cattle.

Ineffective efforts to introduce new crops

At this period in Herefordshire potatoes were only grown in gardens. As part of its efforts to improve food supplies generally the Herefordshire Agricultural Society introduced prizes in 1798 for both first and second crop field potatoes. In doing this it spent no less than £16 10s on the purchase of Lancashire potatoes and a further remarkable £15 15s 2d for the warehousing, packaging and delivery costs. The Society also instructed its members on the best way of treating the soil in which the potatoes were to be planted: "the ground should be well cleaned by ploughing; dung from towns is generally thought better than from the fold and a light soil is always to be preferred to a clay". Alas all this was to no avail. There were no applications for this prize.[11] The members were similarly uninterested in the cultivation of field peas. There were no entries for the class "field peas drilled and kept clean".

Farming after the Napoleonic Wars

The good times were coming to an end. In 1813 and 1814 producer prices for wheat fell very sharply and in 1815 the British Government passed legislation which attempted to artificially fix prices. These became known as the Corn Laws and replaced similar legislation operating in the 18th century. Although the 1815 harvest was then good, 1816 was a year of major crop failures, the 'year without a summer'. It is now known that the abnormal weather was due to the major eruption of Mount Tambora in Indonesia. Especially affected was wheat which was virtually written off. Amongst the farms described in Part III there was one notable casualty. William Thomas, the tenant of Brook Farm, Little Marcle was declared bankrupt and the *Hereford Journal* of 27 November 1816 announced the farm sale. Wheat was not among the items listed for auction, suggesting that the failure of the wheat crop may have contributed to Mr Thomas's downfall. Arable was clearly important. For sale were "one rick of oats, one ditto of barley, one ditto of beans and a quantity of unthrashed peas, vetches, barley and oats in the barns". There were also livestock. Mr Thomas was not a beef farmer but there were "four dairy cows, one three-year-old bull" and pigs were produced commercially: "One sow with eight pigs, one ditto with five pigs, one ditto with three ditto, six store pigs and one fat pig".

Most remarkable was the list of farm equipment. This indicated a radically different type of farming from that practised by John Drew at Brook Farm in 1741. Wagons had only become known in the last part of the 18th century. Mr Thomas had no fewer than four of these expensive items. The traditional 14-foot plough driven by oxen had gone. In its place were no fewer than two "Double-furloughed ploughs," as well as three "Hammock" ploughs and three "light" ploughs. There were three drills and two pairs of harrows. To handle this equipment were horses, not oxen: "seven very useful cart mares and geldings, four three-year old cart colts, two yearling ditto". Mr Thomas was a hop grower as 1,400 hop poles were advertised for sale. He was also producing cider on a commercial scale with 30 empty hogsheads included in the sale.

Farming was deeply depressed after the Napoleonic Wars. On a national level wheat prices fell to 48s 4d per quarter by December 1821. Herefordshire prices would have been around 20% lower. Aided by the powerful landowning lobby, petitions flooded in to Parliament. In response Select Committees on Agriculture were held in 1820, 1821 and 1822 although to little avail.[12] Following exceptionally low prices in 1821 and 1822 part of the hop excise duty of 1822 was remitted. Mr T. C. Yeb, who witnessed this terrible time, vividly described the result of the plummeting demand for cattle:

I have seen whole streets filled with cattle in the years 1821¬–22–23 and no one asked what they were bought for.[13]

The favoured response of Herefordshire landowners to hard conditions seems to have been a one-off percentage reduction of rents for a particular period, described as "a gracious gesture" in the *Hereford Journal.* The landowners clearly hoped that this was a temporary measure and there was actually some discussion in the *Hereford Journal* in 1824 about the possibility of raising rents again. Agricultural prices did indeed improve in the later 1820s and there were no more Select Committees on Agriculture until 1833, but low prices and difficult conditions prevailed throughout the 1830s – the national price of wheat fell below 50 shillings the quarter in 1834, 1835 and part of 1836 – and in the 1840s.[14]

Investment in hops

Although hops were not as important a crop in East Herefordshire as in the Upper Frome valley around Bromyard, statistics produced for Parliament in 1836 show that hops were grown between 1829 and 1835 in the 13 parishes described in Part III and in Putley, the parish described in *Three Centuries of a Herefordshire Village.*

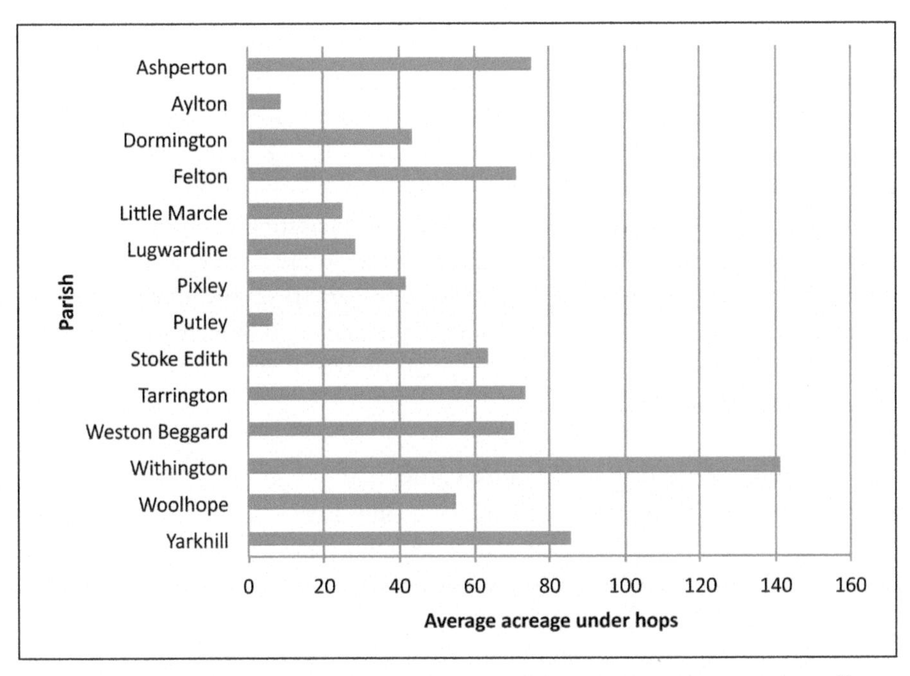

Fig. 2.4 Average acreage under hops in 14 East Herefordshire parishes: 1829–1835[15]

In six parishes (Ashperton, Felton, Tarrington, Weston Beggard, Withington and Yarkhill) on average more than 70 acres each year were allocated to this capital and labour-intensive crop. As a proportion of the parish acreage it was especially important in the tiny parish of Felton. In contrast it was of limited importance in Aylton, Lugwardine and Little Marcle (as well as in Putley). In Woolhope, the largest of the parishes, only 55 acres were on average under hops. With its predominance of limestone soils much of this parish was not suited to the crop.

Hops have always been a notoriously difficult crop, prone to aphids and very expensive to grow. It was quite possible for there to be a total write-off of the crop. Those without significant capital could be at risk in such circumstances as profits in good seasons were needed to compensate for very significant losses in quite a number of years. In 1831 Mr Thomas Smith of The Grove Farm, Yarkhill and Stephen Pitt of Walsopthorne Farm, Ashperton were among the signatories to a petition asking for the excise duty to be waived on hops both for that year and the previous two years because of the very poor conditions. Others fared worse. The *Hereford Journal* in 1835 advertised the bankruptcy sale of James Morris Pritchard of Moorend Farm, Weston Beggard. It may have been the bad seasons in hops that had finally brought about his downfall as included in the sale were 20,000 hop-poles – sufficient perhaps for some 15 acres of hops. The hop harvest at Pixley Court in 1840 was a complete failure. John Davies was recorded in the *Hereford Journal* as selling his whole crop to the landlord of the nearby Trumpet coaching inn for only 6d!

In analysing the agriculture of this period it is interesting to observe that apart from William Thomas of Brook Farm and James Morris Pritchard of Moorend Farm, the other East Herefordshire farmers described in Part III seemed to have survived these difficult times. This may be indicative of the caution of farmers which perhaps showed itself in limited purchases of new equipment as well as in their skill and ability to cope with difficult situations.

The specialised breeding of Hereford cattle

Garrard recorded the measurements of five quality Herefordshire cattle and made engravings of them which were exactly to scale. It is therefore possible to compare the Herefordshire cow and bull in 1800 with the pedigree Herefordshire cow and bull of the later 19th century and also of today.[16]

In this period there was a continuing switch from oxen to horses for general farm use, including ploughing, and with this the nature of the cattle industry was changing. Farmers continued to sell cattle intended for meat to the specialised graziers at the Michaelmas sale in Hereford who in turn sold them for fattening in nearby counties. With a growing population in the United Kingdom and an increase in real incomes over the longer term, the demand for meat rose and there was increasing interest in

DIMENSIONS OF THE HEREFORDSHIRE CATTLE GIVEN IN THIS WORK.

		1			2			3			4			5		
		BULL.			EARL of EGREMONT'S COW.			OX.			DUKE of BEDFORD'S. COW.			FAT OX.		
		Ft.	In.	Qr.	Ft.	In.	Qr.	Ft.	In.	Qr.	Ft.	In.	Qr.	Ft.	In.	Qr.
Height of the - - -	Hind Quarters — — — — — —	4	7	0	4	5	0	5	0	¾	4	5	0	5	2	¼
	Shoulder — — — — — —	4	6	0	4	3	½	5	0	¼	4	3	0	5	2	¾
	Knee — — — — — —	1	1	0	1	0	0	1	3	0	1	1	0	1	1	0
	Hock — — — — — —	1	7	0	1	7	½	1	10	0	1	7	¾	1	9	½
From the Ground to the	Dew Lap — — — — — —	1	6	0	1	6	0	1	7	0	1	6	½			
	Brisket — — — — — —	1	8	0	1	7	¼	1	8	0	1	7	¾	1	8	0
	Chest — — — — — —	2	0	0	1	9	½	2	0	0	1	9	¾	1	9	0
Length of, or from the	Rump to the Extremity of Hip Bone — — — —	2	0	½	2	2	½	2	5	0	2	2	0	3	0	0
	Pole to the Tail — — — — —	7	6	0	6	8	¼	7	8	0	6	7	0	7	9	0
	Face — — — — — —	1	9	0	1	9	0	1	9	0	1	6	½	1	10	0
	Horn — — — — — —	1	0	0	1	2	0	2	0	0	1	2	½	2	6	½
Round the - - - -	Chap — — — — — —	1	10	0	1	6	0	1	10	0	1	7	½	1	10	0
	Cheek and Forehead — — — — —	3	7	0	3	3	½	3	11	0	3	6	0	4	2	0
	Neck — — — — — —	3	5	½	3	0	0	3	7	0	3	0	½	3	11	0
	Chest — — — — — —	6	9	0	6	7	0	7	11	0	6	9	½	9	3	½
	Knee — — — — — —	1	2	0	1	0	0	1	2	0	1	0	0	1	4	¼
	Bone of Fore Leg — — — — —	0	8	½	0	7	0	0	9	½	0	7	½	0	9	¾
	Coronet of Fore Foot — — — — —	1	3	0	1	1	¼	1	3	¾	1	1	0	1	5	½
	Hock — — — — — —	1	5	½	1	2	0	1	7	0	1	4	0	1	8	0
	Bone of Hind Leg — — — — —	0	9	¼	0	8	½	0	10	¾	0	9	0	0	10	¼
	Coronet of Hind Foot — — — — —	1	1	½	1	0	0	1	2	0	1	1	0	1	2	¾
	Horn — — — — — —	0	10	0	0	7	0	0	11	0	0	6	½	0	10	0
Breadth of the - - -	Face across the Eyes — — — — —	0	11	0	0	8	0	1	0	0	0	8	½	1	1	¼
	Hips — — — — — —	2	0	0	2	1	0	2	4	½	2	1	0	2	10	0

The Models were executed from the above measurements, 1, 3, 4, 5, upon a scale of 2¼ inches to a foot.

Fig. 2.5 Dimensions of the Herefordshire cattle engraved by Garrard.
Figures 2.5 to 2.9 reproduced by kind permission of the Syndics of Cambridge University Library

Fig. 2.6 Engraving of a Herefordshire bull

Fig. 2.7 Engraving of a Herefordshire cow belonging to the Duke of Bedford

Fig. 2.8 Engraving of a Herefordshire ox

Fig. 2.9 Engraving of a fat Herefordshire ox

the breeding of Hereford cattle for meat rather than farm work in the larger of the East Hereford farms. Thinghill Court and Stone House Farm, both in Withington parish, continued to play a major role in the development of pedigree Hereford cattle. Matthew Goode of Felton Court was also breeding Herefords from the 1830s and the sale particulars for Aylton Court in 1837 show that Thomas White kept the 'modern' Hereford cattle.

At a national level the Royal Agricultural Society was established in 1839 and from its commencement, Hereford cattle were one of the three specialised breeds of cattle recognised by the society.

The first two volumes of *The Herd Book of Hereford Cattle* were published in 1846 and 1853. They represented a remarkable labour of love by Mr Eyton, the author and publisher, who needed to overcome considerable difficulties. Although Hereford breeders wished to have their names included, they were most reluctant to supply evidence of the pedigrees of their own bulls through jealousy of other breeders! Despite such a handicap, Mr Eyton succeeded in putting together information on 551 bulls of whom no fewer than 96 had been bred by John Hewer (1787–1873), who had worked with his father, William, and inherited his cattle, moving from one modest holding to another in the area owing to lack of capital.

The early Royal Agricultural Society prize winners included a number of the pioneer pedigree Hereford cattle breeders of East Herefordshire. In 1847 Tomboy, owned by Mr William Taylor of Showle Court, Yarkhill, received first prize.

Sheep normally kept

Although East Herefordshire was not famed for its sheep, they had long formed part of the normal crop rotation, and with the increasing population there was a generally rising national demand for both mutton and wool. Prizes were awarded for sheep at the Ledbury Agricultural Society annual meetings and nearly all East Herefordshire farms would have kept a flock at this time. For instance John Baylis of Pixley Court had a flock of 56 ewes and 70 yearlings when his livestock were sold in January 1826, whilst a successor at Pixley Court, John Davies, had a flock of 89 sheep at the time his ram was stolen and killed in 1845.

Growing demand for farm horses

The change from oxen to horses for ploughing and other farm work led to an increased demand for good carthorses. William Vevers (1782–1858) of Dormington Court, well known on the hunting field and in racing and steeplechasing circles, made considerable money from providing his prize-winning steeplechaser stallions for service, but at a more prosaic level he also advertised regularly the services of his prize-winning carthorse stallions. In the *Hereford Journal* of 2 April 1828 it was: "that beautiful GREY CARTHORSE, NOBLE, Winner of the Premium given by the Agricultural Society, for the best cart stallion shown at Worcester in 1826 when he was allowed to be superior to any carthorse in form and action, ever offered to the notice of that Society". Noble's services were not cheap. At that time he was available at one guinea and a crown each mare by the season. In addition each mare was charged five shillings per week for grass keep or six shillings if in foal. Noble's successor, the carthorse stallion Brown Stout, who won first prize at the Herefordshire Agricultural Society annual show in 1838, and Young Brown Stout by Brown Stout were advertised as available for service on similar terms in 1838.

William Vevers was not the only East Herefordshire farmer exploiting the growing demand for carthorses in the first half of the 19th century. John Baylis of Pixley Court was probably breeding and breaking in carthorses in the 1820s as was, a quarter of a century later, John Mason, the tenant of Court Farm, Aylton from 1846 to 1855.

New agricultural societies

The Herefordshire Agricultural Society, which had been established back in 1797, was very much a society for the landowners, the clergy and a very few gentlemen farmers. It was joined in the late 1840s by the Hereford branch of the Farmers Club with fairly similar membership. Indicative though of the new approach to agriculture was the establishment of two societies in East Herefordshire with a much wider membership amongst tenant farmers.

The Ledbury Agricultural Society was founded in 1840 and still exists today. In addition to a ploughing match, the society had, from its inception, classes for cattle, sheep and horses as well as for the best crops of turnips. In 1844 the prize for the turnips was given to Mr Holland of Little Marcle Court. Despite his age, he was nearly 70, he clearly had a keen interest in 'modern' farming. By this time, potatoes had become an established field crop and prizes were awarded for their cultivation. The society also awarded prizes for the best farm implements, for example the best plough, the best seed drill and the best turnip drill, indicating the interest in improved equipment. The much smaller and less ambitious Withington Ploughing Society was founded in 1841, primarily to encourage expertise in ploughing, a vitally important skill, with the major initiators Mr Racster of Thinghill Court, Withington, Mr Apperley of Stone House Farm, Withington and Mr Goode of Felton Court. All these societies had prizes for faithful farm servants. The Ledbury Agricultural Society and the Withington Ploughing Society also optimistically offered a prize for the farm labourer with the largest family who had not needed to apply for poor law funds over the past year and both seemed equally surprised at the very small number of applicants for this.

An important aspect of all the agricultural societies was the annual dinner for members (for men only). The venue chosen for the Ledbury Agricultural Society's annual dinner varied. Sometimes it took place at the Feathers but in 1851 it was at the George, both in Ledbury. For the Withington Ploughing Society, the annual dinner always took place at the Cross Keys Inn, Withington.

Fig. 2.10 The Cross Keys Inn, Withington

Investment in new equipment

Until at least the 1830s, the grain harvest was gathered by the hand-held sickle and the hay mown by scythe, which resulted in heavy pressure on labour during the summer and autumn. With the advent of new agricultural machinery at the larger farms in East Herefordshire the *Hereford Journal*, and from 1832 the newly established *Hereford Times*, included advertisements for all sorts of farm equipment. The agricultural societies stimulated interest in the latest farming machinery, and the *Hereford Journal* report on the Ledbury Agricultural Society's ploughing section mentioned the design of the ploughs used by each competitor. In 1847 the sale by the executor of Mr Thomas Sirrell of Freetown in Ashperton included "25 hogsheads of prime cider, and casks, about 50 empty hogsheads and other casks", indicating the continued importance of cider even if prices were not so high in this period. However there was also a list of modern farm equipment "a four-horse power threshing machine, two-horse ditto, straw-cutter, kiln and cider hairs, seed machine, two winnowing ditto". No longer was the threshing done by hand as it been some 50 years previously. At a time when the population of each parish was still growing this would have had an impact on the farmers' demands for casual labour with a probable consequent deleterious impact on poorer groups in each parish. A number of local iron foundries attempted to enter this potentially valuable market, many failed. Amongst successful firms established during this period was Kells foundry of Ross-on-Wye established in 1838 which was to remain in existence until the First World War.

Duncumb mentioned in 1805 that very little of the land was drained and, indeed, it was only in the 1840s with the improvement in the manufacture of tiles and other equipment that drainage became common.

Improvements in communication

Typically Herefordshire was late in joining the railway age. However it would have enjoyed some indirect benefits in reduced transport costs from the railways established in Gloucestershire and Worcestershire. Gloucester and Bromsgrove stations were opened in 1840 as part of the Birmingham and Gloucester Railway.

Herefordshire had supposedly had the benefit of the canal from Ledbury to Gloucester functional from 1803. The enthusiastic *Hereford Journal* of the time reported: "The expense of carriage of timber by land from Stoke Edith to the canal at Ledbury, eight miles, is sixpence a foot, and the expense of carrying the same from Ledbury to Birmingham by water, 77 miles, is fivepence a foot, including all expenses." However, this report of course had assumed that there would be water in the canal, but the supply of water was so bad that the canal had to be closed for long periods of the year and the resulting shortage of money meant that the canal was not extended further until 1840. Ashperton was reached in that year and a cutting from the River Frome provided the necessary water supply. The continuation of the canal through Yarkhill parish reached Withington in 1844 when there was the inevitable celebration dinner at the Cross Keys Inn. One year later the final stretch to Hereford was completed.

The Great Irish famine

The latter half of the 1840s was one of the dark periods in the history of the United Kingdom. It saw the Great Irish famine. The famine was brought on by the disastrous potato blight (the fungus Phytophthora infestans) which destroyed for the five years

1846–1851 the main food supply for the Irish population. The famine was then further exacerbated by inappropriate government action and inaction and by wholesale evictions by absentee landowners. Probably around one million people died and about two million emigrated in just over 10 years between 1845 and 1855.[17]

The abolition of the Corn Laws

Both the *Hereford Journal* and *Hereford Times* included articles on the horrific Irish famine and charitable collections were made. They also put forward as a matter of urgency the question of the possible abolition of the Corn Laws of 1815 which had prevented imports when the wheat price was below 70 shillings per quarter.

Wheat was still an important cash product in Herefordshire at this time. The local landowners and larger farmers viewed the abolition of import protection with deep misgivings which were fully documented in the *Hereford Times* and *Hereford Journal* of the period. On 17 February 1844 the *Hereford Times* reported in detail a meeting of some 200 landowners and tenant farmers establishing the Hereford Agricultural Protection Society with Earl Somers of Eastnor Castle elected the President. East Herefordshire landowners present included the Reverend Hopton of Canon Frome and the Reverend Money Kyrle of Much Marcle. Mr Edward Foley of Stoke Edith was unable to be present owing to illness (he died three months later) but the Foley estate was represented by Mr C. Mason, the steward. The speakers did not mince their words. "What do these men want? No class of men have obtained their riches more easily, or more rapidly than the manufacturers, and they want to increase their riches by reducing our profit." So expounded one. The meeting raised around £500 with each landowner contributing sums that varied between £10 to £50. A few tenant farmers also contributed, but very much smaller sums. The full list of members published later in the year included professional people and some local clergy but very few of the tenant farmers from East Herefordshire seem to have subscribed. From the farms described in Part III, only William Racster of Thinghill Court and William Vevers of Dormington Court were listed. William Vevers, who, with his successful steeplechasers and racehorses, must have been a very rich man, described himself as a modest tenant farmer and contributed £2.

The Corn Laws were repealed in 1846 and the Hereford Agricultural Protection Society was not destined to enjoy a long or distinguished record. On the contrary, in 1848, a letter to the *Hereford Times* suggested that the remaining funds would surely be more effectively used by the Hereford branch of the Farmers Club and allocated to the testing by chemical analysis of the quality of the soils in Herefordshire, but the society struggled on.

Fig. 2.11 A cartoon in the radical magazine Punch in 1851 viewed the farmers' plight with scepticism. Reproduced by kind permission of the Syndics of Cambridge University Library.

The years following the abolition of the Corn Laws would seem to confirm the gloomiest of forecasts and included poor years for the hop harvest. In 1849 Herefordshire farmers made representations to Parliament on the burden of the excise duty on hops. Although the weather in 1849 and 1850 was good, agricultural prices fell sharply. In 1850 the interest on the capital which had been donated as a prize for the meeting of the Herefordshire Agricultural Society was diverted to become the subscription to the newly formed National Association for the Protection of Agriculture, another organisation which was also destined to deep obscurity.

Sauerbeck's price indices derived from the London market showed wheat selling nationally at an average annual price of about 40 shillings per quarter in 1850–1853 compared with between 50–60 shillings per quarter in 1846–48. Duties on imports of live animals, meat and hams had been abolished at the same time as the Corn Laws and imports again rose. Prime beef in the London market fetched only 36–38s per 'butcher's stone' of 8lb in 1850–1853 compared with more than 40 shillings in 1846–1848.[18] The market price of these products in Herefordshire would have been markedly lower. Nor did the weather help. The winters had, indeed, been unusually mild, but 1852 was one of the wettest on record. An article in the *Journal of the Royal Agricultural Society of England* of 1854 described 1852 as "a long season of the most appalling distress".

Notes

[1] Duncumb, John. (1813). *General View of The Agriculture of the County of Hereford*. London: printed for Sherwood, Neely and Jones. p. 140.

[2] Duncumb, John. *op. cit.* p. 136.

[3] Duncumb, John. *op. cit.* p. 139.

[4] Duncumb, John. *op. cit.* p. 51.

[5] Parker, W. K. (1979). Wheat Supplies and Prices in Herefordshire 1793–1815. *Transactions of the Woolhope Naturalists' Field Club*, Volume XLIII: I. pp. 44–53.

[6] Graph by Nick Newton Design using figures from Parker, W. K. op. cit. A quarter = eight bushels, approximately one-quarter of a ton.

[7] Duncumb, John. *op. cit.* p. 99.

[8] Parker, W. K. *op. cit.* pp. 46 & 52.

[9] Jones, E. L. (1961). Agricultural Conditions and Changes in Herefordshire 1660–1815. *Transactions of the Woolhope Naturalists' Field Club*, Volume XXXVII: I. p. 36.

[10] Garrard, George. (1800). *A Description of the Different Varieties of Oxen, Common in the British Isles*. London: J. Smeeton.

[11] Garrard, T. W. (1898). *Transactions of the Herefordshire Agricultural Society 1797–1809*. Herefordshire Agricultural Society. Herefordshire Archive Service (HAS) AF 57/14/12. pp. 8–10.

[12] Gayer, A. D., Rostow, W. W., Schwartz, A. J. (1953). *The Growth and Fluctuation of the British Economy, 1790–1850*, Volume 1. Oxford. pp. 156–157.

[13] Macdonald, James, & Sinclair, James. (1909). *History of Hereford Cattle*. London: Vinton & Company Ltd.

[14] Gayer, A. D., Rostow, W. W., Schwartz, A. J. *op. cit.* p. 156.

[15] Graph by Nick Newton Design using figures from *Return of acres of hops grown in each parish, 1829–1835, quantity grown and duty paid* (1839). Parliamentary papers, Volume XLVI. p. 519.

[16] Garrard, George. *op. cit.*

[17] www.bbc.co.uk/history/british/victorians/famine_01.shtml

[18] Orwin, Christabel S, & Whetham, Edith H. (1964) *History of British Agriculture 1846–1914*. Longman. p. 95.

PROSPERITY, DEPRESSION, STABILISATION: 1853–1913

Late 1853 saw two events of the greatest importance for the prosperity of East Herefordshire farmers. In October the Crimean War (1853–1856) broke out. In consequence markets for imports were disrupted and home prices rose for the next three years. On a local level and vital for the viability of farming in Herefordshire over the longer term, the railway finally came to Hereford in December 1853.

Transformation with the start of the railway age

Fig. 3.1 Navvies travelling to work on the Hereford and Worcester line, 1861,
© www.herefordshirehistory.org.uk

Herefordshire was one of the last counties to be connected to the national railway network and therefore to markets throughout the United Kingdom. The Crewe to Hereford section had been completed in October 1853 but it was on 6 December 1853 that the very first train arrived in Hereford from Newport. Transport costs plummeted. No wonder the county rejoiced and how they rejoiced! 6 December was declared a public holiday. Some 60,000 people thronged the streets of Hereford, a change from the normal population of 12,000. Lavish entertainments and food were provided for all sections of the community: the county gentry, the farmers, the tradesmen, the workhouse residents and indeed the navvies who had completed this work. A description of all these junkets is given in Part II. The Victorians certainly knew how to enjoy such public occasions.

The farmers in East Herefordshire had to wait a little longer for the connection between Hereford, Worcester and Birmingham. Ballard, the great engineer, wrestled with and overcame the problem of the long Colwall tunnel under the Malvern Hills, and built the Ledbury tunnel and the great Ledbury viaduct using local bricks. The Hereford to Worcester line was finally opened in 1861. In addition to Ledbury there were stations at Ashperton, Stoke Edith and Withington, important for produce from East Herefordshire.

Prosperity and high farming: 1853–1874

The mid-Victorian period was the time of 'high farming' – good quality farming achieved by using the most efficient methods. This period was a heyday for both Hereford cattle and for hops. Cider no longer had a national market and prices were much lower but it could still be sold locally and very considerable quantities were consumed on the farm itself.

The opening of the railways saw the start of a major growth in the importance of Hereford as a livestock centre, both locally and for the neighbouring counties. The new municipal Livestock Market was opened in 1856, replacing the previous insanitary conditions. Auctions were also introduced for Herefordshire apples and pears, though fresh fruit was often sent by railway to the markets in Birmingham. A new Butter Market for farm produce opened in 1861 and indeed still exists[1].

The Foley estate: Lady Emily Foley

Farmers in the parishes of Weston Beggard, Yarkhill, Dormington, Stoke Edith, Tarrington and the western side of Woolhope benefited from being tenants of the Foley estate. This was very much in the control of a remarkable woman, Lady Emily Foley. She had been widowed in 1844 and from that time onwards took on an active concern over many matters including the management of the farms. A detailed description of her is given in Part II but she truly deserves a biography of her own. She was charming, imperious, highly intelligent and benevolent.

Lady Emily Foley was a keen advocate of the fashionable policy of 'high farming'. Partly (although certainly not wholly) as compensation for the abolition of the Corn Laws, the Public Money Drainage Act of 1846 had enabled the government to provide loans at reasonable rates to landowners for drainage purposes. Lady Emily ensured that her farms were well drained. In addition, and this was probably quite rare, she allowed the farmers on her estate to shoot the game, a concession greatly appreciated by her tenants. As part of her policy to encourage good farming Lady Emily Foley had instituted an Annual Farm Inspection of the farms on her estate in 1850. All the farmers were invited to ride round the estate with the judge and the Stoke Edith steward on the final day of the three-day inspection. In keeping with the times the farmers usually enjoyed an excellent lunch provided by the winner of the main prize the previous year. The inspection ended with an invitation to dinner (alas and in keeping with the times the farmers' wives do not appear to have participated in this) when the £20 prize for the best cultivated large farm and the £10 prize for the best cultivated small farm were awarded. The speeches at these events were reproduced almost verbatim in both the *Hereford Times* or *Hereford Journal.*

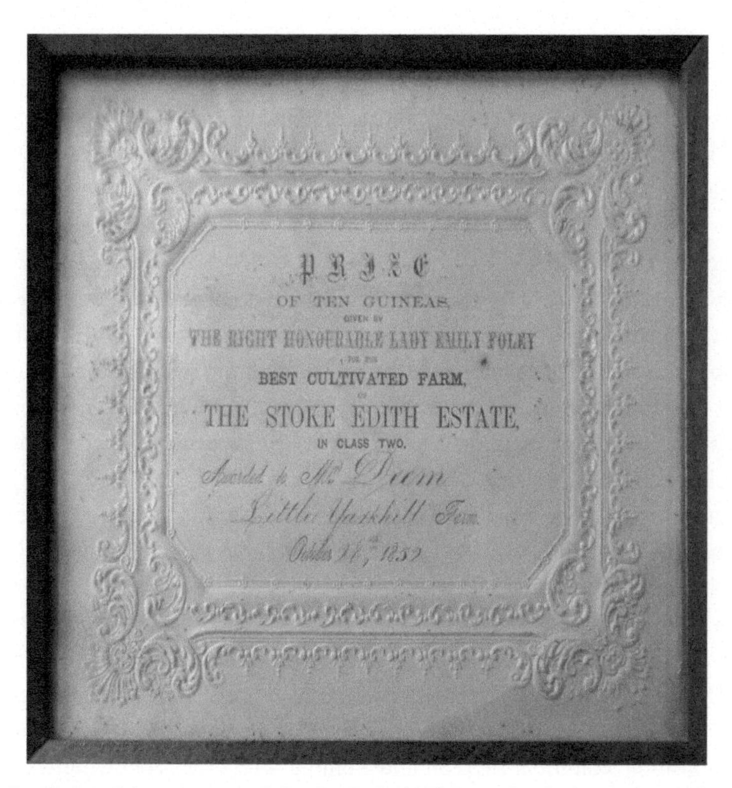

PRIZE
OF TEN GUINEAS
GIVEN BY
THE RIGHT HONOURABLE LADY EMILY FOLEY
FOR THE
BEST CULTIVATED FARM,
THE STOKE EDITH ESTATE,
IN CLASS TWO.
Little Yarkhill Farm

Fig. 3.2 Certificate of the prize awarded to Little Yarkhill Farm for the best cultivated small farm

The Eastnor estate

It seems that Earl Somers of Eastnor did spend some money on improved drainage at Brook Farm, Little Marcle. The scheme of government loans for drainage purposes was extended in the 1860s to include building and Earl Somers invested in some model farm buildings. However, he seems to have been less concerned with the farmhouses themselves as witnessed by the decline of Little Marcle Court described in Part III. Earl Somers does not appear to have been well thought of by his contemporaries – certainly not by his largest tenant Mr Sparkman of Little Marcle Court and Brook Farm. It appears that the ubiquitous and much hated game laws which prevented farmers from shooting even rabbits and hares on their own farms were upheld by the Eastnor estate as indicated by a celebrated court case of 1835 described in Part II.

The Hopton estate of Canon Frome

The rent book for the Hopton estate between 1860 and 1890 shows that it too was spending money on farm improvements and repairs, and the increase in the rent for Walsopthorne Farm, Ashperton in the 1860s indicates that this decade was clearly a time of prosperity. Between 1860 and 1862 Mr Stephen Pitt of Walsopthorne Farm was paying £314 4s per annum in half-yearly instalments for this farm of over 200 acres. In November 1862 this was increased to £366 and in 1867 to £396.[3]

Pedigree Hereford cattle

The coming of the railways opened new markets to commercial livestock producers such as the three successive tenant farmers at Thinghill Court, Withington as well as the Apperley family of Stone House Farm, Withington, who had been pioneers in breeding selected Hereford cattle specifically for meat throughout the first half of the 19th century. There were consequently incentives for breeders to upgrade their herds with quality animals. Hereford cattle matured quickly and were hardy, but potential purchasers needed to be reassured of their bloodlines. It was important to ensure that the admirable qualities of Hereford cattle in comparison with other likely breeds, notably the shorthorn, were well known nationally, not just locally.

From 1856 the breed benefited from the patronage of Prince Albert the Prince Consort. However, despite urging, especially from the Herefordshire Agricultural Society, Mr Eyton resolutely refused to expand on his first two volumes of *The Herd Book of Hereford Cattle*. Mr Thomas Duckham was persuaded to continue the series, publishing Volume 3 in 1858 and Volume 4 in 1859. Following the death of Prince Albert in 1861, Queen Victoria herself became the patron. Mr Duckham then published Volume 5 in 1862, revised Eyton's first two volumes in the same year, and subsequently published Volumes 6–9 between 1865 and 1876. In 1878 the Hereford Herd Book Society was founded under the patronage of Queen Victoria in order to continue publication of the herd book and manage pedigree questions.

The farms and farmers of East Herefordshire described in Part III were well represented in Duckham's volumes of *The Herd Book of Hereford Cattle* and his revisions of Eyton's first two volumes. All three major landowners of East Herefordshire: Lady Emily Foley, Earl Somers of Eastnor and the Reverend John Hopton of Canon Frome estate were recorded as breeders in Volume 3. Volume 3 also included 10 bulls bred by the late William Apperley and 15 by his son John Apperley of Stone House Farm, Withington. Mr Thomas Bradstock of Ross, the grandfather of Percy Bradstock of Garford Farm, Yarkhill and afterwards of Freetown, Ashperton, had three bulls included. Mr Matthew Goode of Felton Court was shown as having nine entries, including a young bull calf called Felton calved on 31 May 1857. Mr Stephen Pitt of Walsopthorne Farm, Ashperton registered his bull Defence the Second. Mr William Taylor of Showle Court, Yarkhill was another most distinguished early breeder. In addition to his own bulls he is recorded as having purchased Exile from Lord Berwick for exporting to Australia. Mr J. Sparkman of Little Marcle Court and Brook Farm, Little Marcle is recorded as having used for his herd of Herefords one of the famous Hewer bulls, Gay Boy. Also recorded are bulls bred by Mr William Yeomans of Stretton Court, Hereford. Mr William Yeomans was the great-grandson of John Yeomans, who had started breeding improved Hereford cattle while still at Thinghill Court in the 1780s. It was William Yeomans' son, John Yeomans, who was later to move to Stone House Farm, Withington in 1905.

Pedigree Hereford cattle were the favoured local breed, but even more importantly their qualities, including hardiness, had been identified as suitable for building up of herds in North and South America. Exceptional prices, many fold higher than the norm, could be paid for selected bulls for export and these rewards were spectacularly achieved by William Taylor of Showle Court, Yarkhill. As a result of the endeavours of breeders, white-faced Hereford pedigree cattle became well known nationally and internationally, with breeders outside Herefordshire as well as within it.

Sheep and other livestock

East Hereford farms had their own flocks of sheep, important as part of their crop rotation. With the increase in population and general rising incomes, demand increased especially for mutton from older sheep rather than for lamb. Wool was also a favoured commodity. Farm sales for this period suggest that a common breed was a cross between the Ryeland and Leicester sheep – the Ryeland Flock Book Society was not formed until 1903. The Hereford Agricultural Society and the Ledbury Agricultural Society both awarded prizes for sheep and of course, for that all-important farm animal, the horse, which by now had almost totally replaced the ox.

The smaller East Herefordshire farms and those on poorer soils such as those in Woolhope were also mixed farms, but seldom appeared in the press. They did not normally enter their stock in the local agricultural societies and their beef cattle were not pedigree but were sold to the local butcher in Hereford or Ledbury with particular reference to the Christmas market. Woolhope in particular with a significant proportion of upland limestone soils always had sheep as an important source of income, and pig rearing with low capital cost was probably more important in Woolhope than in other parts of East Herefordshire as the pigs could be reared under the plentiful orchards there.

Control of common livestock ailments

In both large and small farms the control of common livestock ailments is as critical to the success of farming as market conditions. A short guide of remedies in a useful pamphlet entitled *The farmers and millers guide at the markets, etc. 1853* published by the *Hereford Journal* and reproduced on the following pages provided what would have been the soundest advice available at this period for calves, cows, sheep, pigs and horses.

Boom in hop growing

By this time beer was the esteemed drink for working people nationally, with a growing preference for the lighter brews which required more hops. The population of the United Kingdom continued to grow fast in the first three decades of the 19th century, with the decennial census records showing an increase from around 27 million in 1851 to nearly 35 million by 1881. The main factor behind the increased demand for hops was this growth in population and the apparent increase in consumption of beer per head between 1850 and the early 1870s. Not only was the population growing but the number of pubs in the UK was also increasing.

The heavy red sandstone clay soils which cover most of East Herefordshire apart from Woolhope were eminently suited for hop production. Especially famed for growing hops was the valley of the Rive Frome, which runs through the parishes of

Fig. 3.3 (Pages 45–48) Extract from a pamphlet produced by the Hereford Journal in 1853 giving the diseases of livestock and their remedies[4]

16

THE DISEASES OF LIVE STOCK, AND THEIR REMEDIES.

CALVES.—The most common diseases of Calves are—

1. *Navel Ill.*—The best treatment for this dangerous disease is, 1st, to administer two or three doses (about a wine glass full) of castor oil (linseed oil does just as well, and is much cheaper); and, 2ndly, cordials, which can be made of two drachms of carraway seeds, two ditto of coriander seeds, two ditto powdered gentian; bruise the seeds, and simmer them in beer or gruel for a quarter of an hour; give these once or twice a-day.

2. *Constipation of the Bowels.*—For this doses of castor oil (or linseed oil), of two or three ounces, are the best remedy.

3. *Scouring.*—The farmer may *rely* on the following mixture. Let him keep it always by him; it will do for all sucking animals:—

Prepared chalk	4 ounces.
Canella bark, powdered	1 ,,
Laudanum	1 ,,
Water	1 pint.

Give two or three table spoonfuls, according to the size of the animal, two or three times a-day.

4. *Hoose*, or *Catarrh.*—Good nursing, bleeding, and then a dose of Epsom salts with half an ounce of ginger in it.

COWS.

Their common Diseases and Remedies.

Cleansing Drink.—One oz. of bayberry powdered, one oz. of brimstone powdered, one oz. of cummin seed powdered, one oz. of diapente. Boil these together for ten minutes; give when cold in a little gruel.

Colic.—The best remedy is one pint of linseed oil mixed with ½ oz. of laudanum.

Calving.—The treatment before calving is to keep the cow moderately well, neither too fat nor too lean; remember that she commonly has the double duty of giving milk and nourishing the fœtus; dry her some weeks before calving; let her bowels be kept moderately open; put her in a warm sheltered place or house her; rather reduce her food; do not disturb her when in labour, but be ready to assist her in case of

17

need ; let her have warm gruel ; avoid cold drinks. A pint of sound good ale in a little gruel is an excellent cordial drink.

A Cordial is easily made by 1 oz. of carraway seeds, 1 oz. of aniseeds, ¼ oz. of ginger powdered, 2 oz. of fenugreek seeds. Boil these in a pint and a half of beer for ten minutes, and administer when cold.

Fever.—Bleed ; and then give 1 oz. of powdered nitre and 2 oz. of sulphur in a little gruel. If the bowels are constipated, give ½ lb. of Epsom salts in three pints of water daily, in need.

Hoose.—See CALVES, DISEASES OF, only double the doses.

Hoove or *Hoven.*—Use the elastic tube ; but as a prevention, let them be well supplied with common salt, and restrained from rapid feeding, when first feeding, upon rank grass or clover.

Mange.—½ lb. of black brimstone, ¼ pint of turpentine, 1 pint of train oil. Mix them together, and rub the mixture well in over the affected parts.

Milk Fever or *Garget.*—Two oz. of brimstone, 1 oz. of diapente, 1 oz. of cummin seed powdered, 1 oz. of powdered nitre. Give this daily in a little gruel, and well rub the udder with a little goose grease.

Murrain.—½ lb. of salts, 2 oz. of bruised coriander seeds, 1 oz. of gentian powder. Give these in a little water.

Poisons swallowed by oxen are commonly the yew, the water dropwort, and the common and the water hemlock. 1½ pint of linseed oil is the best remedy.

Purge, in poisoning—either 1 lb. of salts in a quart of water or gruel, or 1 pint to 1½ pint of linseed oil.

Redwater.—Bleeding, says Youatt, first, and then a dose of 1 lb. of Epsom salts, and ½ lb. doses repeated every eight hours until the bowels are acted upon. In Hampshire they give four ounces of bole *ammoniac*, and two ounces of spirits of turpentine in a pint of gruel.

Scouring.—Give ½ oz. of powdered catechu, and 10 grains of powdered opium in a little gruel.

Sprains.—Embrocation : 8 oz. of sweet oil, 4 oz. of spirits of hartshorn, ½ oz. of oil of thyme.

Sting of the Adder or Slowworm.—Apply immediately to the part strong spirits of hartshorn ; for sting of bees apply chalk or whitening mixed with vinegar.

Worms.—Bots : give ½ lb. of Epsom salts with 2 oz. of coriander seed bruised in a quart of water.

18

Yellows.—Two oz. of diapente, 2 oz. of cummin seed powdered, 2 oz. of fenugreek powdered. Boil these for ten minutes in a quart of water, and give daily in a little gruel.—*Youatt on Cattle*, 557.

SHEEP.

Common Diseases of, and their Remedies.

Apoplexy.—Bleed copiously; then give 2 oz. of Epsom salts in a pint of water.

Blackwater.—Keep the bowels open with Epsom salts, and give a teaspoonful of elixir of vitriol, or sulphuric acid, diluted with seven parts of water, in an infusion of oak bark.

Blackmuzzle.—Mix an ounce of verdigrease (acetate of copper), 4 oz. of honey, ½ pint of vinegar; simmer them together over a fire for ten minutes in an earthen pipkin. Apply it to the mouth on a piece of rag.

Cough or *Cold.*—Bleed; give a solution of Epsom salts.

Fly.—Fly powder; two pounds of black sulphur, half a pound of hellebore; mix them together, and sprinkle the sheep from the head to the tail with a dredging box.

Sheep Wash.—The farmer will find this an excellent recipe: half a pound of powdered white arsenic (arsenious acid), four pounds and a half of soft soap. Boil these for a quarter of an hour, or until the arsenic is dissolved, in five gallons of water. Add this to the water sufficient to dip fifty sheep. The quantity of arsenic usually recommended is too large.

Foot Rot.—One drachm of verdigrease (acetate of copper), 1 drachm of blue vitriol (sulphate of copper), 1 drachm of white vitriol (sulphate of zinc), 2 ounces of water, 2 drachms of nitric acid, 2 drachms of butter of antimony; pare away the horn, and apply the lotion upon a feather to the part affected.

Rot.—To prevent, let the sheep have always a lump of salt to lick in their troughs.

Scab, or *Schab.*—Apply a lotion formed of 1 oz. of corrosive sublimate, 4 oz. of sal ammoniac, dissolved in 4 quarts of rain water. This is a powerful stimulant, and must be used with caution.

Scouring.—See CALF, Diseases of.

Ticks.—See FLY.

Wounds.—Wash the part, and apply a lotion formed of vinegar 1 pint, spirits of wine 1 oz. spirits of turpentine 1 oz. Goulard's extract 1 oz. If the wound be a recent one, it is

19

better to stitch it up with separate ligatures, which can be easily withdrawn, and dress with cold water.

PIGS.

Common Diseases of, and their Remedies.

For the common diseases of Pigs, the following recipe may be employed :—½ lb. of sulphur, ½ lb. of madder, ¼ lb. of salt-petre, 2 oz. of black antimony; mix these together, and give a table spoonful night and morning in its food.

HORSES.

Common Diseases of, and their Remedies.

Cough, or *Colds*, are best treated by cold bran mashes, with ½ lb. of linseed, and 1 oz. of salt-petre each mash.

Gripes, or *Colic*.—In the absence of a veterinary surgeon in this dangerous complaint, the following is the best remedy for a horse :—1½ pint of linseed oil, 1½ ounce of laudanum, given in a little warm gruel. Some persons assist the operation of the above with a glyster, composed of ½ lb. of Epsom salts, ½ lb. of treacle, dissolved in three quarts of warm water.

Mange.—See Cows, for which the remedy is the same.

Powder Alterative for diseased skin or surfeit; mix together ½ lb. of sulphur, ½ lb. of saltpetre, ¼ lb. of black antimony, give a large table spoonful night and morning in their corn.

Sprains and Wounds.—Mix 1 oz. of Goulard's extract, 1 oz. of spirits of turpentine, 1 oz. of spirits of wine, 1 pint of the strongest vinegar; rub this by the hand, or a piece of tow, gently on the part affected.—*Farmer's Encyclopædia.*

Yarkhill, Weston Beggard and Dormington. In 1871 for the first time *Kelly's Directory* identified separately individual hop growers. With the exception of farms in Woolhope parish, most of the farms mentioned in Part III were growing hops.

The second half of the 19th century could well be described as the peak for hop production in this part of Herefordshire. Herefordshire generally grew the quality varieties of hops for which there was a ready demand. New technologies were reducing costs. From 1862 hop poles, a heavy expense, could be treated with creosote increasing their lifespan. On the larger farms hop poles were replaced with wiring of the hop vines. It was discovered that spraying with soft soap and quassia mixed with water could reduce the prevalence of blight.[5] It seems also to be true that costs of production in Herefordshire and Worcestershire were lower than in Kent and Sussex, the other major producers. This is clear from the minutes of evidence in the report of the Parliamentary Select Committee on Hop Duties in 1857. Hop growers in different parts of the country had been asked to break down the cost of production per acre in their part of England and Mr William Taylor of Showle Court was the only grower who gave evidence for Herefordshire.

According to Mr Taylor rents per acre were low in Herefordshire at £1 to £1 10s per acre, as was the tithe charge for hop production at 6s per acre. Mr Taylor was growing 24 acres of hops on his two farms, Showle Court and Lower Hope Farm. He put the cost of production (labour, fertiliser and maintenance of hop poles, rent, etc.) at £18 19s per acre. The cost of drying varied between 22s and 25s per cwt. Wages of labourers varied between 2s and 2s 6d a day for the men. Most labourers had cottages to rent at a very cheap rate. He was not prepared to break down the labour cost. Asked why the acreage under hops in Herefordshire over the previous 20 years had fallen from 10,600 acres to 4,600 acres he replied that this was easily explained: "It was customary to make the return by hop acres, and often there were two hop acres upon a chain acre. … I think there is quite as much land under hops in the county of Hereford now as there was at any time since I can remember." Obviously yield varied with the season but in an average year William Taylor expected 10 or 12 cwt per acre. In 1854, despite blight, the yield was 15 cwt per acre. In 1855 it was 17 or 18 cwt per acre, the second highest he had ever had. He grew "the Cooper's white, the Canterbury grape, the Mathern white, the grape and a small amount of Jones's".[6]

The excise duty on hops was abolished from 1862. It would appear, though, that this had been a relatively modest burden and it had possibly been borne more by the consumers rather than the producers. The impact in any case was probably more than offset by the abolition of the import duty on hops at around the same time.

Decline in cider production

Long over were the heydays of the late 18th and early 19th century when quality cider from Herefordshire was renowned nationally and, indeed, internationally as an esteemed drink. Its place was now taken by imported wine. Although farms continued to produce cider, but this was now mainly for the consumption by the farmer and labourers, with sales only within the locality.

Depression: 1875–1899

Prosperity was not to last and the period 1875–1899 is sometimes referred to as the Great Agricultural Depression. From 1875 onwards, farming incomes throughout the United Kingdom were affected by low prices for cereals and for wool. The end of the Civil War in the United States was followed by the major development in the early 1870s of their railway system. This in its turn, combined with the development of steamships, greatly reduced the cost of transport of the US exports of wheat. Prices of wheat fell sharply to around 45 shillings per quarter in 1874 and 1875[7] and remained at this level until 1883. The prices of other cereals, such as oats and barley, continued to fall throughout these years. Compounding the problem was the exceptional run of disastrously wet weather and cold winters between 1875 and 1882, with only the good summer of July–September 1881 to alleviate the situation.[8] Wool, which had been highly profitable in the 1850s and 1860s, was now subject to competition from the sheep stations of Australia, although the price of mutton, which had also increased in the 1850s and 1860s, remained buoyant.

East Herefordshire farmers responded to the changing situation by radically reducing the proportion of their land under arable in favour of increased livestock production. Even so individual farms who had not responded soon enough could be badly hit. One farm that may have failed to do so was Withington Court. It was in the hands of receivers in 1880 and the list of the fields in a map prepared at that time shows a predominance of arable. Individual farmers in East Herefordshire also suffered from the livestock diseases prevalent in those years. The spread of liver rot affected many flocks of sheep throughout Herefordshire and George Hall of Garford Farm, Yarkhill lost no fewer than 70 ewes to this ailment.[9] Adding to these difficulties, cattle were affected by pleural pneumonia at this time, but it is not known whether any of the farms in Part III were so affected.

The demand for hops also started to falter, but Herefordshire with its lower costs increased its share of national production. In the 1870s to 1890s William Henry Davies, later of Claston Farm, Dormington, appeared to have been making significant profits from large-scale hop production on land in Weston Beggard and Dormington. At his peak he was producing 1,000 pockets[10] per year, suggesting he was growing hops on at least 80 acres of land on the several farms he was renting at this time.

There was a fall in prices of fatstock between 1883 and 1888, although this affected lower quality beef herds rather than the high quality beef herds prevalent in East Herefordshire. There must have been some benefit for local beef producers from the further expansion in 1888 and then 1897 of the important Hereford Livestock Market. High prices were still achieved for prize-winning Hereford bulls in the 1880s and 1890s and many of these continued to be exported, but from the early 1890s onwards there was a more general fall in prices of fatstock, affecting all grades.[11] Consumers in the UK were demanding more meat but a much higher proportion of this was satisfied by frozen beef from North America and Australia, the very countries that had been building up their herds through quality prize-winning pedigree Herefords.

It seems probable that it was those smaller farms in Woolhope parish which were most affected by the situation. Throughout the 1880s and 1890s there seems to have been a fair change of tenant farmers in this parish, indicating the difficulties of making a living. However important farms elsewhere were also affected. For instance Little Marcle Court farmhouse, increasingly run down, had been lived in by farmworkers since 1871, and in 1891 Garford Farm, Yarkhill was lived in by farmworkers as were Moorend Farm, Weston Beggard and Freetown, Ashperton. In these cases the land was farmed by larger local farmers, probably on very favourable terms.

Landowners were reducing rents generally. Information is not available for the Foley or the Eastnor estates but at Walsopthorne Farm, the Canon Frome estate reduced the rent from £396 per year to £341 8s in 1880. In November 1887 it was reduced further to £293, lower than it had been in 1860. The rent for Court Farm, Woolhope, owned by the Dean and Chapter of Hereford Cathedral, was also reduced from £92 in 1873 to £70 in February 1889. In addition, Henry Williams, the farmer at Court Farm in 1889, was allowed £10 a year off the rent for expenditure on manure for a five-year period.

Stabilisation: 1900–1913

Export of pedigree Hereford cattle highly profitable

Quality Hereford pedigree cattle could still yield a satisfactory income with prices for prize-winning animals in the early 20th century far above the norm. The establishment of the American Herd Book had reduced the demand from that country but South America was opening up. By this time, William Henry Davies had moved from Hillend

Farm, Weston Beggard to Claston Farm, Dormington. In 1903 he not only exported his prize heifer Vera to Argentina but also a significant proportion of his pedigree herd. Quarto, Mr H. W. Taylor of Showle Court, Yarkhill's prize bull which had won the Champion Prize for the best Hereford bull at the Royal Agricultural Society of England show in Bristol in 1913, was exported to Argentina in the same year. Meat prices recovered somewhat from 1906 and remained higher right up to 1914 with probable alleviation for the commercial East Hereford herds.

Reduced demand for hops

Hops, however, were suffering from competition from imports and from lower overall demand – a consequence of the success of temperance groups. On 16 May 1908 two special excursion trains were commissioned from Hereford to enable the major hop farmers from East Herefordshire join with others from different parts of the country in a mass demonstration in Trafalgar Square demanding the imposition of tariffs on foreign imports. In a debate of 31 July 1909 the government was urged to meet these demands, but the argument received little sympathy from Lloyd George, the Chancellor of the Exchequer. He pointed out that the demand for beer had fallen over the past 20 years and highlighted the success of Herefordshire in increasing its share of total output. Most Herefordshire hop growers were able to continue, but a casualty of this failing demand was the bankruptcy in 1903 of Henry Hall of Dormington Court. Perhaps inspired by William Henry Davies, Henry Hall had made the risky decision of increasing his output of hops from around 30 acres to over 80 with all the exceptionally large capital, as well as recurrent expenditures implied. To compound the problem he had financed this expansion largely through borrowed money.

Profitability of fruit

Increasing incomes in urban areas of England and cheap transport costs had increased demand for fresh fruit. From the 1870s onwards, Mr Riley of Putley Court had pioneered dessert apples and plums with soft fruit (strawberries, gooseberries and blackcurrants) as an undercrop in place of former cider orchards. Other larger East Herefordshire farms, including Withington Court, Thinghill Court, Withington and Pixley Court, followed his example and were growing soft fruit in the early 1900s, with Pixley Court establishing a jam factory as part of this endeavour. There was also a demand for cider apples from the two local commercial cider producers, Westons of Much Marcle (established in 1878) and Bulmers of Hereford (established in 1887).

Fig. 3.4 Two horses ploughing by Brian Hatton, 1899, © Hereford Museum Service

Low farmworkers' wages

Wages were second only to rent as a major expense for hard-pressed farmers. There had been out migration from most parishes since the 1860s. The development of the railways had provided some opportunities for the more ambitious and the Godwin tile works at Withington some limited alternative employment, but for most East Herefordshire countrymen farm work continued to be the only available source of employment. Much of this work was skilled. The wagoner was responsible for expensive farm horses, preparing them for work and then bedding them down at the end of the day. Sheep are notoriously prone to ailments and the development of liver fluke could destroy a whole flock. A skilled and careful shepherd was therefore of great value.

However, Mr Sidney Box, an early union organiser, encountered hostility from both farmers and clergy when he established the Herefordshire Agricultural Workers' Union in 1912. In his memoirs[12] he listed the average agricultural wage in Herefordshire in 1912 as 14s 2½d per week and pointed out that it had increased by a mere 3½d since 1901. As this was the average wage, an unskilled farmworker would have received less. A cottage was often available at a cheap rent but the condition of the housing could be poor. It is sobering to think that Mr Box's aim was to limit wagoners' working hours to 75 per week in the summer. He did not succeed in this aim, but he did obtain a 2s increase in the average wage by August 1914.[13]

Farming on the eve of the First World War

The financial position of farmers had stabilised in the new century, but the position of landowners was less favourable. Rents had not risen for at least 50 years, and indeed in some cases were significantly lower than they had been at the start of the Great Agricultural Depression, whilst maintenance costs were higher. The production of cereals had continued to fall in the first decade of the 20th century.

The United Kingdom was to enter the First World War highly dependent upon imports and without any consideration as to the consequent vulnerability of the country. The equipment and farming methods hardly changed from the 1870s until the First World War and, indeed, as indicated in Chapter 4 below, sometimes remained the same right up until the Second World War.

Notes

[1] O'Donnell, Jean. (9 February 2010). *Hereford's Markets, Past, Present and Future*. Herefordshire & Wye Valley Life.

[2] By kind permission of Joy Edwards.

[3] Herefordshire Archive Service (HAS) BL 93.

[4] *The farmers and millers guide at the markets, etc. 1853*. The *Hereford Journal*. By kind permission of Tom Nellist.

[5] Grundy, J., Paske, H., Walker, P. (2007). *A Pocketful of Hops* Bromyard & District Local History Society. pp. 5–6.

[6] *Report from the Select Committee on Hop Duties; Together with the Proceedings of the Committee, Minutes of Evidence and Appendix*. (1857). The House of Commons. paragraphs 4644–4825.

[7] Perry P. J. (1974). *British Farming in the Great Depression 1870–1914*. David & Charles.

[8] Perry P. J. *op. cit.*

[9] Journal of the Royal Agricultural Society of England. (1881). London.

[10] A hop pocket is a sack, approximately six feet long and weighing about 80 kilos, in which dried hops are pressed and stored.

[11] Orwin, Christabel S, & Whetham, Edith H. (1964) *History of British Agriculture 1846–1914*. Longman. p. 259.

[12] Box, Sidney. (1950). *The Good Old Days: Then and Now*. Reliance Printing Works Halesowen, Worcs. p. 1.

[13] Box, Sidney. *op. cit.* p. 6.

WAR, DEPRESSION, WAR AND IMMEDIATE POST-WAR: 1914–1949

Fig. 4.1 The War Memorial at Withington: one of many in East Herefordshire

The First World War: 1914–1918

From the early years the First World War took its terrible toll on the young men of East Herefordshire. The loss is clearly visible in the many names on the crosses in each of the parishes, many of them from families of farmworkers and farmers. John and Rebecca Yeomans of Stone House Farm, Withington were to lose both their sons during this war. Clement and Eliza Jane Bayliss of Moorend Farm, Weston Beggard lost their only son. William Stephens and his wife, Mary Anne, of Baregains Farm, Little Marcle were informed of the death of their younger son, Albert, in June 1915. There were few families that did not lose at least one family member.

Britain dependent on imports of food

At the time war was declared the area under arable in United Kingdom had fallen for more than 40 years and was standing at an all-time low. In terms of final output the country was dependent on imports for 79% of its needs for wheat and flour (grain equivalent). Its dependence on imported meat products seemed rather less with imports supplying 33% of the needs for beef and veal and 44% of its requirements for mutton and lamb.[1] However this was illusory as many UK animals were fed on imported grain. Despite these facts the government took a remarkably sanguine and laissez-faire approach to food. When war was declared the President of the Board of Agriculture, Lord Lucas, declared that he saw "no occasion whatever for public alarm over food supplies".[2] Lord Milner's cross-party Board of Agriculture committee of 1915, charged with increasing agricultural output, urgently recommended measures to increase output of cereals. Given the expense and difficulties of ploughing they recommended the provision of guaranteed prices using deficiency payments. The proposal was rejected outright by the government.

High prices and food shortages

Prices rose sharply between 1914 and 1916, benefiting most farmers but making conditions very difficult for the farmworkers whose wages had hardly increased over the same period: in 1916 retail prices were 60% above their 1914 level. The poor wheat harvest of 1916 and the relative failure of the potato crop followed by the Battle of the Somme changed government attitudes. With merchant shipping losses from U-boat attacks there was a serious possibility in late 1916 and early 1917 that the UK would have to capitulate because it could not feed its population. In October 1916 the government took over all dealings with wheat and in November this was extended to supplies, distribution, consumption and prices of all basic foods. Lord Devonport was appointed Government Food Commissioner on Boxing Day 1916 to organise this and the Ministry of Food established in early January 1917.[3] It was at this point that County War Agricultural Executive Committees with District Committees working under them were established with the responsibility for identifying fields that could be ploughed up for planting of cereals and potatoes. Ploughing up land could involve the farmer in heavy expenditure. To compensate for this the Corn Production Act of 1917 guaranteed minimum prices for wheat and oats on a sliding scale for the crop years 1917–1922. To assist farm workers the Board of Agriculture had already recommended a minimum weekly wage of £1 25s. Under the Act, District Committees had powers to authorise minimum wages higher than this.

The requirement to plough up land seems to have been the cause of considerable conflict between the WAEC and the Herefordshire branches of the National Farmers' Union. Relations reached such a low level that the annual NFU report covering 1917

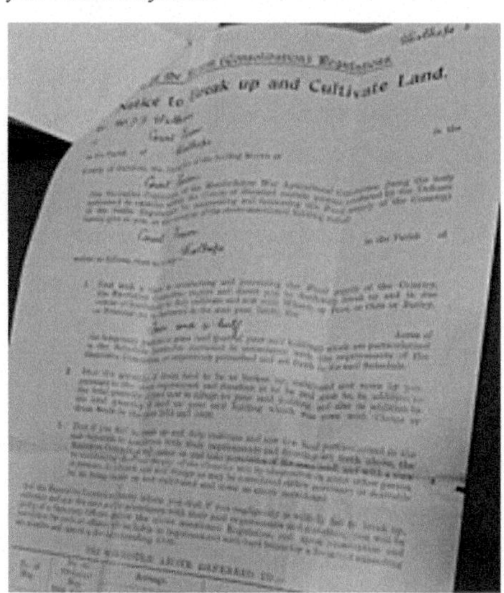
up and Cultivate Land.

Fig. 4.2 Notice from Herefordshire WAEC requiring Court Farm, Woolhope to plough up four and a half acres [4]

for the newly amalgamated branches of the South and North Herefordshire branches states that members were no longer prepared to cooperate with the WAEC demands for such ploughing. Most county WAEC papers were destroyed at the end of the war but there is extant a rare Herefordshire WAEC notice sent to Mr Dansey Watkins of Court Farm, Woolhope. Mr Watkins was required to plough up four and a half acres called Ox Pasture. He was also required to plough up any land that had been under clover in 1915 or 1916. In his reply Mr Watkins states he has already ploughed up the pasture. He makes no mention of the land under clover. Although Mr Watkins may not have been aware of this it was the custom of the WAECs to issue such reminders even in cases where the ploughing had already been carried out since this piece of paper protected tenants from penalties where their leases specifically prohibited the ploughing of permanent pastures.

Shortages of agricultural labour

With so many workers away fighting there was an acute shortage of skilled labour throughout the war. The 1915 annual report for the South Herefordshire branch of the NFU speaks of the dire shortage of labour and the consequent near impossibility of fully satisfying the government's demand for food. Herefordshire farmers were reluctant to employ women outside their normal domain of seasonal work – weeding and harvesting for farmworkers' wives and poultry and butter for farmers' wives and daughters. In June 1915 a Farmers' Aid Women's Society was set up to encourage more understanding. Mrs Bradstock, the wife of Percy Bradstock of Garford Farm, Yarkhill and Mrs Bray, the wife of Mr G. H. Bray of Dormington Court were two of the three initiators behind the scheme. The South Herefordshire branch of the NFU for 1915 was not encouraging: "As a theoretical proposition there is much to be said for this, but in practice it is beset by many difficulties and especially so in a county like Hereford."[5] They were more appreciative of the contribution of the soldiers awaiting shipment to France.

With the introduction of conscription in 1916 the labour position further deteriorated. In this year John Yeomans of Stone House Farm, Withington, whose two sons were fighting in Belgium and France, requested exemption for his wagoner explaining that six of his farmworkers had already enlisted. His request was refused.[6] In 1917 the Women's Land Army was formed but the numbers were always small compared with the Second World War – just over 2,500 registered in Herefordshire during the course of the First World War.[7] German prisoners of war were also employed from 1917.

Further rises in prices

Retail prices rose still further to significantly more than double the 1914 level in 1918 and 1919. The index of agricultural prices continued to rise from 60% above its average level in 1911–1913 to more than two and a half times in 1919 and only just short of three times in 1920, the peak year.[8] Actual prices for both wheat and oats were far above the guaranteed price so the government Exchequer was spared.

Changes in agricultural production

Exports of pedigree Herefords were not impeded during the First World War. No fewer than 1,700 pedigree Herefords were exported between 1914 and 1918.[9] On the other hand the acreage under hops was controlled and cut to almost half. In the country as a whole the total area under hops fell by more than half from 36,700 acres in 1914 to 15,600 in 1918.

Major sale of tenant farms 1916–1919

No fewer than four landowners in East Herefordshire took advantage of the improved prices in the war and post-war period to sell off land. Those which affected the farms in Part III were the Eastnor estate sale of 1916 and the Stoke Edith estate sale of 1919/1920, but the Canon Frome estate and the much smaller Wessington Court estate in Woolhope also sold land during this period.

Eastnor estate sale

In 1916 the Eastnor estate sold all its land in Pixley, Aylton and Little Marcle. This included five farms described in Part III: Pixley Court in Pixley parish, and Brook Farm, Laddin Farm, Lillands and Little Marcle Court in Little Marcle parish. The details given in the prospectus reveal clearly the low returns and significant costs incurred by the landowner since the start of the Great Agricultural Depression in 1875.

The five farms were large by the standards of the day and mainly on good soil with good facilities. Yet only at Brook Farm was the estate receiving even slightly more than £1 per acre at the time of sale, where the total rent was £207 2s for the 199-acre farm with its farmhouse, extensive farm buildings, hop kilns and two cottages. For the four other farms which had similar amenities, the rent was less than £1 an acre. At Pixley Court, the largest of the farms with its 282 acres and three cottages, the rent was £267. At the Laddin with its 185 acres it was £165. At Lillands, a 211-acre farm with four cottages, the rent was £186 and at Little Marcle Court the rent was £180 15s for 191 acres. These rents can be contrasted with the rent for Walsopthorne Farm in Ashperton in 1867 at the height of 'high farming' when the Canon Frome estate was charging £396 each year for a farm of 215 acres – only slightly under £2 per acre. Little Marcle Court in 1916 was probably in a poor state of repair. It was euphemistically described in the prospectus as an "OLD-FASHIONED FARMHOUSE of considerable interest". However the estate had spent quite considerable sums on farm buildings not long before the sale. All the farms had modern, mostly square, hop kilns and Lillands had a newly-built range of farm buildings.

Pixley Court was bought by the sitting tenant. The other farms were purchased by new owners. The actual prices are not known. Land prices had increased from their low level of 1914 but not as much as they would do in the succeeding three years. The purchases made in 1916 did not, at least at the time, seem to have imposed a severe burden on the buyers. (The sitting tenant who had been farming Lillands in 1916 bought the farm in 1921 when it was again put up for sale.)

Stoke Edith estate sale

It was different three years later when in December 1919 Paul Foley of the Stoke Edith estate put up for sale 3,370 acres of land in the parishes of Weston Beggard, Yarkhill, Dormington, Stoke Edith, Ashperton and Woolhope. These sales included nine farms from Part III (Moorend Farm in Weston Beggard parish, Garford Farm, Showle Court and Yarkhill Court in Yarkhill, Claston Farm and Dormington Court in Dormington, Perton Court in Stoke Edith, Freetown in Ashperton and Park Farm in Woolhope). All except Garford Farm, Freetown, Perton Court and Showle Court were sold privately to the sitting tenants by early 1920. The sitting tenant of Garford Farm bought Freetown, a larger farm with better access to water. The new owner of Perton Court may have had some connection with the Stoke Edith estate. Mr Dent, well known for his pedigree cattle, remained as the tenant.

The peak year for sale prices of agricultural land nationally in the period 1900–1939 was 1920 when prices were 30% higher than the average in 1937–1939.[10] Prices of land fell back after 1920 and never reached anything like the level again until the Second World War. In 1920 farmers had little alternative but to purchase: it was after all their source of income. Almost all would have needed to borrow. It did not help matters that Paul Foley was said to have boasted that he was selling the land at its highest price and was intending to buy it back when the prices collapsed. His prognosis on prices was correct but not one single farmer sold his land back to the Foley estate. The financial problems were never talked about but the economies which had to be made were clear in the returns by these farms in the National Farm Survey of 1941–1943.

The interwar period: depression

The 1920s

To help ensure jobs for the returning soldiers the government had 'unpegged' sterling from its value in gold in March 1919, allowing sterling to depreciate by a huge 35% against the US dollar. This, together with low interest rates and pent-up demand from the war years of shortages, produced an inflationary boom from April 1919 to April 1920. The post-war boom and the associated inflation came to an abrupt end in 1920 when the policy was sharply reversed with the bank rate rising to 7% in April 1920. Between October 1920 and October 1921 output fell by 15% and unemployment rose to 22%.[11] For the Treasury 'economy' was now the watchword.

Depressed price for cereals

All this had its inevitable impact on agriculture. All the farms in East Herefordshire described in Part III were mixed farms, largely pastoral but with the arable significantly increased from its low level of 1914. This increase was immediately sharply reversed from 1921. There was a good reason for this. The 1920 Agriculture Act had endorsed the earlier policy of guaranteed minimum prices for wheat and oats. According to the Act four years' notice had to be given for the guarantees to be suspended. With the calamitous fall in the international price of wheat, this would have inflicted a very severe burden on the Treasury. The government reneged on the agreement. The Corn Production Acts (Repeal) Act received Royal assent in August 1921. (The Act did however agree compensation for land already planted with wheat and oats.) This had, naturally, the most serious effect on the east of England, traditionally the main corn-growing area. However it did affect those in Herefordshire who had been induced, or forced, to plough up their land. The United Kingdom retained a liberal policy towards imports and with excess supplies of grain in North America flooding the British market, prices of corn remained exceptionally low. The area under arable in Herefordshire fell back and was lower in 1929 than it had been even in 1914. The government's lack of faith was not forgotten.

Increased dependence on livestock and orchards

Herefordshire in the 1920s was therefore truly the home of traditional Hereford cattle and orchards.

The market for cattle started well. With arable crops reserved during the war for human rather than animal consumption, livestock numbers had fallen and the herds of both dairy and beef needed to be rebuilt. The few large farms in East Herefordshire with pedigree cattle experienced a bonanza. The average price of a pedigree Hereford in 1914 was £37 4s; in 1919 it had risen an astonishing fivefold to £206 5s and then increased almost two and a half times further to reach £473 8s in 1920. Herefords were not to reach this average price again until after the Second World War.

For producers of prize-winning cattle such as the Bradstocks of Freetown there continued to be a good market overseas with 1,250 export licences issued during the 1920s, mostly for animals destined for South America where the prices remained high.[12] In the home market the average price for the 3,264 bulls sold between 1921 and 1930 fell to £50. Farmers producing stock cattle, such as those in Woolhope parish, would have fared badly in the 1921 collapse in prices, especially those who had bought young animals for rearing 1920 and had then sold them at the reduced price. To compound matters there was a severe outbreak of foot-and-mouth in 1922 with all the markets closed. During the remainder of the 1920s the livestock farms in East Herefordshire were able to struggle on, aided by cheap prices for animal feed. There was a small increase in the demand for milk and agricultural prices stayed fairly stable in the latter half of the 1920s.

There remained a market for cider apples in this period. Most farms continued to produce for their own purposes, and Westons Cider of Much Marcle and Bulmers of Hereford provided commercial outlets at modest prices.

After the initial problems of the early 1920s there was an increased demand for fruit in urban areas. John Riley of Putley Court had established fruit growing back in the 1870s. When the estate was broken up in 1923, separate lots were sold as specialised fruit orchards with graded products. Such farms continued to provide fairly satisfactory incomes with lower grade products of orchard fruit, especially apples, plums and pears, sold for processing at factories set up in Ledbury producing jams. Of the farms described in Part III, Thinghill Court, Withington produced soft fruit in the 1920s and possibly also Yarkhill Court, Yarkhill and The Hyde, Woolhope.

Thomas Edward Davies of Pixley Court, who had been continuing to grow soft fruit and also process it into jams, seems to have been badly affected by the depression of the early 1920s and the jam factory and Pixley Court itself was put up for sale in 1923. Pixley Court was purchased by Edward Thompson from receivers in 1928.

Difficult times for hop growers

The output of hops had been restricted in the latter two years of the war and control of sales and prices continued for another four years. As part of the economy measures the government had imposed a large tax on beer in 1920. Partly in consequence of this, demand had fallen substantially. Even though the total acreage under hops in the United Kingdom at 27,000 acres in 1922 was well below that of 1914, there were still excess stocks of hops unsold. The Hop Controller therefore restricted sales of the 1923 harvest to three-quarters of the average sales in 1920–1922 and a good average price of £13 per cwt was then achieved for the 1923 crop. However the 1924 harvest was so great that controls were not possible. The average price fell to just over £8 per cwt and there were substantial unsold stocks.

At this difficult time the market was then liberalised. The English Hop Growers Association, a voluntary body comprised of some 90% of the hop growers, took over these stocks and agreed to sell only through the Association and to accept restrictions on sales.[13] The 10% of hops growers that did not belong to the Association did not limit their production and profited by the situation to the detriment of the others. Feelings ran extremely high. A number of East Herefordshire farmers drove to Pomona Farm, Weston Beggard to remonstrate with Noel Croft, the owner who had not joined the scheme. Words were exchanged. Indeed, there was some rumour that the whole matter become so inflammatory that it ended up in the criminal courts, but this was not something passed on to an enquiring child asking about it 25 years later!

The Association went into liquidation in 1928 and average prices fell from £10 per cwt in 1927 and 1928 to just over £4 in 1929 and a little under £4 in 1930. Little Marcle Court, which had been resold in 1921, was another large farm that experienced difficulties in this period. In 1922 the owner, Mr Gordon Williams, was recorded as a farmer and hop grower. Perhaps as a result of investment in hops, Little Marcle Court ended up in the hands of receivers in 1929.

The hard years of the 1930s: further depression

The hardship experienced by many farmers throughout the 1930s, and especially in the first half of this decade, is clearly shown in cold figures; the gross output of agricultural holdings in England and Wales fell from £220.6 million in 1927–1928 to £199.8 million in 1933–1934. It did not reach the 1927–1928 level until 1936–1937. It then remained on a plateau for the remaining two years of the decade.

Fall in livestock prices for pedigree cattle

The arable farms of eastern England were those who had first felt the impact of tumbling prices for cereal crops in the 1920s and had sometimes switched to livestock production. The livestock producers in Herefordshire initially derived some benefit from lower feedstock prices but then were faced with the excess output.[14]

Tragically in late 1929 H. J. Dent of Perton Court, Stoke Edith parish, distinguished as a most successful breeder of Hereford cattle, was found dead, killed by his own shotgun. He was quite possibly a victim of these difficult times. E. Heath-Agnew, the author of *A History of Hereford Cattle and their Breeders* describes these years in a chapter entitled 'The Survivors 1930–1939'.[15] Surprisingly in April 1930 at the Hereford Herd Book Society spring sale the recession had yet to hit and bulls continued to be sold for an average price of nearly £50, the average price received between 1921 and 1930 and an average price not to be exceeded until 1938. A satisfactory 250 exportation certificates were awarded, divided equally between Russia and South America. Freetown Admiral, the outstanding bull bred by Mr P. E. Bradstock of Freetown, Ashperton, won both the Grand and the Senior Male Championship at the Royal Agricultural Society of England show in 1930 and the next two years. The average price at the spring sale of nearly 400 bulls was only £36 in 1931, but unexpectedly in 1932 the Hereford Herd Book Society benefited from a major purchase of 400 cattle by the Russian government. In 1933 it was Freetown Admiral's son Freetown Rear Admiral who was Grand and Junior Champion at the Royal Agricultural Society of England show. It was only in 1938 with the prospect of war looming that prices finally improved and the average price for pedigree bulls at the spring sale averaged £52 5s. In the 1939 spring sale they edged further upwards to £53 10s.

Establishment of the Hop Marketing Board in 1932

The Agricultural Marketing Act of 1931 permitted the majority of producers of any agricultural product to set up a marketing board and compel the minority to cooperate. However as most imports were still permitted duty-free, it was largely ineffectual. The one exception was hops where growers negotiated the control of imports with the brewers, who were the sole buyers. The Hop Marketing Board was set up in July 1932. It was solely responsible for the negotiations on quantities and prices with brewers and was given the power to limit the amount each grower could sell. Edward Thompson of Pixley Court was a founder member of the board. Following its establishment the average price of hops rose about 70% compared with the year before. Throughout the 1930s the hop producers were restricted in how much they could produce but could rely on a reasonable price for the crop sold.

Establishment of the Milk Marketing Board in 1933

A new Agricultural Marketing Act of 1933 also permitted producers of an approved scheme to restrict imports. It was under this arrangement that the Milk Marketing Board, which would have such an impact over the next 50 years, was established. This was a benefit especially to some of the smaller farms of East Herefordshire, providing better outlets for milk, particularly that sold for manufacturing purposes rather than for liquid sales.

Orchards

Orchards remained an important source of income. There was a continuing demand for dessert apples, pears and plums from the more prosperous parts of the country. Bulmers and Westons retained their own orchards but also purchased some local cider apples. John Ball of Court Farm, Aylton exceptionally marketed his own cider not only locally but as far off as Wales.[16] Most farms in Part III then maintained significant acreages under orchards as evident later in the individual returns in the National Farm Survey 1941–1943 and the Agricultural Census of June 1941.

Farmers' recollections

Despite these initiatives the 1930s were truly difficult times. Theodora Reeves, in her biography of the Powell, Steadman and Sparkman families, recalled that Rupert Powell of Awnells Farm, Much Marcle, was obliged to sell wheat, beans and oats for only 6s per cwt and eight prize Hereford heifers in Ledbury market in 1934 for an average price of only £18 12s 6d each. Most of the farmers reviewed in Part III survived, though there were stories to pass on to the succeeding generations. Mr Skittery of Lillands, Little Marcle found, when taking a hop sample to Worcester in 1930, that there was no buyer at all for his hops that year. The vines were pulled and used as bedding for the animals. Reg Bayliss of Moorend Farm, Weston Beggard remembers that two seasons of unsold hops were stored on the farm in 1930. Hazel Court, Tarrington became vacant at this difficult time and prices of land were very low. In 1930 it was sold to a newly married young couple, the Williamses. It was to remain in the family until the end of the 20th century.

Peter Davies's reminiscences *A Herefordshire Tale*[17] recalled the hard struggles of the 1930s at Claston Farm, Dormington. His father, Philip Davies, a tenant of the Stoke Edith estate, had had to borrow in order to purchase the farm in the Foley sale of 1919: "With great difficulty, father managed to buy Claston which had then been reduced to 170 acres. He eventually secured a loan for the farm." Although Claston was a largish farm by the standards of the day and had a hop quota, nevertheless Philip Davies had a milk round which enabled him to receive the retail price for milk to generate additional income. Peter's mother Mildred, a daughter of Mr Thompson of The Hyde, Woolhope, made butter to sell on the milk round and one of Peter's jobs was to turn the separator. Another was to help his father with the milk round before he went to school.

Government subsidies and advisory facilities

As is often documented, the United Kingdom entered the Second World War unprepared militarily. What is sometimes overlooked is the lack of preparedness in the food supplies. It is not possible to conduct a war when one cannot feed the population. In the First World War there had for some time been a well justified concern that the country would need to capitulate because of the lack of food. It is then surprising that only relatively modest steps were taken to increase food production, even in the later 1930s when war seemed quite likely.

Some action had been taken by the government. From 1925 a modest subsidy, sometimes ineffectual, had been available for sugar beet. The Wheat Act of 1932 had provided a subsidy but only for a restricted quantity of 27 million cwt of wheat. The Agriculture Act of 1937 increased this to 36 million cwt and added minimal subsidies to barley and oats. It also aimed to provide some assistance for purchases of lime and basic slag. There were other subsidies for fat cattle. However in 1937–1938 estimated subsidies came to £11.5 million, equivalent to only around 4% of the estimated agricultural output of £264.5 million despite the modest efforts to encourage arable.[18] The fact remains that the acreage under arable in England and Wales in 1939 was still lower than in 1914. This was especially so in Herefordshire. In 1939 only 20.7% of Herefordshire land was under tillage (crops and fallow land). This reflected complacency at least amongst some politicians. As late as March 1938 Mr Chamberlain in the statement reminiscent of the Minister of Agriculture in 1914 had stated "The idea that we can be starved out in wartime seems to be entirely salacious".[19]

There was one important development compared with pre-1914 conditions and one which would prove invaluable in the Second World War. This was the establishment in

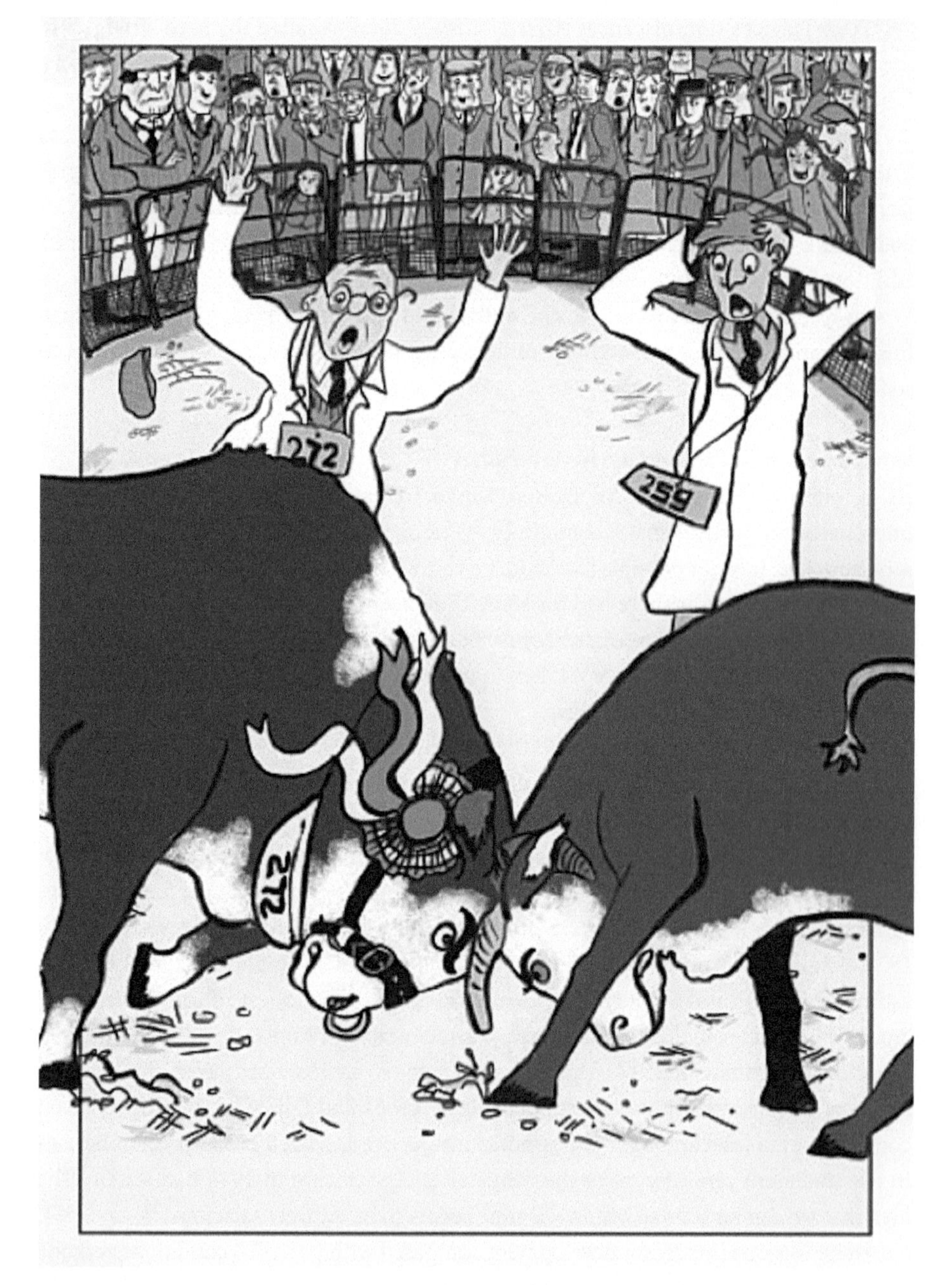

Fig. 4.3 "I should have had the First Prize!": cartoon by Amanda Summers

the 1930s of publicly financed advisory services to farmers. County Council Agricultural Executive Committees established in 1917 had remained in existence since that time. In Herefordshire a subcommittee of this was specifically concerned with agricultural education. It was staffed by four paid and well-qualified officials. Mr Evans BSc was assisted by Mr C. Saville who advised on orchards and horticulture. Traditionally it was farm women who were responsible for butter and cheese making and for poultry. Miss O. Jenkins with a National Diploma in Dairying advised on dairy production and Miss Winifred Davies with National Diplomas in both Dairying and Poultry Keeping advised on poultry. From March 1933 the Agricultural Education Subcommittee produced the Herefordshire County Council Agricultural Quarterly Journal. It was edited throughout the 1930s by Mr Evans and normally had practical articles by all four advisers. It also included articles written by veterinarians or university research groups. Mr Evans pointed out that the advisers were happy to provide advice with no cost to the farmer. In addition agricultural courses were run, though to his disappointment these were mainly patronised by the sons of the better-off farmers.

An entertaining incident with a prize-winning Hereford bull in 1939

The dark days just prior to the outbreak of war were briefly lightened in July 1939. Mr H. C. Dent, one of the two sons of the late Mr Dent of Perton Court, had been only 19 when his father died. He initially increased his knowledge and skills in pasture stations in Australia but returned in 1935 to take over the tenancy of Eastwood Farm, Tarrington. Drawing on family skills, his pedigree bull Perton Rear Admiral won first prize in his class at the Agricultural Show held in July 1939 in Liverpool. To the great enjoyment of the crowd and local press, watching at a safe distance, a less successful contender, Grange Amilute, engaged the champion in a fight in the bull ring with a scattering of buckets, etc., a contest only brought to a conclusion when the bulls had their horns entangled with each other and could be safely separated.

The Second World War: 1939–1945

If the politicians were not prepared for the war, the administrators were. Largely owing to the deep concern of a few senior civil servants in the Department of Agriculture, a detailed programme had been worked out and agreed with Ministers.

Consequently the day war was declared the County War Agricultural Executive Committees sprang into action and had legal control over what was being produced. In Herefordshire, the Herefordshire Agricultural Quarterly Economic Journal ceased to be published during the war as the journal's four advisers were attached to the

Herefordshire War Agricultural Executive Committee (WAEC) or its subcommittees. The Ministry of Food was spun out of the Ministry of Agriculture and central control imposed on the wholesale markets. By the end of September the civilian population had been registered for ration books. The administrators wished to impose rationing immediately but the government believed that this would be bad for civilian morale so it was only in January 1940 that rationing was first imposed.

The potential problems of feeding the population were even graver than in the First World War. The United Kingdom was dependent upon imports for 50% of its food requirements and the dependence was again actually more than this given the heavy import content of animal feed. The major aim was to reduce the import of bulky products, particularly cereals and sugar, in order to release shipping for other requirements. It was also necessary to change the diet of the population away from meat to vegetables and cereals. Meat consumption was cut by a third and so was sugar.

A second Domesday Book: the National Farm Survey of 1941–1943 and the annual Agricultural Census of June 1941

To feed the population it was vital to increase radically agricultural output and especially the area under arable in as short a time as possible. To assist with this a National Farm Survey was undertaken by the War Agricultural Executive Committees between 1941 and 1943. Every holding over five acres was inspected, the condition of the land described and a grading A–C given to the farmer. Those given a B were given additional advice. Those given a C were in danger of having their holding taken over. In addition, the normal June Agricultural Census of 1941 provided full information of what was being produced that year. Supplementary questions were asked about the machinery on the farm, the use of family labour and the rent paid for tenanted property. The original completed questionnaires are to be found in individual folders covering each parish. They give a remarkable picture of farming at this period, contributing as they do to almost a modern Domesday Book. The information contained in them is summarised for each of the farms in Part III.

The National Farm Survey of 1941–1943 and the Agricultural Census of June 1941 show the farming at the start of the war and responses to war conditions during the harvest years of 1939 and 1940, but not the further significant responses of 1942 and 1943.

Most of the larger farmers ploughed up a certain amount of land under instructions from the Herefordshire WAEC for the 1940 harvest in Autumn 1939 and for the 1941 harvest in Autumn 1940. They also voluntarily increased their acreage under crops.

The acreage under tillage (crops and fallow land) increased by 60% between June 1939 and June 1941 to account for 33% of the land under agriculture compared with just under 21% in June 1939.

Identification of the land to be ploughed up was just one aspect. Even more challenging was the provision of machinery, tractors, ploughs, binders, etc., not to mention the manpower to undertake this monumental task. It is not surprising that the minutes of the Herefordshire WAEC Subcommittee on Machinery on 1 August 1941 reveal a cacophony of woes. Ominously, the meeting was attended by Mr Tymms, the Ministry of Agriculture's Machinery Inspector. He recorded problems of the low output of tractor drivers and "a large number of discrepancies in the time sheets". On a more hopeful level the subcommittee recorded the arrival of a considerable amount of new equipment including two Fordson tractors making 24 altogether and five ploughs making 25 altogether. The subcommittee put in a healthy shopping list for 39 potato diggers, 11 disc harrows and 14 additional Fordson tractors.

The number of pigs on Herefordshire farms dropped by almost half between 1939 and 1941 and the numbers of poultry by nearly 20%, both changes reflecting the extreme difficulty in obtaining feed. There was some decrease in the numbers of sheep but little change in the numbers of cattle.

Herefordshire farms were mixed pastoral farms. In the early 1930s some farms in the United Kingdom had specialised in pig rearing and poultry production using the cheap imports of animal feed, but this had not generally been the case in East Herefordshire: if there were pigs on the farm there would normally be only two or three sows or perhaps some piglets being reared on their own. Looking at the individual Agricultural Census returns for June 1941 it seems that only The Hyde, Woolhope had been producing pigs on a commercial scale during this period with the census return listing 147 pigs. Nearly all the farms had poultry but the size of the poultry flock was extraordinarily small by modern standards, normally around a hundred birds. The only exceptions were in the parish of Woolhope: The Hyde which was an accredited poultry producer had 2,500 birds and the smaller Yare Farm 713 birds. It was common to have a flock of sheep and in June 1941 the lambs were still on the farm but about to be sold. Nearly all farmers had cattle but rarely more than 60 or 70 head and the smaller farms many fewer. It is not easy to see which of these were dairy cattle as opposed to beef. With the exception of farms under 100 acres nearly all the farms in Part III had a hop quota. Many had substantial acreage under orchards but only six farms, Aylton Court, Eastwood Farm, The Hyde, Thinghill Court, Yare Farm and Yarkhill Court, had soft fruit.

Most of the farmers listed in Part III were given an A grade for competence. There were exceptions. Mr Meredith of Perton Court, Stoke Edith was given a B grade. Although he was a competent pastoral farmer he had very little knowledge of arable farming. The farmer at Baregains Farm in Little Marcle was given a C grade and steps were taken to oust him. Although seemingly unrecorded in the minutes of the Herefordshire National Farm Survey Subcommittee the tenant of the important farm of Showle Court was called into question and by early 1942 had been replaced by the young Tom Barnes.

When the National Farm Survey of 1941–1943 and the Agricultural Census of June 1941 are taken together a vivid picture emerges of the struggle that so many East Herefordshire farmers, farmworkers and their families, like the rest of the farming community in the country, had endured in the previous 20 years and particularly in the early 1930s. This showed itself in the lack of modern facilities and in the poor upkeep of the farms.

Lack of electricity

In the 18th century visitors complained about the state of Herefordshire roads. The late 1930s equivalent was the lack of electricity over much of the Herefordshire countryside. In England as a whole electricity was available to 30% of agricultural holdings.[20] In contrast in Herefordshire in 1942 only 14% of agricultural holdings had access to electricity. Only two other counties (Devon and Cornwall) in England had so low a percentage. However the situation in Herefordshire was even worse than in these other counties. In Devon and Cornwall 77% and 83% respectively of the electricity was from a public supply. In Herefordshire it was only 64%.

Electricity from the mains grid was available in Lugwardine, although costly, and in addition a number of the wealthier farmers in Withington, Weston Beggard and Yarkhill clubbed together to have electricity specially installed at an even more considerable cost. For all the other parishes where the farms had installed electricity from private sources it was usually just for lighting purposes rather than for power. Only one of the farms in Part III, Aylton Court, had a milking machine in 1941 but it was run on a generator as Aylton Court only had private electricity for lighting purposes. Elsewhere milking, that time-consuming activity, was invariably done by hand. 23 of the farms described in Part III had no electricity at all: Weston Corner Farm in Withington, Moorend Farm in Weston Beggard, The Grove Farm and Showle Court in Yarkhill, Hynett Farm and Old Court in Lugwardine, Claston Farm in Dormington, Perton Court in Stoke Edith, Eastwood Farm and Hazel Court in

Tarrington, Walsopthorne Farm in Ashperton, Baregains Farm, Laddin Farm, Little Marcle Court and Lower House Farm in Little Marcle, and all the farms in Woolhope. One can imagine the extra work involved in farm activities.

Drainage, ditches, hedges and farm buildings

The majority of the farmers in Part III had responded to the financial problems by delaying expenditure on drainage, ditches, hedges and farm buildings, so much so that it is interesting instead to see which of the farms had, in contrast, succeeded during these hard times in maintaining that vital long-term expenditure. They were mainly the larger and presumably the more prosperous hop farms: Freetown, Garford Farm, Lillands, Pixley Court, Stone House Farm, Thinghill Court and Withington Court. However some remarkable smaller farms were also similarly successful: Beans Butts in Woolhope, Lower House Farm in Little Marcle and The Grove Farm in Yarkhill.

Tractors versus horses

Most of the farms of a hundred or more acres had a tractor although the number of tractors in Herefordshire in 1941 was well below the average for the country.

Despite the existence of tractors all the farms had farm horses. Thinghill Court with 522 acres had three tractors but also had 11 heavy horses. H. C. Dent, farming Eastwood Farm with its 167 acres and other land in Lugwardine as well as land from the Stoke Edith estate had six tractors, but even so he had three farm horses.

Farmworkers

Some of the smaller farms were run by the farmer and his family but most employed farmworkers. Large farms employed a considerable number of workers. Comparing the farms in Part III over the previous 90-year period it is quite surprising that the number of full-time workers does not seem to have fallen substantially. In 1851 William Racster of Thinghill Court was employing 23 workers on 500 acres. In 1941 Mr Hawkins was employing 17 full-time workers of whom 14 were men and three were women on 522 acres. In 1851 Thomas Pitt was farming 248 acres at Freetown and employing six men, two boys and three women. In 1941 Percy Bradstock was farming 351 acres employing seven full-time male workers and four full-time women.

Further changes during the Second World War

The Ministry of Agriculture assigned each County WAEC a target for conversion of pasture to arable and this was then subdivided by district. The minutes of the

Herefordshire National Farm Survey Subcommittee show substantial additional acreages of pasture ploughed up for the 1942 harvest with another addition for the 1943 harvest. The 1943 addition affected 12 of the farms included in Part III in the Ledbury district alone.

Farm	Acres
Aylton Court, Aylton	7.3
Baregains Farm, Little Marcle	15.5
Bent Orchards, Woolhope	6.9
Canwood Farm, Woolhope	12.0
Court Farm, Aylton	4.9
Court Farm, Woolhope	5.0
Laddin Farm, Little Marcle	8.0
Lillands, Little Marcle	10.5
Overbury Farm, Woolhope	8.7
Park Farm, Woolhope	6.6
Showle Court, Yarkhill	13.0
The Hyde and Sapness Farm, Woolhope	13.1

Fig. 4.4 Acres of land required to be ploughed up by Ledbury district WAEC for 1943 harvest[21]

The identification of additional fields to be ploughed up would have been a challenging one. Herefordshire farmers have long memories and many years after the war at parties and other gatherings complaints could still be heard on the lines of "Your grandfather compelled our farm to plough up our most productive meadow". Farmers received fixed prices for their products, deliberately set to provide higher incomes based on average yields. A failure of the crop though would be a financial burden given the costs of preparing the land.

Although the farms remained mixed farms the extraordinary growth in arable inevitably led to a further reduction in some livestock. However Ministry of Agriculture annual Agricultural Census figures for Herefordshire for 1941–1945 show that the number of cattle remained approximately the same partly because the government was especially keen to maintain milk production, an important source of nutrition. The diversion of cereal crop to human consumption together with the decline in imports however continued to radically reduce the availability of animal feed and in this period the numbers of pigs in Herefordshire declined by a further 23%, poultry by 15% and sheep by 8%.

Each year during the Second World War and indeed until 1950 summer camps were arranged for secondary schoolchildren, primarily to help with the fruit picking. Arable production is more labour intensive than pastoral and from 1941 farmers could make use of the Women's Land Army. The experience was not altogether a happy one. All farmers are conservative and under the conditions of Herefordshire where much work is hard labour the farmers are particularly so. As one former Land Army girl stated in a throwaway phrase when reminiscing: "The farmers didn't like us". Because of the problems of billeting soldiers on farms in Herefordshire many of the Women's Land Army were attached to the Herefordshire WAEC and lodged in hostels. The women played an indispensable role in providing farm labour, sometimes skilled. The Herefordshire WAEC Subcommittee on Machinery of 1 August 1941 in an innovative gesture and a reflection of their difficulties with existing tractor drivers had selected 12 WLA women for training as tractor drivers and were agreeably surprised at the aptitude shown by some of them. There were romances. Peter Davies of Aylton Court met his future wife, Phyllis Jakeman, a Land Army girl at Pixley Court when they were supervising the movement of produce at Ashperton station.

The farmers normally preferred the prisoners of war who were available towards the last two years of the war. On occasion the prisoners of war could be resentful and unhelpful but on the other hand some, often those from a similar rural background, became family friends after the war. The German prisoner of war who worked at Claston Farm stayed on the farm all his life and looked after Philip and Mildred Davies in their old age.

Fig. 4.4 Phyllis Jakeman (later Davies) in her Women's Land Army uniform – a town girl, previously employed in a London department store, she was proud of winning third prize in the WLA milking competition [22]

The human cost

There were inevitably losses of young men amongst the local country families, albeit fewer than in 1914–1918, but each a tragedy for family and friends. One was the elder son of the late Henry James Dent of Perton Court and brother of Henry Cooke Dent, then at Eastwood Farm, Tarrington. Oscar William Robert Dent was killed in the Normandy invasion. His son, John Dent of Withington Court with his wife Elizabeth have continued the long family tradition of successful breeding of pedigree Hereford cattle.

Immediate post-war: 1945–1949

The period 1945–1949 saw in many practical ways a continuation of wartime conditions. The County War Agricultural Executive Committees were wound up when war ended but many of the regulations and controls remained. The Agricultural Education Subcommittee of the Herefordshire County Council Executive Agricultural Committee was reconvened and the Agricultural Quarterly Journal reinstated. Rationing did not end until 1953 and was indeed more severe in 1947 and 1948 than it had been during the Second World War as during this period both bread and potatoes had to be rationed.

During this period there was a modest adjustment to peacetime conditions. The proportion of land under tillage fell from 42% in 1945 to 37% in 1950, still far above the pre-war level to which it has never returned. The reduction in tillage facilitated a revival in the numbers of livestock. The number of cattle rose by 17% and there was a slight increase in the number of sheep. The largest increase, though, was in the numbers of poultry: at 880,000 it was over 50% more than in 1945. There was, even as early as this period, the start of deep litter, a more intensive method of production.

There was immediately a fundamental difference for farmers though. In contrast to the 90-year period prior to 1939, from the Second World War onwards farming has been considered strategically important even in peacetime and consequently deserving of very substantial financial support. The initial demonstration of this was the passing of the 1947 Agriculture Act. Under the Act guaranteed prices were negotiated annually between the Ministry of Agriculture and the NFU and the farmers were compensated for any shortfalls in their actual receipts. The workings of this Act and the many changes in the support over the second half of the 20th century and their consequences for East Herefordshire farming are taken up in the following chapter.

Notes

[1] Whetham, Edith H. (1978). *The Agrarian History of England and Wales 1914-1939*, Volume VIII. Cambridge University Press. p. 15 (derived from table 6).

[2] Whetham, Edith H. *op. cit*. p. 15.

[3] Whetham, Edith H. *op. cit*. pp. 89 & 90.

[4] Hereford Cathedral Archive (HCA) 6009.

[5] National Farmers' Union Annual Report, South Herefordshire 1915: Herefordshire Archive Service (HAS) BA 49/186.

[6] Laws, Bill. (2016). *Herefordshire's Home Front in the First World War*. Logaston Press. p. 62.

[7] Laws, Bill. *op. cit*. p. 132.

[8] Whetham, Edith H. *op. cit*. p. 230.

[9] Whetham, Edith H. *op. cit*. p. 230.

[10] Whetham, Edith H. *op. cit*. p. 137.

[11] Skidelsky, Robert. (2014). Britain Since 1900 – A Success Story? Vintage. p. 183.

[12] Heath-Agnew, E. (1983). *A History of Hereford Cattle and Their Breeders*. Duckworth. p. 133.

[13] Whetham, Edith H. *op. cit*. p. 190.

[14] Whetham, Edith H. *op. cit*. p. 260.

[15] Heath-Agnew, E. (1983). *op. cit*. pp. 146–159.

[16] Herefordshire Federation of Women's Institutes (1989). *The Herefordshire Village Book*. Countryside Books. p. 19.

[17] Davies, Peter. (2007). *A Herefordshire Tale: Claston, Hops and the Davies Family*. Peter Davies.

[18] Whetham, Edith H. (1952) *British Farming 1939–1949*. Thomas Nelson. pp. 15 & 16.

[19] Short, Brian. (2014) *The Battle of the Fields*. Boydell Press. p 59 quoting Wilt, Alan F. (2001) *Food for War: Agriculture and Rearmament in Britain before the Second World War*. Oxford University Press.

[20] Finnegan, Oliver & Glover, Catherine (Eds.). (2014). *British Farm Surveys, 1941 to 1943:* Reports and Statistical Analysis. List and Index Society. p. 107 (derived from table A 17).

[21] MAF 80/1058 Minutes Farm Survey Subcommittee.

[22] By kind permission of Penelope Cunningham.

FARMING AS A SUPPORTED INDUSTRY: 1950–1999

Fig. 5.1 Mr John Poyner at the Trumpet and District Agricultural Society Tractor Run 2017

1950 onwards is a natural break in the history of East Herefordshire farming. From this time onwards the agricultural industry has generally been recognised as of national importance and in need of financial support. An East Hereford farmer struggling during any of the difficult periods from 1875 to the start of the Second World War with laissez-faire governments and cheap imports would have been astonished at the reversal in attitude and the consequent benefits to farmers' incomes generally in the second half of the 20th century. However the support received varied radically during this time and the changes had considerable impact on the individual farms and farmers. Associated with this, and of the greatest importance for life in the countryside, was the erosion in the numbers employed, especially on the larger farms, and the replacement of farmworkers with ever larger and more complicated machines. No longer was the farm the principal, in fact in many cases the only, employer of labour in East Herefordshire.

Guaranteed prices, capital subsidies, marketing boards: 1950–1972

Under the 1947 Agricultural Act farmers were protected against market fluctuations by guaranteed minimum prices for key agricultural products (cattle, sheep, pigs, milk, eggs, barley, wheat, oats, rye, mixed corn, potatoes, sugar beet and wool). The advisory services and marketing boards set up in the 1930s – the Hop Marketing Board in 1932, the Milk Marketing Board in 1933 and the Potato Marketing Board in the same year – continued in existence and were used to provide advice to farmers and promote agricultural products. This provided support to most of the products of the farms in East Herefordshire given in Part III. The exception was those important orchards – these were supposedly protected through seasonal and other import tariffs.

In the early post-war world guaranteed prices were not such a severe strain on the Exchequer, but from around 1953 onwards international prices started to come down. In order to reduce the burden the government started to move away from guaranteed prices, replacing them with subsidies for capital equipment. However, from 1956 long-term assurances for agriculture stated that for any product, apart from livestock, the guaranteed price in any one year should not be less than 96% of the previous year's figures. For livestock production the reduction was to be no more than 9% in any three-year period. To further assist farmers the Egg Marketing Board was set up in 1956.

Although officially the government continued to be wedded to a free trade policy in fact from 1964 onwards the government also initiated some tacit control on imports. 'Voluntary limits' were sought on some commodities although there were also later direct quotas. By 1969 there were quotas on butter and 'voluntary arrangements' on poultry.[1]

Traditional farming

With the security provided by government commitment and support, these years in East Herefordshire were exceptionally benign. The Ministry of Agriculture annual Agricultural Censuses for the period show that the remarkable increase in arable output in Herefordshire achieved during the Second World War was maintained during the second half of the 20th century.

In the Second World War the increase in yields had been achieved mainly by ploughing up more land. Between 1950 and the early 1960s not only was the area under wheat higher but the average yield per acre in the UK doubled. Wheat was a profitable crop grown on most farms and there was a fall in the output of turnips and swedes previously used for animal fodder. With higher incomes, silage, which required significant capital investment, became a popular alternative to hay on some of the larger East Hereford farms such as Pixley Court.

Despite the greater emphasis on cereals the old staples of Herefordshire, cattle, hops and orchards all prospered. After an early post-war boom, the number of sheep did decline from the 1950s onwards, but most farms still had a modest flock, sometimes of the old established Ryelands.

Hereford cattle

The 1950s and 1960s were good years for the leading breeders of Hereford pedigree cattle. For the first time since 1920 the export market for the highest quality pedigree Herefords to the US revived in 1950 as the American breeders wanted to combat dwarfism in their stock. Amongst the bulls exported to this country in 1951 was P. E. and T. F. Bradstock of Freetown's bull, Free Town Contrite, who had been both Grand Male and Reserve Supreme Champion at the Royal Agricultural Society of England Royal Show in Shrewsbury in 1949 and was bought by the Wyoming Hereford Ranch. Other leading East Herefordshire breeders exporting to the US in the 1950s included Mr and Mrs P. M. G. Fraser of Westhide who exported their two bulls Westhide Governor and Westhide James in 1953, and Mr H. R. Grifiths of Little Tarrington who exported Tarrington Onward in 1950.[2] Argentina remained an important market. Mr Dean Dent of Woodmanton Farm, Yarkhill, a distant relative of Henry James Dent of Perton Court, exported his bull, Woodmanton Guardsman, to Argentina for £2,800 in 1954. In addition to the established exports to Australia, New Zealand and North and South America, the 1960s saw prize animals exported to European countries both in the Eastern bloc and the EC.

Prices for these finest prize-winning bulls were many fold higher than the average. In the 1950s prices at the Hereford Herd Book Society show and sale averaged around £280 and in the 1960s around £380. Although this was still lower than the peak year of 1920, Hereford cattle continued to provide a satisfactory income at this level.

The domestic demand for quality Hereford bulls benefited from the combination of the rapid growth of artificial insemination and the government concern that the development of specialist dairy rather than dual purpose herds was leading to wastage of the many calves deemed not suitable for herd replacement and which also had exceptionally low qualities for beef. A calf subsidy which had been introduced in 1947 was restricted in 1952 to steers of beef type and heifers suitable for beef breeding. In 1947 artificial insemination by one of the three colour marking beef breeds (Aberdeen Angus, Galloway and Hereford) was made free. The scheme was so successful that it was withdrawn in 1952.

Increasingly Herefords were a favoured bull. In 1936–1937 35% of licensed beef bulls were Herefords. By 1950–1951 this had increased to 49% and by 1970–1971 it had reached 79%. Hereford/ Friesian cross bull calves in the dairy herds normally had beefing qualities and could be sold at good prices. The Hereford was similarly favoured for artificial insemination, providing all beef inseminations in 1970. Freetown Vanguard was said in 1975 to have sired a remarkable 50,000 offspring during his 10 years of service.[3]

Most of the larger farmers in East Herefordshire had their herd of commercial beef cattle, often pedigree Herefords, but also pedigree cross. In this period Claston Farm was buying crossbred yearling bullocks for fattening and sale to the Midland finishers. No doubt others were doing the same.

Dairy cattle

For many smaller or moderate-sized farms, such as Lower House Farm in Little Marcle, Moorend Farm in Weston Beggard, Old Court and Hynett Farm in Lugwardine, Hazel Court in Tarrington, Bent Orchards, Overbury Farm, Park Farm and Yare Farm in Woolhope, dairying was important. Bent Orchards had invested in a fine new milking parlour in 1947 powered by their own generator and Aylton Court, a much larger farm in Aylton parish, was also well known for its pedigree Friesian herd. The Milk Marketing Board lorry came round each day to collect the churns containing quite modest quantities of milk whilst calves could be reared on any excess quantities. By this time, the Milk Marketing Board, most of whose board members were elected, was not only a purchaser and transporter of fresh milk, but also a processor of high-value milk products. It provided farmers with negotiating power, especially with that part of the product sold for manufacturing where producer prices had traditionally been notoriously low. By the 1960s collection by tanker was becoming the norm with an adverse impact on the smallest farmers. However, for most farms the service was satisfactory and the monthly cheque useful.

Since towards the end of the Second World War the Milk Marketing Board had been a provider of useful artificial insemination services to the farming community. In 1968, taking advantage of the dip in prices of quality Hereford pedigree bulls in consequence of the foot-and-mouth epidemic, the Milk Marketing Board bought six quality bulls. In addition to selling the milk, farmers owning dairy herds could also rear half-bred beef calves.

Every outbreak of foot-and-mouth epidemic can have dire consequences. The 1967–1968 outbreak afflicted Mr and Mrs Walker and Mrs Walker's mother, Mrs Brewer, at Lower House Farm, Little Marcle and led to the destruction of all their cows. They gave up farming shortly afterwards.

Hop production

Above all for the farms of 100 or more acres on the rich Herefordshire sandstone hops were at least as important and profitable as they had been way back in the period of 'high farming' in the 1860s. The acreage varied but of the 36 farms included in Part III no fewer than 21 had a hop quota. This highly capital-intensive crop continued to require big investments and be very susceptible to the weather, with rain at the wrong time making the hops very difficult to harvest. There could be, and indeed were, annual failures. In *A Herefordshire Tale* Peter Davies described the loss of his entire 33 acres of hops at Longworth, Bartestree in 1964 when the hop yards were struck by lightning and the hops collapsed during a heavy thunderstorm. Fortunately he was fully covered by insurance. However, the total quantity of UK hops to be provided under quota was negotiated each year between the Hop Marketing Board and the brewery representatives. This quota was sold at an average cost plus an agreed profit margin. The demand for hops grew considerably during this period so the size of the quota considerably increased. When individual farmers experienced a harvest failure it was often possible for them to at least partially compensate by selling their unused quota. Thus risk in this most risky of crops was appreciably reduced and prices uniformly good.

At least three of the farms illustrated in Part III greatly increased their hop acreage between 1950 and 1973. In the early post-war period Stone House Farm, Withington had put a large acreage under orchards, unusually producing its own cider, but then switched to hops, taking advantage of the shortage of hops and good prices. Claston Farm in Dormington similarly expanded its hop production, firstly by renting the hop yard at Eastwood Farm, Tarrington from 1946–1956 and then by purchasing additional acreage of land at The Vauld, Marden in 1954 where hops were grown until 1972. David Skittery of Lillands increased the hop acreage from 20 to 50 acres in 1966.

Orchards

The only part of traditional farming which did less well were the orchards. There was no specific government support for fruit growing. Although the sector was supposedly supported by tariffs, these did not seem to be effective. The acreage in Herefordshire under orchards halved from over 22,000 acres in 1950 to only around 11,000 in 1970.

Potatoes

With the new consumer demand for potato crisps and instant potato products the acreage under potatoes, which had radically expanded in the Second World War, continued to increase in this period.

New machinery and equipment

A major change in this period was mechanisation, as even the small farmers of East Herefordshire now had the confidence, and indeed the money, to purchase some farm equipment. Electricity finally came to rural Herefordshire, although it took its time and only arrived in Woolhope in 1959. (Mains water took much longer and was in place by the 1970s.) The need for casual farm labour was therefore considerably reduced, and there was also a reduction in the number of full-time farmworkers required.

Those lovely farm horses were the first to be affected. That brand-new tractor made them redundant. Stout and Bouncy, the horses on Yare Farm, Woolhope were no longer required. Then there were the new balers. It was no longer necessary to build a wheat or haystack with that special thatch to keep it dry and in some instances hay was replaced with silage which required specialised equipment.

Until the 1950s hop picking had always been done by hand and late September/early October were lively times for Herefordshire. The gypsy caravans would arrive as indeed they had done for hundreds of years. They would be joined by hop pickers from the

Fig. 5.2 Reg Bayliss of Moorend Farm, Weston Beggard practising with new equipment at a YFC meeting at Monksbury Court, Yarkhill [4]

Midlands, especially from Dudley, as well as those from South Wales. Traditionally hop picking had been considered an enjoyable working holiday. It was said in Herefordshire that the police in the Midlands also took their holidays then and there were always a number of colourful stories in the local *Hereford Times*. However in times of high wage rates and high employment it was becoming difficult to attract labour. Piece rates needed to be increased and hop picking by hand became increasingly problematic. On the larger farms hop pickers vanished to be replaced by machines. Most were bought from the small number of producers of hop-picking machines and were extremely expensive. Dormington Court purchased its first machine in 1953 and Claston Farm in 1957, but Les Bowcott of Monksbury Court, Yarkhill, a son of Thomas Bowcott (1879–1947) of Felton Court, who had a special aptitude in engineering, designed his own.

The British manufacturers of farm machinery prospered and gave special lectures to the Young Farmers' Clubs on the new machinery and how to use it. The YFC members competed to show their skill with the new equipment. Reg Bayliss of Moorend Farm, Weston Beggard was exceptionally successful in these competitions.

New types of farming

The mid-1960s saw the beginnings of new types of agriculture on certain of the larger farms in East Herefordshire.

Intensive poultry, pig and milk production

In 1964 the historic and large farm, The Hyde, Woolhope, changed hands. It was farmed, not by an individual farmer, but by a consortium financed by money from the City of London. None of those participating had previous long-term involvement in agriculture but they saw the prospects in an agricultural industry so well supported by government. The consortium had formed a joint venture with Sun Valley Poultry in 1963, a company which had been founded in 1960 and produced poultry on an intensive scale under 'factory' conditions in Hereford. The consortium expanded Sun Valley and the company's several farms specialised in different activities. The number of poultry in Herefordshire continued to show a sharp upward trend to just under two million in 1979 compared with 800,000 in 1955. There were pigs at The Hyde and another of the farms concentrated on milk production.

Instant trees

An interesting new endeavour was pioneered by Thinghill Court, Withington in the late 1960s. Taking advantage of modern agronomy advances, Stuart Hawkins

Fig. 5.3 Instant trees on Thinghill Court land in 2017

combined with Wyevale Nurseries in Hereford to produce 'instant trees' for sale to those authorities wishing to beautify new developments. This enterprise continued until the 21st century. Although Wyevale Nurseries are no longer associated with Thinghill Court some trees are still containerised on Thinghill land.

The Common Agricultural Policy: 1973–1999

With its entry into the Common Market in 1973 the UK adopted the Common Agricultural Policy (CAP). This had been devised for countries with a higher proportion of their population than in the UK engaged in agriculture and living in more rural areas. It consequently paid much greater attention to protection, with the subsequent burden falling more on consumers in terms of higher prices rather than the previous policy of subsidies with the burden on government finances. Agriculture moved to a system of guaranteed intervention prices protected by quotas and tariffs, whereby surplus stock is taken off the market when prices fall by the European Community stepping in and buying it up.

The policy was highly effective in increasing output in the EC above that needed for domestic use. From the 1980s much comment was made on the EC surpluses of 'butter mountains' and 'wine lakes'. Consequently to counter the growing cost of such surpluses the EC intervention support prices generally started to be somewhat reduced.

Arable farming prospers

Certain arable products, including wheat, were specially favoured by EC policy. Partly in response to the CAP the area under wheat in the UK in 1975–1980 was more than double that of 1965–1970.

The EC support resulting in increased returns from cereal production was of significant benefit to a number of the larger farms described in Part III and encouraged a further switch to arable in East Herefordshire. Not only were the prices higher but the yield per acre jumped with the use of herbicides and then fungicides. It was around this time that Canwood Farm, Woolhope converted from mixed farming to specialised arable farming with considerable success. In 1986 at Claston Farm 350 acres of the 600-acre farm were down to cereals.

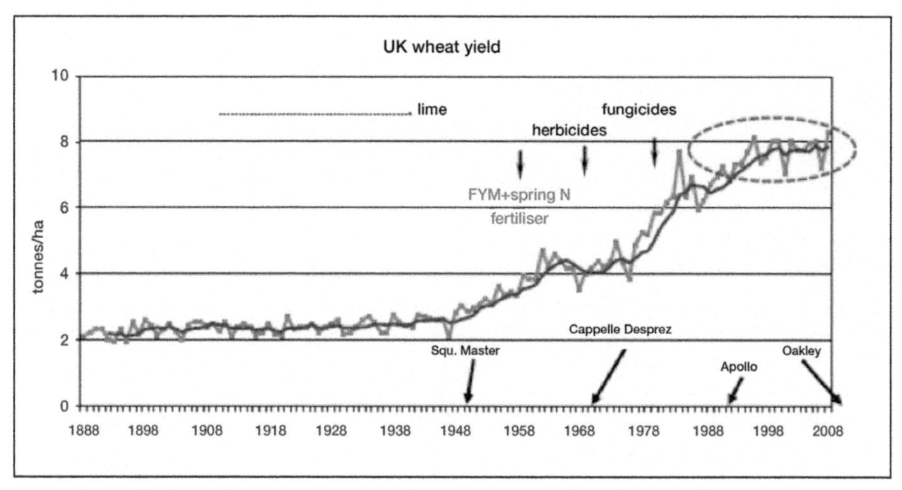

Fig. 5.4 NIAB calculations of the average yield per hectare of wheat in England 1888–2008 [5]

With the advent of more arable farming the landscape of the parishes of East Hereforshire changed, apart from the majority of the parish of Woolhope. To ensure economies of scale, the larger farms acquired more land and the traditional fields were amalgamated to facilitate the large, complex machinery. Gone were many of the hedgerows, some identifiable as far back at the Tithe Maps of the 1840s. With the growth of herbicides and fungicides traditional flora and fauna declined.

Problems with hop production

The deadly Progressive Verticillium wilt (PVW) which was untreatable had afflicted hop growers in Kent for many years but had by this time spread to East Herefordshire. According to Peter Davies in *A Herefordshire Tale*, Perton Court hop yards had probably been affected in 1972 and Claston Farm was an early sufferer with an outbreak in 1973. By 1981 11 growers in East Herefordshire had been affected and the number affected by PVW continued to rise remorselessly, although it was possible from 1981 onwards to obtain permission to replant hop yards with PVW resistant varieties. A further blow was when the Hop Marketing Board which had supported hop growers effectively for 50 years was considered inconsistent with EC competition law and was abolished in 1982.

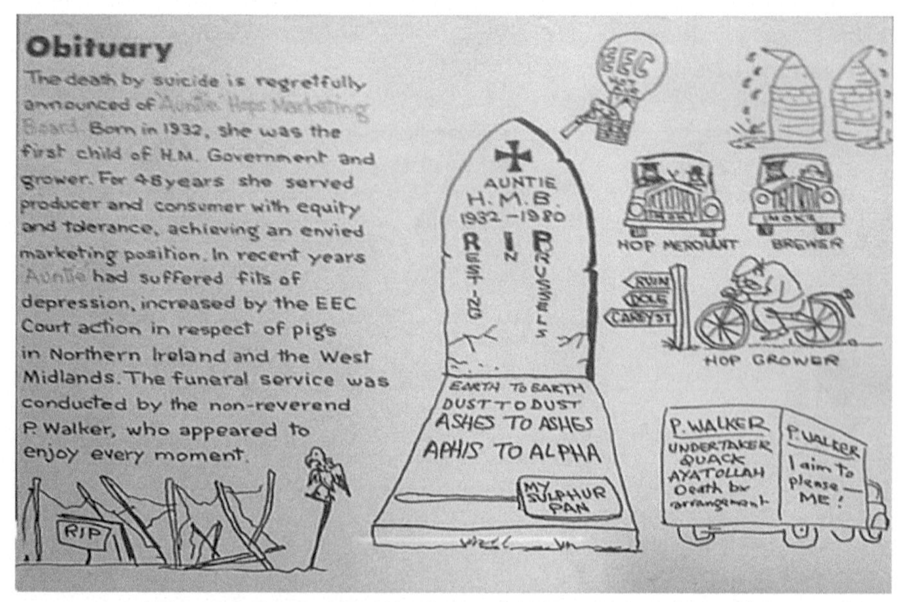

Fig. 5.5 Cartoon marking the demise of the Hop Marketing Board [6]

Through an initiative of Peter Davies, Weston Quality Hops Ltd was established in 1983 as a joint marketing board which received approval by the EC as a produce marketing group in 1988. However as Peter Davies pointed out in A Herefordshire Tale the Hop Marketing Board's arrangement made with the British brewers to take the basic quota each year had meant that only poor quality hops were left after the quota was satisfied with the result that it had not been possible to build up an export market. The UK brewers had also become dissatisfied with the inability to make forward contracts for the purchase of hops which were standard elsewhere.

In the early 1960s, West Germany and the UK were growing about an equal quantity of hops. However the Germans adopted a vigorous export strategy, largely by making agreements with brewers worldwide to brew German lager beer, but using only German hops. Sadly the HMB never changed the original marketing agreement with brewers, and by the 1990s the German growers were producing six times as many hops as growers in the UK.[7]

In 1993 the ever resourceful Peter Davies pioneered the laboursaving and more environmentally friendly hedgerow hops but still the numbers of hop growers fell radically. A final blow at the end of the century was the collapse in world price. Peter Davies related that in 1995 he was able to arrange a five-year contract for his hedgerow hops at £250 per zentner (1 zentner = 1.97 cwt). Two years later his purchaser went bankrupt and the price in 1998 was about £50 per zentner. By 1999 of the farms in Part III only Thinghill Court in Withington, Walsopthorne Farm in Ashperton, Lillands in Little Marcle and Dormington Court land were producing hops.

Soft fruit

Soft fruit continued to be produced at The Hyde and Pixley Court was one of a number of farms already growing blackcurrants under contract from one of the major soft drink companies. The decline of hops gave an added incentive to soft fruit production and it was in the mid-1980s that Pixley Court started its major expansion of blackcurrant and raspberry production.

Hereford pedigree cattle

Increased competition

Although under the CAP the number of cattle in general also rose, some farsighted observers had pointed to possible weaknesses in Hereford cattle even in the prosperous post-war years. With the increasing scientific approaches to breeding, statistical data on weight gain, food conversion and progeny were readily available in the US for Hereford cattle and other breeds but the English breeders, confident of the quality of their animals, had largely ignored this. From the 1960s onwards, customer demand had been increasingly changing in favour of leaner cuts with butchers preferring larger animals. Continental breeds, principally Charolais and Simmental, which had these characteristics, accounted for 47% of all artificial beef inseminations by 1984 whilst the share by Herefords had dropped to 44%. There were also some changes in marketing cattle in this period. The increasing use of semen meant that more sales were made from farms rather than at auctions. The numbers of pedigree Herefords sold at the Hereford Herd Book Society shows and sales therefore fell sharply throughout the 1970s and 1980s.

On the positive side Hereford cattle were still known to be quality, low-maintenance animals, good at conversion from grass and average prices still reflected this. However no longer was there that remarkable premium available for the highest quality bulls which had so inspired the breeders. Typically the champions at the Herd Book Society shows and sales during the 1970s and 1980s reached two to three times the average price rather than five to ten times as had been experienced on many occasions in the past.

The numbers sold at the Hereford Herd Book shows and sales continued to fall in the late 1980s and early 1990s although prices were somewhat higher. In January 1995 only 16 bulls were offered for sale but with an average price of £1,485. The Champion, Louda Zodiac, sold for 2,400 guineas (£2,520).

Spread of BSE

The breeders of Hereford cattle were by the late 1980s facing a crisis far worse than simple competition from other breeds. Bovine Spongiform Encephalopathy (BSE) had first been observed in a dairy herd in the UK in December 1984. The disease was officially recognised in 1986 and from July 1988 all animals showing BSE symptoms were required to be slaughtered. In July 1989 Europe had banned the export of British cattle born before July 1988 and the offspring of affected animals. On 20 March 1996 the health secretary, Stephen Dorrell, officially announced a probable link between the cattle disease and the human disease CJD. Exactly one week later the EC imposed a worldwide ban on all exports of British beef (live cattle, meat and products). The ban on meat and products from animals born after August 1996 was lifted by the EC in 1999 but remained in Germany until 2000 and in France until 2002. The ban on the export of live cattle to the EC from the UK remained in force until 2006. Individual countries outside the EC imposed their own restrictions.[8]

Dairy farmers

From 1984 quotas had been imposed on milk production, benefiting those who had quotas and ensuring that dairying was normally profitable, but making it difficult for those who wished to enter the business. Although compensation for infected cows was available, tuberculosis was an increasing danger throughout this period, and could destroy a farmer's livelihood. The dairy farmers of East Herefordshire suffered less than the beef producers in the 1990s as a result of the BSE crisis – not for them was a halving of their market. The Milk Marketing Board which had served the dairy farmers so well was not abolished until 1994 and the full impact of this privatisation was not seen until the 21st century. Park Farm, Woolhope continued as a milk producer and Thinghill Court, Withington built up an extensive dairy herd. Showle Court, Yarkhill was establishing itself as a specialist organic milk producer from 1983 with the fodder for the cows produced on the farm itself and a sophisticated milking parlour especially designed by Roger Clay, the brother of Tom Clay, owner and farmer of Showle Court from 1983.

Fig. 5.6 Shorthorn cow in Showle Court rotary milking parlour designed and built by Roger Clay

Sale of land with farmhouses and buildings converted to residential use

With the sole exception of Lower House Farm, Little Marcle, so stricken by the 1967–1968 foot-and-mouth disease that the Walkers and Mrs Brewer gave up farming in 1970, all the 36 farms described in Part III survived at least until the late 1970s, often with approximately the same historic acreage as enjoyed for 150 or more years.

However, with wilt destroying most of the previously profitable hop yards and with livestock production seriously damaged by BSE, farming seemed less attractive to the families of some of the farmers who were reaching retirement age or had died. In contrast, with mains water and electricity in place, a substantial house in remarkably beautiful country with a modest acreage for leisure pursuits was a most attractive proposition for those with financial capital. With land and property prices remaining high, land from six of the 36 farms were sold off and the farmhouses and some buildings sold for conversion to residential use between 1972 and 1999. As a result, many of the former manor houses have been restored to their former magnificence.

In the late 1970s most of the land of Old Court, Lugwardine close to Hereford was sold for housing. In 1988 when Percy Cooke, the farmer at Old Court, completely retired, the farmhouse and barn were sold for residential use. Perton Court land in Stoke Edith had been run as part of the Stoke Edith estate throughout much of the post-Second World War period and in the 1980s Perton Court itself, its buildings and cottages were sold as housing. In 1986 Peter Davies of Claston Farm bought Dormington Court. Retaining the land, he sold off Dormington Court for development as a hotel, and the farm cottages and the hop kilns for residential accommodation. In 1989 Frederick Davies retired and most of Aylton Court land was sold to the neighbouring farm of Lillands in Little Marcle. Little Marcle Court in Little Marcle was sold in 1995 and Weston Corner Farm, Withington also ceased to be a farm in this period.

Exit from European Exchange Rate Mechanism

In 1993 farming in general, including East Herefordshire, received a welcome and most unexpected boost. The United Kingdom left the European Exchange Rate Mechanism in September 1992, the predecessor to the euro and the measure by which the EC (from 1993 the EU) intervention prices were decided. With the effective devaluation of sterling, the guaranteed intervention price, which is decided in euros, was worth more in sterling. In the country as a whole, farm incomes in 1994–1996 were at their highest level ever in real terms and were around double those of the previous three years 1990–1993.[9] However, unfortunately this prosperity was not to last.

Notes

[1] Bowers, J. K. (1985). *British Agricultural Policy Since the Second World War.* Agricultural History Review. p. 72.

[2] Heath-Agnew, E. (1983). *A History of Hereford Cattle and Their Breeders.* Duckworth. p. 204.

[3] Grundy, Joan E. (2002). *The Hereford bull: his contribution to New World and domestic beef supplies.* Agricultural History Review. pp. 81–84.

[4] By kind permission of Reginald Bayliss.

[5] By kind permission of Bill Clark, Technical Director, NIAB. www.niab.com/

[6] By kind permission of Edward Thompson.

[7] Davies, Peter. (2007). *A Herefordshire Tale: Claston, Hops and the Davies Family.* Peter Davies. p. 82.

[8] www.theguardian.com/uk/2000/oct/26/bse3

[9] Department for Environment, Food and Rural Affairs. (2012). *Agriculture in the United Kingdom 2011.* DEFRA. p. 3 (derived from chart 2.1).

FARMING IN THE EARLY 21ST CENTURY

Fig. 6.1 The hop kiln and farm buildings at Aylton Court converted for residential use

Changes in farms and farming

Further sales of farms

The sale of land and the sale of farmhouses and buildings for conversion to residential use continued at the beginning of the 21st century. Mr Tremayn of Court Farm in Aylton had sold most of his land in the years before his retirement in 2000, leaving only 20 acres at the time of the final sale in 2000. Eastwood Farm land was sold and the farm house, hop kilns and farm buildings turned into residential accommodation around 2000. Following the death of Mr Harrison in 2002 the historically large farm of Brook Farm in Little Marcle was sold to David Watkins. David Watkins continues to farm the land but the farmhouse and many of the buildings at Brook Farm have been converted into residential accommodation, as have those at Yarkhill Court, which ceased to be a farm in 2009. Stephen Dale continues to live at Canwood Farm, but most of the land was sold in 2012 and the farm buildings and remaining ten acres converted into a greatly esteemed art gallery and sculpture park in 2016. Bent Orchards land and farmhouse was sold to another Woolhope farmer at the end of 2016.

Of the 36 farms described in Part III, 21 remain as family farms at the time of publication.

Foot-and-mouth strikes again

The 21st century started badly when foot-and-mouth struck at a national level in 2001 with an epidemic far worse even than that of 1967–1968. Those living in the Herefordshire countryside at that time will long remember those dreadful funeral pyres. Farming was desperately affected by the slaughter of so many animals, not just from the farms with confirmed foot-and-mouth cases but also from farms associated with them. Even farms not directly affected were gravely hampered by the embargo on the movement of all livestock. Countryside tourism, important in Herefordshire, came to a temporary halt.

The Grove, Yarkhill was one of the farms that suffered from the epidemic itself and now no longer has livestock. Bent Orchards, Woolhope was seriously affected by the embargo which prevented the sale of its milk and subsequently switched from milk to suckler calves.

Changes in EU support

From 2003 onwards, guaranteed intervention prices were abolished. Consequently, prices followed those of international markets. Most EU support to farmers was instead in the form of a fixed payment through the Single Payment Scheme, a payment which varied according to the hectarage given over to farming activities. In addition, a modest amount, around one quarter of the total fixed payment, was towards environmentally friendly schemes. However, certain farming activities, including horticulture and the smaller orchards received no assistance resulting in a system that favoured arable farmers.

The Single Payment Scheme was replaced from 2015 by the Basic Payment Scheme, payable to holdings of five or more hectares, but dependent on adherence to 'cross compliance'. Amongst other requirements this means that arable farmers have to produce at least three kinds of arable products. The Single Payment Scheme was calculated in euros, as is its successor. The payment therefore varies according to the rate of exchange between the euro and the pound sterling. As this has oscillated very considerably, significant differences in these annual payments have occurred. Prices, especially of cereal products, can vary sharply depending upon international commodity prices and the rate of exchange between the US dollar and the pound sterling. However, despite the difficulties of incomes varying from year to year depending on prices and yields, farming in East Herefordshire at the beginning of the 21st century has enjoyed some good years.

Some revival in farming

Although the annual DEFRA report Agriculture in the United Kingdom 2016 makes it clear that income from farming in 2013 was still below the record years of 1994–1996, the ten years from 2003 to 2013 saw a welcome revival generally in agriculture from the post-BSE depths.

Wheat and rapeseed

From 1875 to 1939 the proportion of land under arable had been low and the arable crops grown mainly intended for the feeding of the livestock. The much larger proportion under arable since the Second World War has been maintained in the early 21st century in East Herefordshire with Garford Farm, Yarkhill exclusively an arable enterprise and a few other farms in the area almost entirely given over to arable. Since 2003 prices on the local market have followed those on the international market with the international prices for both wheat and rapeseed usually more than compensating for the sharp increases in the price of inputs, despite rapeseed being an expensive and difficult crop to grow. Although there were fluctuations in the market with particularly low prices in 2009 and 2010 following the global financial crisis, prices were well above the 2003 levels until 2015 when prices fell back to around the level of a decade before. There seems to have been a modest recovery at the time of publication partially attributable to the fall in the pound sterling.

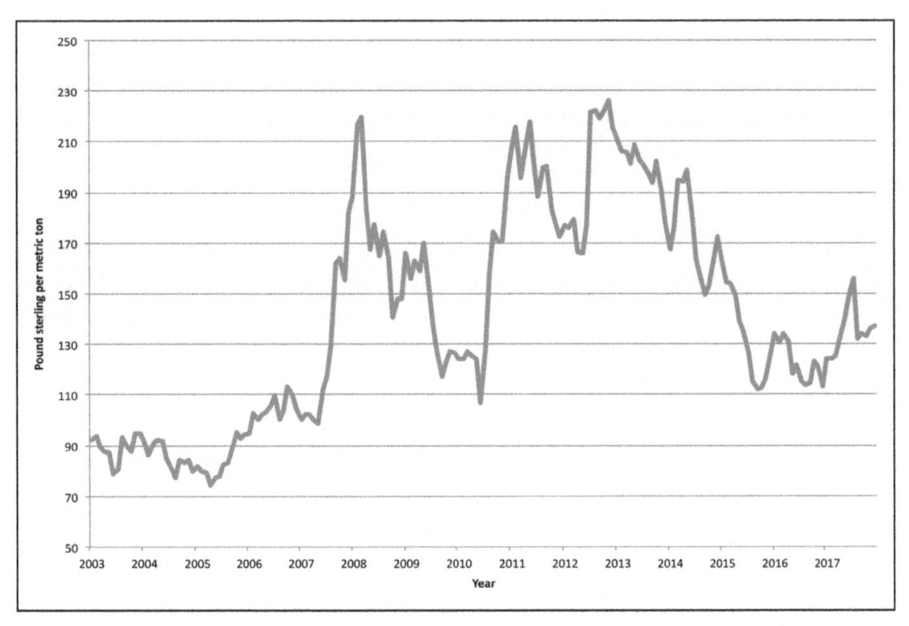

Fig. 6.2 Monthly international price of wheat per metric ton: 2003–2017 [1]

International prices for rapeseed oil have also been highly favourable up to 2013, again apart from the years 2009 and 2010. Although market conditions have again not been so good in the years 2014 and 2015, prices are still above the depression years of 2003–2006.

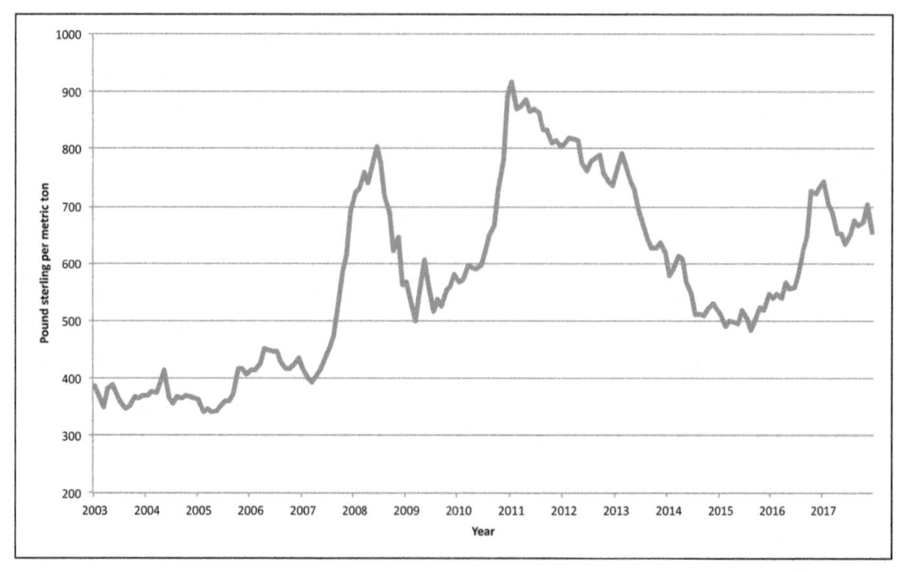

Fig. 6.3 Monthly international price of rapeseed oil per metric ton: 2003–2017 [2]

The landowner champions of the Corn Laws of the first half of 19th century would have been heartened to know that the UK in the early 21st century was self-sufficient in wheat as well as, for them, the largely unknown crop of rapeseed, and indeed in some years a net exporter of both. It is a remarkable contrast to the dependence on imported food which so imperilled the country at the start of the Second World War.

Potatoes

In the Second World War farmers had been normally obliged to grow at least one acre of the traditionally boom-or-bust crop of potatoes for the war effort. This was sometimes done reluctantly as not all land designated was suitable. In contrast potatoes are grown under contract in the 21st century at a number of East Hereford farms, including Felton Court supplying Tyrells and Hynett Farm, Lugwardine supplying McCain. Herefordshire recalls with pleasure the success of William Chase, originally made bankrupt from a disastrous year in potatoes who then developed the superb brand Tyrells Crisps in a mere six years 2002–2008 and purchased that fine historic farm Laddin in Little Marcle in 2007. His next enterprise, Chase Distilleries, based at Rosemaund, another historic farm of East Herefordshire and a former government experimental station, uses potatoes as the base for its specialised vodka and gin, as well as making cider apple based gin.

Cider, perry and single variety apple juices

The East Herefordshire farms described in Part III have always been renowned for their cider apples. To provide for an ambitious expansion of their export market in the late 20th century Bulmers, who together with Westons of Much Marcle are the principal local purchases of cider apples, had encouraged the planting of orchards through the signing of new long-term contracts. Some of the former hop farms including Freetown, Ashperton, had consequently replaced at least part of their hop yards with orchards. However, hardly had the countryside recovered from the outbreak of foot-and-mouth when the unexpected and serious news was broken that Bulmers had overextended itself and was likely to go bankrupt. Fortunately for the many East Herefordshire suppliers of cider apples, including Freetown in Ashperton and Lillands in Little Marcle there was a happy ending. Scottish & Newcastle purchased Bulmers in 2003 and with its marketing expertise was able to honour the company's commitments and indeed expanded the market for cider.

In addition to the apples supplied to Bulmers and Westons, a feature of early 21st-century East Herefordshire has been the growth of artisanal ciders and specialised apple juices, as well as perry made from pears, all promoted at the April and October Big Apple festivals. Once Upon A Tree of Putley, a company launched in 2008, received the BBC Food & Farming Best Drinks Producer Award in 2012. Jus, producing single variety apple juices at Lillands, Little Marcle, won Best in Show at the Malvern Autumn Show in 2016.

Fig. 6.4 Jane Skittery at the Jus stall at the Big Apple festival in Putley Village Hall 2017

Soft fruit production of national importance

Soft fruit production is another area in which East Herefordshire has become increasingly important in the early 21st century.

The development of soft fruit, especially blackcurrants, originally grown on contract, was Edward Thompson of Pixley Court's initial response to the decline in the profitability of hops and the problems of wilt in its hop yards in the mid- to late 1980s. At the time of publication Pixley Berries is the only English producer of fresh (as opposed to concentrated) pasteurised blackcurrant, raspberry and other juices, supplying these ingredients direct to a large number of important European companies and selling its own products, Pixley Berries cordials, in leading supermarkets.

Fig. 6.5 Pixley Court blackcurrant fields May 2016

A feature of early 21st-century Herefordshire farming has been the strengthening of direct links between supermarkets and growers. Strawberries is another area which has seen a major expansion with Thinghill Court, Withington, amongst its many activities, growing strawberries for sale in the principal supermarkets.

A remarkable company not described in Part III in the parish of Ledbury, Haygrove Ltd, was started in 1998 on a single hectare of rented land by Angus Davison, a great-nephew of Edward Thompson of Pixley Court, as his university project to grow strawberries. It is now a large international company with farms in Portugal and South Africa as well as England growing strawberries, raspberries, blueberries, blackberries and cherries.

Fig. 6.6 James Hawkins (left) and the manager of the Thinghill Court strawberry enterprise with Thinghill Court free-range eggs and strawberries at the Yarkhill Field to Fork Festival 2014

Rising popularity of Herefordshire beef

Following the problems experienced in the livestock industry with BSE and foot-and-mouth, the early 21st century has, in contrast, seen a resurgence of consumer interest and demand for specially selected British beef breeds, of which Herefords are one of the most sought after. In 1998 Waitrose had pioneered a scheme for the promotion in their stores of beef specifically described as Hereford which had to be the progeny of a pedigree Hereford bull and from a selected number of farms. Other supermarkets followed suit and the number of registered Herefords sold under this scheme has risen year by year. With this interest behind them the second decade of the 21st century has witnessed a remarkable rise in the number of active herds of pedigree Hereford cattle in the United Kingdom. In 2007 there were 570 such herds, increasing to 635 by 2010. The numbers have grown each year since to reach 933 at the end of 2017. In the Internet age many sales are privately negotiated. However the Hereford Cattle Society Shows and Sales remain important features of the Society as well as social events. At the Spring Cattle Show and Sale of April 2018 the 26 bulls reached an average price of £4,321 with a top price of 8,200 guineas. Meanwhile the Free Town herd at Freetown, Ashperton continues its hundred-year tradition for winning the highest prizes for its bulls.

Fig. 6.7 Free Town Maelstrom: Supreme and Grand Male Champion at the National Horned Hereford Show 2015 [3]

Fig. 6.8 Edward Davies with completed hop pockets ready for export to the United States 2015

Hops still grown

The last decade of the 20th century appeared to witness the death of that hop industry which, together with the orchards and herds of Hereford cattle, had for over three centuries been such an attractive feature of East Herefordshire farming. However to use a misquotation associated with Mark Twain "the reports of its demise have been greatly exaggerated". Peter Davies of Claston Farm, Dormington pioneered the labour-saving dwarf species. Other growers, including Thinghill Court, are producing wilt-resistant varieties of dwarf hops. The growing interest in craft beers has expanded the market in the United States for English hops. Some growers, including Edward Davies of the remarkable and historic farm of Walsopthorne Farm, have never ceased producing hops.

Notes

[1] Graph by Nick Newton Design using figures from www.indexmundi.com/commodities/?commodity=wheat

[2] Graph by Nick Newton Design using figures from www.indexmundi.com/commodities/?commodity=rapeseed-oil

[3] By kind permission of the Hereford Cattle Society.

SOME FARMING FAMILIES

Fig. 7.1 John Charles Davies and family in 1912 in their car, make unidentified [1]

The great continuity of families often stretching back one hundred and sometimes as many as two or even three hundred years is evident from the history of the individual farms described in Part III. This continuity is clear even when following the male line and the surnames. It is even more significant when account is taken of the fact that the farmers naturally usually married sisters of their neighbours. Mr George H. Bray, the chairman of the Herefordshire County War Agricultural Executive Committee in the Second World War and the owner of Dormington Court as well as another large Dormington farm, Priors Court, was not only a distinguished breeder of Hereford cattle but the uncle of three other exceptional breeders of the day: Mr Harry Moore of Shucknall Court in Weston Beggard, Mr Edward Lewis of The Haven in Dilwyn, north-west Herefordshire, and Mr Jack Weyman-Jones of Bodenham Court. It was indeed reasonable that when Mr David Prothero started work in the 1960s at the

Hereford Herd Book Society (as the Hereford Cattle Society was then named), he was warned to remember that all the farmers were interrelated.

Farming families with associations of almost 100 years or more

The Bowcotts of Felton Court

There was an 18th-century Bowcott in Felton parish who may have been an ancestor but it was Thomas Bowcott (1879–1947) who in 1903 married Annette Morris, the granddaughter of Marie Morris, the then tenant of Felton Court, and took over Felton Court in 1920, having previously been farming in the adjacent parish of Moreton Jefferies. (His father, Thomas Bowcott (1847–1910) had farmed in the nearby parish of Much Cowarne.) The farm passed first to Thomas and Annette's son, Thomas Edward Bowcott (1909–1975). It was then purchased by the Edwards family when their son, Robert, married Joy, Thomas Edward Bowcott's daughter, in 1963. It is now farmed by Joy and Robert's son and his wife, Richard and Clare Edwards.

The Bradstocks of Freetown, Ashperton, the Dents of Withington Court and Perton Court, Stoke Edith and the Leakes of Stone House Farm, Withington

The Bradstock, Dent and Leake families are all distinguished breeders of pedigree Hereford cattle.

Richard Bradstock and his son Tony are the third and fourth generations of the Bradstock family to have been breeding prize-winning Hereford cattle at Freetown. Three generations of Bradstocks have been President of the Hereford Cattle Society: Percy, Tom and Richard. Tony's great-grandfather, Percy Bradstock, who came to Freetown from Garford Farm, Yarkhill, was brought up by his relative H. W. Taylor at Showle Court, Yarkhill following the early death of his parents. Earlier generations of Bradstocks farmed at Ross-on-Wye and Percy Bradstock's paternal grandfather appeared in Volume 3 of the Hereford Herd Book of 1858.

John Dent of Withington Court, who has owned pedigree Herefords all his professional life, is the grandson of H. J. Dent of Perton Court, a most distinguished breeder in the early 20th century. John's uncle, H. C. Dent, the son of H. J. Dent, rented Eastwood Farm, Tarrington from 1933 to 1943, and was the owner of Perton Rear Admiral who won first prize at the Agricultural Show in Liverpool in July 1939 and was an international judge for Hereford cattle. Thomas Dent of Leyton Court, a successful breeder of Herefords from the 1880s, was a great-great-uncle. Dean Dent of Woodmanton Farm, Yarkhill, whose descendants still farm in East Herefordshire, is also distantly related.

Rachel Leake of Stone House Farm, Withington is the third generation of her family to breed Herefords at this historic farm long associated with the Apperley family. Prior to moving to Stone House Farm in 1919 an earlier generation of the Leakes were breeding Hereford cattle in nearby Morton Jefferies.

The Cryer/Davies family of Bent Orchards, the Sayce family of Yare Farm and the Williams family of Overbury Farm, Woolhope

For 90 years (1926–2016) three generations of the same family farmed Bent Orchards. Tom and Mabel Cryer from 1926 until Tom died in 1938. Then Mabel and their two daughters, Mollie and Betty Cryer, joined by David Davies after his marriage to Mollie, and finally by David and Mollie's son, John, and his wife, Susan, with their family of three girls.

Three generations of the Sayce family have been at Yare Farm since before the First World War. They are probably related through the female line to the family who farmed Yare Farm in the late 19th century.

Similarly, three generations of the Williams family have farmed Overbury Farm, moving there from South Herefordshire in 1938 just before the Second World War.

The Hawkins of Thinghill Court, Withington and the Thompsons of Pixley Court

The Hawkins of Thinghill Court and the Thompsons of Pixley Court have been associated with East Herefordshire since the 1920s. Both farms are large and highly innovative.

James Hawkins runs a considerable number of initiatives based on Thinghill Court, some in association with his brother, Paul. James's great-grandfather, Thomas Hawkins, purchased Thinghill Court in 1920 following the death of his maternal uncle, John Smith, who had farmed Thinghill Court since the 1870s. However Thomas himself was very close to his uncle and had been living at Thinghill Court since at least 1911 when the census of that year shows him as a farm pupil.

Edward Thompson is the third generation of his family to farm Pixley Court and is now assisted by members of the fifth generation. Pixley Berries has a national and international reputation for its blackcurrant, raspberry and other juices.

The Skittery family of Lillands, Little Marcle

The great-grandfather of Michael and James Skittery of Lillands, William Ward Skittery, took over the tenancy of Lillands in 1888 and then bought the farm in 1921. There was an earlier connection. William's father, William Mathias Skittery, born in

Shepton Mallet, was the stepson of James Ward of the nearby Flights Farm and he had actually looked after Lillands for a few years in the 1860s when the then tenant, Mr Hartland, who was also a successful auctioneer, was the official tenant.

The Watkins family of Park Farm and Court Farm, Woolhope

Graham Watkins is the fourth generation of the Watkins family to farm at the historic Park Farm, Woolhope. His great-grandfather, Gwilliam Watkins, and his great-great-uncle, Gwilliam's brother, John, born in the neighbouring county of Radnorshire, came to Woolhope in the difficult years for farming at the end of the 19th century. Gwilliam took over the tenancy of Park Farm in 1898 and his brother Croose Farm slightly earlier. In 1911 John's son, Dansey, took over Court Farm, Woolhope. From the start of the First World War until after the Second World War four separate Watkins households were farming in Woolhope at Park Farm, Croose Farm, Court Farm and Wessington Court.

Farming families with associations of over 200 years

There are at least three family dynasties, the Davieses, the Godsalls and the Powells, whose male ancestors are known to have been farming in East Herefordshire within a 10-mile radius for well over 200 years and who have during this time farmed at least one of the farms mentioned in Part III.

The Davies dynasty

The many male descendants of Thomas Davies and his wife Eliza (née Shale) are associated with a number of East Hereford farms, including six described in Part III (Moorend Farm in Weston Beggard, Claston Farm in Dormington, Walsopthorne Farm in Ashperton, Pixley Court in Pixley, Aylton Court in Aylton and Beans Butts in Woolhope).

Thomas Davies himself came from a family who can be traced in East Herefordshire for at least two previous generations. His grandfather, John Davies of Tarrington, had married an Elizabeth Bailis in 1760. His father, Barnaby (1763–1829), was born in the beautiful and historically important 15th-century yeoman house of Coldmore, originally in Woolhope parish but from 1886 included in the parish of Putley. Barnaby married Mary Jones from a gentry landowning family in Pixley parish.

Edward and his son Herbert Davies of Walsopthorne Farm, Ashperton and Peter Davies of Claston Farm, Dormington are descended from Thomas Davies's youngest son, William Henry, of Claston Farm (1860–1943). He was Edward Davies of Walsopthorne Farm, Ashperton's great-grandfather and Peter Davies of Claston Farm, Dormington's grandfather. The Davies family associated with Pixley Court and Aylton Court are descended from Thomas Davies's elder son, John Charles Davies (1856 –1932). He was a successful businessman who lived from 1901 at Hill House, Ledbury and had a remarkably large family of 15 children. As part of his aim to establish each of his sons with a farm he rented and then purchased Pixley Court and later purchased Aylton Court.

With such large families the Davieses were naturally connected through marriage with other East Herefordshire farming families. Peter Davies's wife, Pam, was a Skittery of Lillands, Little Marcle and his mother, Mildred, was the younger daughter of Alfred Thompson of The Hyde, Woolhope.

The three Godsall dynasties

Showle Court, Yarkhill and Park Farm, Woolhope

Walter Godsall, farmer of Showle Court, Yarkhill, died in 1705 and was a great-grandfather of Anthony Godsall who farmed Park Farm, Woolhope in the second half of the 19th century. One of Walter's granddaughters, Margaret, married John Vevers of Yarkhill Court in 1779, a typical example of interrelationships on the maternal side.

Eastwood Farm, Tarrington

The Godsall family, associated with Eastwood Farm, Tarrington from at least the late 18th century until the close of the 20th century, were interrelated with the Godsalls of Lower House Farm, then in Ashperton, but the relationship with the Godsalls of Showle Court, Yarkhill, if any, would have predated the 18th century.

Weston Corner Farm, Withington and Hynett Farm, Lugwardine

There is also a Godsall family associated with Weston Corner Farm, Withington from before 1841 when John Godsall (1812–1886) was farming there until the last half of the 20th century. The family can be traced back to the 18th century in Withington parish records and there is possibly a connection with Walter Godsall of Showle Court.

Descendants of John Godsall's son, John Godsall (1841–1912), were associated from the late 19th century with three other East Herefordshire farms. John Godsall had farmed Hynett Farm from about 1871 until the death of his father in 1886, and his daughter, Editha, married Reuben Price of Hynett Farm, Lugwardine in 1893. John Godsall's son, William Godsall, farmed Hoar Farm (later called Underhill), Woolhope from around 1910 until after the Second World War. Another son, Charles Harold Godsall, farmed Moor Court, Stretton Grandison, and his descendants still continue to farm there as well as run a highly esteemed bed-and-breakfast enterprise.

The Powells of Laddin Farm, Little Marcle

Mr David Powell of Awnells Farm, Much Marcle can trace his ancestry back to before the 16th century. In 1604 John Powell owned Preston Court in Preston, the adjacent parish to Little Marcle, bordering Gloucestershire. In that year, his daughter, Mary Powell, married John Coke, who built Hall Court, Kynaston in 1608 so that Mary could have a home is beautiful as Preston Court. John Coke later became an extremely able MP and royal administrator who was knighted in 1624 and twice rescued the navy from serious decay.

The Powells had particular difficulties as royalists after the Civil War of the 17th century. They lost Preston Court and other land. For a time Richard Powell, a descendant, was obliged to work as a farm labourer at Laddin Farm until, through some influence with the new owner of the Little Marcle estate, his son received the tenancy of Laddin Farm, Little Marcle, beginning the long association of the Powell family with this farm. In 1709 Thomas Smith of Huntleys Farm, Much Marcle left a ring to his "sweet sister Penelope of the Laddin" who was possibly married to Thomas Powell. When Edmund Philipps of Putley Court died in 1724, his will mentions "£60 to be paid unto John Powell of the Leddon [Laddin] in the parish of Little Marcle". John Powell of Laddin Farm died in 1758 and was succeeded by his brother, Henry Powell, who then gave up the tenancy in the 1770s.

The Powells were a large extended family; consequently various members owned or were tenants of a number of other important East Herefordshire farms from the 18th century onwards and they intermarried with local farming families. Joseph Dobbs (?–1799) who took over the Laddin from Henry Powell in the 1770s is said to have been Henry's son-in-law. His son, Samuel Dobbs, married Elizabeth Powell. The Dobbs family who farmed the Laddin until 1892 were therefore closely related to the Powell family.

In 1871 Alice Sparkman (1856–1909), the daughter of John Sparkman of Brook Farm, Little Marcle, married Thomas Powell (1844–1908), a descendant of the early 18th-century Powells of the Laddin. This branch of the family had been successful farmers in Much Marcle and associated with a number of historic farms there. Henry Powell, Thomas's great-grandfather, had leased the manor of Hellens with 192½ acres from Edward Walwyn, the then squire, from 1783 to 1789 and it was Henry's son, John, Thomas's grandfather, who undertook the journey to Oxford described in Chapter 8 below.

Thomas and Alice Powell had a large family of eight sons and three daughters. They were to live in three Much Marcle farms associated with the Powell family, firstly in Moor Court, the Much Marcle farm where Thomas had been born. (His father, James, had also been farming the larger Much Marcle farm of Chandos Farm since 1857.)

In the 1890s Thomas and Alice moved to the large farm of Hallend, Kynaston, which had come on the market at this time of agricultural depression and had been bought by James. In 1900 they moved again to the historic Hall Court, Much Marcle, the tenancy of which had become vacant. After Thomas and Alice died, five of their sons, James, Rodney, Harold, William and Rupert, for a while formed a farming consortium. Their eldest son, James John Stedman Powell, took over Hall Court and married Joan Thompson, the elder daughter of Alfred Thompson of The Hyde, Woolhope. In 1919 the consortium purchased Moorend, Ashperton which was then farmed by Harold and his new wife. In 1922 they purchased Awnells Farm which became the home of Rupert and his wife Ethel, the parents of David Powell. David Powell generously donated the beautiful Awnells Farm to the Countryside Restoration Trust in 2000 and remains farming there. Awnells is nationally famed for its traditional orchard and also for its herd of Hereford cattle which are descended from two heifers given by John Sparkman to Alice in 1871 on her marriage to John Powell.

Farming families of the 18th and 19th centuries

Some other families who farmed in East Herefordshire for a number of generations are no longer represented in the area.

The Apperley dynasty of Stone House Farm, Withington

The most distinguished of these farming families were the Apperleys of Stone House Farm, resident at Withington from about 1690 until 1905. John Harvard Apperley was an early pioneer in the breeding of pedigree Hereford cattle, a minor squire and a founder member of the Hereford Agricultural Society in 1797. The Apperleys continued to own Stone House Farm and other land in Withington until the beginning of the 21st century.

The Bosleys of Baregains Farm and Lower House Farm, Little Marcle

The Bosley family can be traced to Little Marcle from the mid-18th century until the 1870s. A record in the Herefordshire archives shows the tenant of Baregains Farm in 1767 to be a John Bosley. The Bosley family still appeared as occupants of the farm in the census records of 1841, 1851 and 1861.

It seems probable that Thomas Bosley, the young tenant of Lower House Farm in 1836 at the time of the famous trial for poaching described in Chapter 8 below, was related to the Bosleys of Baregains Farm. He remained at Lower House Farm until the 1850s when he moved to Bentleys Farm, Bosbury.

The Hoopers of Beans Butts and the Mailes of The Hyde, Woolhope

The Hooper family held the copyhold of the smallholding of Bean Butts from 1731 until 1885 and played an important part in Woolhope life during this time.

The Mailes were copyhold farmers of The Hyde between 1738 and 1847. The Mailes were also associated in the mid-19th century with Overbury Farm and the Crown Inn at Woolhope. Louisa Hodges, née Mailes, started the Butchers Arms, Woolhope, initially a beer house, now a successful country inn, on her marriage in 1870 and was the landlady well into the 20th century.

The Pitt family of Walsopthorne Farm and Freetown, Ashperton

At the beginning of the 19th century Francis Pitt and his wife had the tenancy of White House Farm, Canon Frome, one of the more important tenant farms of the Hopton family. Three of their sons were to take over tenancies of other important farms in the vicinity, indicative of the high esteem in which the Pitt family must have been viewed in the neighbourhood.

One son, Stephen, became the tenant of Walsopthorne Farm after this historic farm came into the possession of the Hopton family in 1823. Stephen, aged 23, is recorded as the tenant in 1828 and he and his wife, Ann, reared their children there. One of their sons, William, took over the farm after his father retired to Over Court, Sutton. William himself moved to this farm in the 1890s after the death of his father.

Following the death of Thomas Sirrell in 1846, Thomas, another of Francis's sons, took over the tenancy of Freetown. Freetown, along with Showle Court, was a prize farm of the Foley estate. Lady Emily Foley took a strong personal interest in the farms and would have certainly wished to have had an exceptional tenant there. In 1854 Thomas received the prize for the best maintained large farm of the Foley estate. Thomas's son, John, took over the tenancy of Freetown in his turn but gave up farming in the 1880s, perhaps disheartened by the increasing agricultural problems of this era.

John, the third of Francis's sons to take over the tenancy of a local farm, confusingly shared the same name as his nephew, Thomas's son. This John Pitt farmed Pigeon Farm, Weston Beggard and married a daughter of William Henry Davies of Claston Farm, Dormington. In later life the daughter was living with her parents, which suggests that the marriage was not a success.

The youngest son, called Francis after his father, farmed at White House Farm, Canon Frome all his life.

Abraham Pitt, his son, George Pitt, and his grandson, also called George Pitt, who were associated with Yare Farm, Woolhope in the second half of the 19th century and early 20th century, do not seem to have been related to Francis Pitt of Canon Frome.

The Vevers family of Yarkhill Court and Dormington Court

Throughout the second half of the 18th century and right through the 19th century the Vevers family played a major role in farming. They were associated with a number of large farms but especially with Yarkhill Court (from the 1770s until about 1904) and Dormington Court (1798–1874) as hop farmers and early breeders of Hereford pedigree cattle. They were a junior branch of a landowning family from the north of England and many of their interests were associated with those of the landed gentry. Like many landowners and larger farmers, they were enthusiastic supporters of hunting.

One of the most renowned members of this family was Mr William Vevers (1782–1858) of Dormington Court. He was distinguished nationally for the breeding of horses – flat racehorses, steeplechasers, shire horses and carthorses – and was also famed for his prowess in foxhunting.

A unique farming family

The Yeomans family of Thinghill Court and Stone House Farm, Withington

There is one family that is missing and it is one that played an important role in Herefordshire from the 18th century onwards and especially in the breeding of fine Hereford cattle: the Yeomans family. Generations of the Yeomans family appear in that classic book *The History of Hereford Cattle* by James Macdonald first published in 1886 and then revised in 1909 with additional material researched by James Sinclair.

John Yeomans was already experimenting with improved Hereford cattle when he moved from Thinghill Court in 1785 to Howton Court. His great-grandson, another John Yeomans, was also a highly successful breeder at Stretton Court, Huntington near Hereford. This John Yeomans achieved a record price when he sold almost his whole herd for export in 1892 at the height of the demand for Hereford cattle. His wife Rebecca's family were the Haywoods of Blakemere, a family also long distinguished as cattle breeders. John and Rebecca and their family, Haywood, Walter, Jane and Honor, were to move from Stretton Court in 1905 to Stone House Farm in Withington, a farm long renowned for its association with early breeding of Hereford cattle. Haywood and Walter were both killed in the First World War bringing to an end this long tradition. John Yeomans gave up the farm in 1919.

Jane and Honor, undeterred by the loss of their brothers and of the young men they would have married, played an important role in their community. In the Second World War Honor took on a difficult position at the Rotherwas Munitions Factory. Jane supported the Woman's Land Army members. Both sisters played the most active role in the development of the Yarkhill Young Farmers' Club and in encouraging its members after the Second World War. They devoted much of their lives to supporting in every way the children of their friends and neighbours, giving memorable parties and greatly enhancing the life of all those who knew them. In gratitude this book is dedicated to Jane and Honor and to their two young brothers who like many of their generation were so tragically killed in the First World War.

Notes

[1] By kind permission of Penelope Cunningham, great-granddaughter of John Charles Davies.

GLIMPSES OF FARMING LIVES

Fig. 8.1 Lucky mementoes found under the attic floorboards of Dormington Court. By kind permission of Cheryl Shearer

The 18th century

Superstitions

In the preindustrial age with much uncertainty of life there would remain dependence upon traditional remedies and a belief in the effectiveness of superstitions. Found carefully wrapped under the attic floorboards when renovating Dormington Court were a 300-year-old man's shoe, a child's shoe and the remains of a woman's garment, possibly a bodice. Traditionally, shoes were hidden to provide protection against evil and bring good fortune. A century and a half later Lady Emily Foley would put bars around St Edith's Well in Stoke Edith to deter those who saw the waters as a cure for their troubles. The farmers would have had their own remedies for the ailments of their livestock. There would have been a local bonesetter. A midwife was supposed to be registered by the diocese – ecclesiastical records list the names of women who were granted licences by the Church of England to practise midwifery – but each village would have had a woman known to be skilled in this important area.

Education

A modest number of 18th-century East Herefordshire small-scale squires, such as the Apperleys of Stone House Farm, Withington, and the Philips and the Broomes of Withington Court, would probably have received some classical education as would a very few of the largest tenant farmers, notably the Drews of Brook Farm, Little Marcle and the Vevers of Yarkhill Court. On the whole though, the farming community did not especially esteem education at this time. Looking at 18th-century wills it would seem that some farmers, including Walter Godsall of the important farm Showle Court, Yarkhill whose will was marked with a cross, could not even sign their names. There are therefore few written records in the public domain relating to the lives of the farmers in East Herefordshire from this period.

Outside contact

It is true that the professional groups, particularly the local clergy, would have reasonable links throughout England. In the latter half of the 18th century landowners such as the Foleys of Stoke Edith and the Hoptons of Canon Frome would be sending back full information on the demand for products at a national level as well as innovations in farming to their stewards in Herefordshire. Most of the farming community would probably only know about this information at second-hand through just seeing what the landowners were doing on their own estates. Like farmers everywhere – and at most times – they would be cautious about adopting new ideas.

The notorious nature of Herefordshire roads already described meant that venturing on a journey of even four miles was quite an undertaking. Travelling more was an adventure. Nowhere else is this better seen than in a letter dated 1790 transcribed below from Edward Walwyn, the owner of the historic estate of Hellens, Much Marcle to Thomas Powell, a neighbour in Much Marcle and an important and ambitious farmer from a long-established farming family. Edward is giving instructions for a journey to be undertaken by Thomas's son, John, who was about 23 years old at the time. Not only did Edward feel it necessary to give instructions about the journey itself but also guidance on how to deal with people like the innkeeper and his wife.

Monday, 5 April 1790

John to meet me at the Kings Arms in Holywell Street Oxford on Saturday next by 4 o clock in the evening.

The road and distances from Hellens to Oxford are as follows:

from Hellens to Gloucester through Newent	15 miles
from Gloucester to a large inn upon the London Road called Frogmill	13 miles
From Frogmill through Northleach to the town of Burford	17 miles
And from Burford to Oxford is	18 miles
In the Whole	63 miles

I would have John set out from Hellens at One O clock on Friday. He will get to Gloucester by 4. Feed his horse and Rest there one hour. And he will get to Frogmill that Night between seven and 8 o clock. He must see that his horse has a good Stall, Corn and Hay. I suppose he can take care of himself without my giving him Instructions. Only this be a general rule, that where ever he travels let him see that he has a CLEAN BED AND CLEAN LINEN. Whenever that happens not to be the case he must first speak to the mistress of the Inn and if that does not do THEN TO THE MASTER.

From Frogmill he must set out on Saturday morning by 6 O'CLOCK and go to Burford to Breakfast, which is 17 miles.

He must feed his horse and rest there Two Hours and a half (2½) hours and he would easily get to Oxford by 4 o clock in the evening.

See that John understands and follows the directions above for his journey.

E Walwyn

Let John put this part of the letter in his pocket which will be of service to him upon the road.

Fig. 8.2 Letter from Edward Walwyn, owner of Hellens estate, Much Marcle, to Thomas Powell, a farmer of Much Marcle [1]

Until wagons were introduced in about the second half of the 18th century, the only transport available for the farm would be a simple cart or 'wain'. This must have severely constrained social contact, especially for the women of the family. The major enjoyments of the farming community and the country people generally throughout most of this century would probably be those family celebrations of weddings, christenings and indeed funerals. Harvest too was a time of rejoicing when according to William Marshall writing in the 1780s, an excess quantity of cider would be available.

One major social event would come each half-year when the tenant farmers were due to pay their rents. It was customary for this payment to be made at the local inns. The locations of the Crown & Anchor in Lugwardine, the Trumpet Inn in Pixley, the Tarrington Arms (known as the New Inn in the 18th century and until recently as the Foley Arms) in Tarrington, the Cross Keys Inn in Withington and the Crown Inn in Woolhope are shown on the maps in Part III and all still exist. As compensation the farmers were then normally entertained to an excellent dinner. Mr Gregory of Court Farm, Woolhope in a letter of 1728 complained to the Dean and Chapter about the expenses involved in providing such a meal at the Crown Inn at Woolhope.

Fig. 8.3 The Crown Inn, Woolhope

The *Hereford Journal* of the late 18th century also shows that local auctions would be held at local inns. The Tarrington Arms was a favoured location situated as it was on the Hereford–Ledbury toll road. The Trumpet Inn situated on an important crossroads was also popular. Again it was customary for good refreshments to be available at such auctions.

Fig. 8.4 The Trumpet Inn, Pixley: an old coaching inn

The first half of the 19th century

Social life

Increasingly from the first half of the 19th century market days in Ledbury, Bromyard and Hereford would provide opportunities for social as well as commercial contact, not only for the farmers but also for the farmers' wives and families.

For the younger adults who could be spared from the farm in the late autumn and winter and who were lucky enough to have family or other possibilities for accommodation in the market towns there were, in the slacker months of the winter period, entertainments in Ledbury and Hereford. The *Hereford Journal* of October 1811 advertised "The First CARD and DANCING ASSEMBLY will commence at the Feathers Inn, Ledbury on Wednesday, 6 November next. Dancing to commence precisely at eight o'clock." The existence of similar advertisements for dancing assemblies can be found in the local papers of the period.

There were other grander occasions in Hereford, some dating back to the 18th century. These included concerts and dances which coincided with the Quarterly

Assize Sessions. Attendance was mainly confined to the landowning families and other gentry. Following her marriage to Edward Foley, Lady Emily Foley was guest of honour at the first ball of the season in December 1832. The Hereford races though no doubt drew a much wider audience.

The Hereford Agricultural Society, which had been founded in 1797, confined its membership to landowners and a very few of the larger farmers such as Mr Apperley of Stone House Farm, and Mr Williams and later Mr Racster of Thinghill Court. The Ledbury Agricultural Society, founded in 1840 and the much smaller Withington Ploughing Society established in 1842 had a much wider membership amongst local farmers. Ebullient speeches at the strictly male annual dinners following the competitions were often quoted in full in the *Hereford Journal* or *Hereford Times* and invariably reference was made to the excellent quality of the food. In 1849 Earl Somers, the president of the Ledbury Agricultural Society, donated a haunch of venison.

Important national events were similarly celebrated. The coronation of the new Queen Victoria in 1838 was the subject of much rejoicing, as was her marriage in February 1840 and the arrival of her first child, the Princess Royal, in November 1840. These celebrations were often balls and women were therefore included. However such celebrations were confined to the better off. William Apperley of Stone House Farm was a steward at the ball held at Hereford to celebrate the marriage of Queen Victoria to Albert.

Other smaller events were organised. One celebration of the coronation which ended in disaster was at Yarkhill. According to the *Hereford Journal*'s account of an inquest, W. C. Barnett:

> *… was celebrating the Coronation Day in the village, and a quarrel arising, Barnett turned round to fight a man named Wilson, when in striking his antagonist Barnett's foot slipped, he fell backwards, and injured his spine. The jury returned a verdict that the deceased came to his death from an injury received in a fall, whilst aiming a blow at an adversary, being at the time in a state of intoxication. The deceased was not addicted to drinking, but on the contrary was a remarkably sober, civil and well conducted man. He was farming Bailiff to Mr Vevers of Yarkhill Court by whom he was highly valued, and during the time he had been in his employ had never been intoxicated till the unfortunate evening of the Coronation when he had partaken too freely of the strong beer which on that joyful occasion was provided to celebrate the day – he was 34 years of age.*

No doubt other East Herefordshire farmers similarly provided barrels of beer for their employees but fortunately not with such sad consequences. There were at least some more sedate celebrations on Coronation Day and those which favoured the poor. For example, the vicar of Little Marcle and his wife entertained the village children to lunch with the favoured menu of the time: roast beef and plum pudding.

Hunting with privately-owned hounds and steeplechasing

Hunting was popular in Herefordshire at this time, but not as well organised or large-scale as it became in the last half of the 19th century. There were only a few packs of hounds owned by rich individuals and the members of the hunt largely comprised the better off. It was a Mr Terrett's foxhounds which hunted around Ledbury during the Napoleonic Wars. The *Hereford Journal* of 19 February 1812 stated that "Mr Terrett's foxhounds will meet at Sutton Wall tomorrow, at Ledbury Turnpike, on the Worcester road the 25th, and at Redmarley kennel on Thursday the 27th at 10 o'clock each morning."

Associated with hunting from early times were the popular steeplechase meetings. These were held at most of the county towns, including Ledbury. Usually the horses at these meetings were expected to have been hunted during the previous season. Almost certainly a number of the larger farmers described in Part III, such as William Apperley of Stone House Farm, Withington, would have enjoyed an occasional day's hunting. The most distinguished though was William Vevers of Dormington Court. The *Hereford Journal* stated that "as a rider to hounds he's been known in the county ever since boyhood, and few better men across country, even at his present age, are to be found in any part of England." Famed nationally for the breeding of steeplechasers, racehorses and carthorses, his most famous steeplechaser was a horse called Rattler, "a horse of great speed and equal to 20 stone which when blemished, and 10 years old, he sold to the French government for 300 guineas. He proved one of the best stallions ever imported into France."

The game laws

Some farmers were able to enjoy hunting, but the game laws which normally prevented tenants from shooting any game on their farms, including rabbits and hares, were bitterly resented by farmers and farmworkers alike. It is sometimes forgotten that in addition to the social aspects for the guests of gentry, the letting of shooting could be a significant source of income for landowners at this time as well as in later periods. Only those with a landed income of at least £100 a year or agents specifically designated by these landowners, such as gamekeepers, were entitled to a game licence. The penalties for poaching were savage. Mantraps were made illegal in 1826 but those found guilty of poaching could still be transported.

The fact that most landowners rigorously protected their game was illustrated in a dramatic case involving three young men of Little Marcle at the Hereford Assizes of early 1836. Thomas Bosley, the 19-year-old farmer of Lower House Farm, John Dallimore, the eldest son of John Dallimore senior of Brook Farm and John Peddingham, also said to be a farmer's son, were accused of poaching in Ast Wood on the night of 20 September 1835. The shooting in Ast Wood had been let to the local squire, Mr William Henry Gwillim of the Brainge. The gamekeeper, Edwin Cooper, and his witness, James Morris, saw the young men enter the wood around 11 p.m. and then observed them emerging at 12.45 a.m., each with a gun and accompanied by a pointer dog. The gamekeeper explained that "The wood in question was out of the direct road to the defendants' homes" and claimed that after the three men had left, he and James Morris heard three guns go off.

The counsel for the defence, Mr Sergeant Ludlow, immediately conducted a spirited rebuttal by first asking where the gamekeeper came from. Although the reply was hedged, it was clear that he came from Eastnor. Having ascertained that the gamekeeper was indeed employed by Mr William Henry Gwillim of the Brainge to whom Earl Somers, owner of the Eastnor estate, had let the shooting, Mr Sergeant Ludlow then asked Earl Somers's family name which Edwin Cooper reluctantly gave as John Cocks to possible rural amusement. Although the gamekeeper maintained that Earl Somers had nothing to do with the prosecution, the defence clearly thought that, on the contrary, Earl Somers was behind the decision to prosecute. Mr Sergeant Ludlow submitted there was no evidence against the defendants of an intent to kill game and the *Hereford Times* reports that "he trusted that the jury would become dried to the condition of mummies in that box, before, upon such testimony as had been advanced, they would bring in a verdict which would subject the defendants to transportation". According to the press account he also rather surprisingly "observed that the object of the prosecution was to prevent the defendants from shooting game and dwelt upon the hardship of not allowing a farmer to shoot a few partridges upon his own land". Although the judge presiding over this fascinating case remarked on the irrelevancy of attributing motives to the prosecution, after a short adjournment the jury obligingly recorded a verdict of not guilty.

The condition of farmworkers

Farming continued to be virtually the only activity in the East Herefordshire countryside until well after the Second World War and the majority of those living in the country were in some way concerned with it. Most of those employed were farmworkers hired for the year on a very low wage. Those whose livelihood was dependent upon different types of seasonal employment were no doubt worst affected by the introduction of threshing machines in the 1830s and 1840s which reduced employment in the winter. The wagoners responsible for the horses, the stockmen and the specialised shepherd might receive slightly more, but earnings generally were very low. There would be a few skilled occupations – nearly all the parishes would have at least one blacksmith. With wagons on every farm the occupation of wheelwright was also a skilled one and with so much cider consumed so was that of the cooper. The remuneration these skilled men received was therefore somewhat higher than other farmworkers. In the heavily wooded areas, especially around Woolhope, there would be some sawyers who were independent of any individual farmer, but their remuneration would still be quite low.

In addition to the farming family it was common for there to be several farmworkers who lodged with the household and probably ate with the family. On occasion the farmworker would be a relative of the farmer. It could not have been easy to have been a living-in farm labourer in the first half of the 19th century, especially if you were resident in any of the farms owned by Earl Somers of the Eastnor estate. The farmers of Pixley and Little Marcle seem to have had little compunction in bringing their farm servants before the magistrates. Mr Davies of Pixley Court appears to have been particularly litigious but there are also newspaper records relating to other farms. Farm servants were normally hired for the year and woe betide them if they left before this. In August 1842 Henry Bolton was committed to prison for deserting his master Mr Nutt of Lillands, Little Marcle. In August 1847 Mr Dallimore of Brook Farm complained to the magistrates that his resident farmworker, John Green, had left on Sunday morning after breakfast and had not returned until the next day. What is more he had done so before. The servant was fined 6d to be deducted from his wages and ordered to pay 7s 6d court costs. As described in Part III, Mr Davies of Pixley Court was less successful in 1848. The magistrates did not believe his version of the events. It was Mr Davies who then had to pay the court expenses.

The first half of the nineteenth century included some very difficult times for farmers and even worse for the poor. The local poor law could be very harsh and a landowner who could be sympathetic to the tenants' needs could make all the difference. The poor of the parishes in which the Stoke Edith estate was the principal landowner received periodic attention. In the 1820s the poor of the Stoke Edith parishes received a gift of beef, tea and sugar at Christmas time. After Edward Foley married Lady Emily Graham in 1832 there were references to the poor children in the different parishes receiving clothing at Christmas. In May 1833 after a difficult farming year 10% of the rent was deducted for the Stoke Edith tenants. There is no record ever of any such reduction for the farms owned by Earl Somers of Eastnor. Perhaps because of this there seems on occasion to be also deep hostility between the farmers and labourers. In July 1842 for instance a valuable carthorse mare belonging to Mr Dallimore of Brook Farm was so brutally stabbed that it had to be put down. This is likely to have been an act of vengeance. Mr John Davies of Pixley Court appears to have been a most difficult man. The killing in 1845 of the ram of his flock of sheep, so much more valuable than any other animal, seems to have been inspired by a wish to impose maximum financial loss.

LADY EMILY FOLEY: 1805–1900

Fig. 8.5 Lady Emily Foley by Joseph Brown after Frederick Richard Say, published 1840, © National Portrait Gallery, London

Lady Emily Foley had the good sense to die in the early hours of 1 January 1900, thus missing the momentous 20th century. She had a big impact on her own century. The youngest daughter of the 3rd Duke of Montrose, she and her brother, William, with whom she was very close, could remember the celebrations following the Battle of Waterloo. In her old age she would have admired (or been shocked at) the first cars.

Her influence in East Herefordshire is such that amongst the descendants of East Hereford families memories of her doings emerge when tapped, even though she has been dead for almost 120 years.

Social success

Throughout her life Lady Emily Foley clearly greatly enjoyed social occasions. She was charming and the portrait in the National Gallery suggests she was very beautiful when young. She certainly added to the social scene right from her arrival in Herefordshire in 1832 following her marriage to Edward Foley in August of that year. Herefordshire society was clearly thrilled at having the daughter of a Duke resident in the county. The *Hereford Journal* in the autumn of that year records the visit to Herefordshire of her parents, the Duke and Duchess of Montrose. Honoured by the interest of such a great nobleman, the city dignitaries presented the Duke with the Freedom of the City of Hereford in October 1832.

To while away the short cold days of winter the gentry of Herefordshire used to organise monthly assemblies with dancing and supper, starting at 9 p.m. Lady Emily Foley was made patron for the first assembly of the season on 8 November 1832. No ball was complete without Lady Emily leading off with the first dance. Such was her role at the great ball celebrating the arrival of trains to Hereford on 6 December 1853.

Concern for the poor

Not only concerned for her own enjoyment, Emily Foley showed practical sense in caring for the poor of the parishes. She seems to be especially fond of children. On Christmas Eve, 1832, she and Edward Foley distributed to the Sunday School children of the neighbouring parish of Weston Beggard jackets and trousers to eight of the boys and cloaks to twelve of the girls – important gifts to keep them warm in the winter. She made a regular practice of doing this in the other parishes owned by the Stoke Edith estate. In 2012, an elderly lady at the Herefordshire Family History Society lecture on Victorian Herefordshire suddenly recalled her great-grandmother telling her of the occasion Lady Emily Foley arrived at Tarrington School and distributed cloaks to all the girls – blue for those who lived in Tarrington and green for those who lived in Stoke Edith.

Knowledgeable on farming

Lady Emily was not just a benevolent landowner, though. After Edward Foley's death in 1844 she took over the administration of the Foley estate with the aid of a steward. The Game Laws which caused such resentment in the countryside were not abolished until the 1870s, but, unlike many of her peers in Herefordshire, she permitted her tenants to shoot game on their farms. She was a highly intelligent person and interested in ensuring the estate was farmed to the highest standards of the time but wishing to achieve this with the goodwill of her tenants.

Typically Lady Emily Foley did so by instituting from 1850 an Annual Farm Inspection of the estate. This was done very thoroughly over three days by a well-known agriculturalist. The declared intention was to award the prize of £20 for the best cultivated large farm and £10 for the best cultivated small farm. To this end on the last of the three days the tenants were invited to ride round the estate with the judge and steward, and Lady Emily Foley would often join them. Normally they stopped for lunch at the invitation of the farmer of the best cultivated large farm from the previous year. The day ended, as it so often did in the high Victorian era, with an excellent dinner. Lady Emily Foley and her brother, Lord William Graham, would present the prizes and then tactfully withdraw to allow their guests to enjoy the good food and plenty of alcoholic refreshment provided at Stoke Edith House, which was followed by a round of singing.

A great-nephew's reminiscences

The best, and certainly the most entertaining, description of Lady Emily Foley is a vignette of her old age and is given by one of her great-nephews, James Graham, the future 6th Duke of Montrose.[2] It recalls a visit he made to her at the age of 10 in 1887 and it merits retelling in detail.

James received a telegram summoning him to visit his great-aunt, the Lady Emily Foley, immediately. He arrived at Hereford station, briefed with the normal family-type instructions for that extra specially polite behaviour to a distinguished elderly relative. There he was greeted by a tall footman in fine livery, complete with white powdered hair and a cockaded hat and transported the eight miles to Stoke Edith in a yellow phaeton complete with coats of arms on either door and drawn by two horses with a postilion riding one. A further outrider preceded the procession; all were similarly attired and with wigs.

On arriving at Stoke Edith house, James found his great-aunt waiting for him in an armchair at the top of a long flight of steps, surrounded by members of her household to whom he was personally introduced.

James Graham was allowed to attend the formal dinner at Stoke Edith House with its many courses all served on silver plates. Lady Emily Foley had in her younger days been the toast of many a county ball. She maintained her love of beautiful clothes and jewellery, dressing for dinner in beautiful décolleté gowns and adorned with a different set of jewellery each night.

James had arrived on the Saturday and so was able to observe on Sunday that other great tradition of Lady Emily Foley, the formal procession walking across the park to church with the footman at a discrete distance carrying a cushion with her bible and prayer book. This ritual has been preserved for us in an old photo of 1897 reproduced as Fig 8.6 below.

Life at Stoke Edith House may have been formal and grand but Lady Emily Foley also loved and understood children. When James Graham was led to his room on arrival he found a number of presents including, to his great joy, a model of the three-decker warship, the Great Harry of Henry VIII's reign.

The reminiscences of the 6th Duke of Montrose give a marvellous description of a remarkable lady, immensely kind, authoritative, old-fashioned and with a great zest for life. Lady Emily Foley was all of these but a great deal more. In addition to all her other activities she played a role in the design of the spa town of Malvern. In her final years she was attending meetings discussing the establishment of a teacher training college in Hereford which took place in 1902. She was indeed active to the end.

Fig. 8.6 Lady Emily Foley aged 92, August 1897 walking to church accompanied by Miss Mary Herbert, photographed by Miss Winifred Herbert, © www.herefordshirehistory.org.uk

SOME FARMWORKERS

William Field: 1826–1890

It is not easy to trace farmworkers over their lives. However there are exceptions. One such is William Field. He was born in Preston Wynne in 1826. In 1841 the census records show he was aged 15 and employed as a farmworker in Small Ashes Farm, Marden, living in the household. In 1851 he was at Withington Court. In 1861 he was employed at Hillhampton, Ocle Pychard, on a farm of 280 acres a mere two miles away from his previous place of employment. He was still living in the household and was described as a carter. In 1866 when he was in his late 30s, he married Alice Bayliss and moved back to Preston Wynne, although the 1871 census shows that he and his wife were living on the common and so presumably in very poor accommodation. In 1881 William and Alice were living at the Marsh Farm, Preston Wynne with a family of two, William now aged 12 and John 5. He died in 1890 at what was, for that time, the ripe old age of 64.

The Farley farmworker dynasty of Little Marcle: late 18th–early 20th centuries

The *Hereford Journal* of February 28, 1849 includes a brief statement that a little boy called William Farley had been sent for trial for setting fire to a clover rack at Brook Farm, Little Marcle. His younger brother, George, was acquitted.

Did little William end up on a convict ship bound for Botany Bay? Far from it. The 1851 census shows both William and George safely at home with their family in Little Marcle with their father, John Farley (1812–1893), mother, Harriet, and paternal grandmother, Eleanor. William was 11, George 9, and there were two younger children, Richard 5 and John 2.

The Farleys came from a family long associated with this small parish. The children's paternal grandfather Richard Farley (1773–1833) had been christened in Little Marcle and married Eleanor King in Little Marcle church in 1803, so the family had been resident in Little Marcle from at least the late 18th century. Although members of the family would remain in the parish until the 20th century, never again would they hit the local press.

John and Harriet remained in Little Marcle until John died in 1893. John seems to have been well thought of and was for a time nominated as a constable for the parish. In 1861 three of the four boys were resident farmworkers in Little Marcle: there is no census record in this year for George. The youngest, John, was still living with his parents but, although only 12, he was described as a carter's boy: farmworkers' families needed to earn their living from an early age. William, described as a farm labourer, and his wife, Charlotte, were living close to the rectory. Richard was living in at Baregains Farm and described as a carter's boy. William moved to Ledbury sometime in the 1860s and remained there until he died in 1916. George, Richard and John were recorded in the 1871 census. Richard died in 1877 but George and the younger John were to remain in Little Marcle. John and his wife, Mary Ann, lived in part of Little Marcle Court for some 20 years with their large family. By 1906 they had moved to the cottage of Priors Acre. The 1911 census shows that they had lost four of their 12 children by this time. Alfred, their youngest son, then living at Priors Acre, served in the First World War. According to Mrs Reeves in her 1972 history of Little Marcle, when John Farley died "his wife did not collapse or have a nervous breakdown. They owned a donkey and trap – and so Mrs Farley decided to become the local carrier."[3]

WOMEN FARMERS

Fig. 8.7 Editha Price with turkeys and hens at Hynett Farm, Lugwardine c. 1922 [4]

In the 21st century Rachel Leake, descended from many generations of East Herefordshire farmers owns and farms Stone House Farm, Withington with its pedigree Hereford cattle, Ryeland sheep and arable. Jane Skittery of Lillands produces and sells Jus prize-winning single apple juices.

It is not difficult to identify many women in the latter 20th century who played a specially important role in the operation of their farms. Amongst such were Mabel Cryer and her daughters who owned Bent Orchards in Woolhope, running the farm for some years on their own and continuing to be actively engaged in the farming throughout their long lives. Gwyneth Williams together with her son, Mark, farmed Hazel Court in Tarrington together following the death of her husband. Doris Prosser (née Cooke) of Old Court, Lugwardine and Eliza Jane Baylis of Moorend Farm, Weston Beggard were others.

The role of earlier generations is difficult to identify. The farming community lived an active outdoor life and written diaries are rare. Unlike their male counterparts, women are seldom included in the local newspapers.

In addition to their myriad household activities, women were normally responsible for poultry as well as for the production of butter, as indeed appears to be the case with Editha Price of Hynett Farm, Lugwardine. Sometimes the entire dairy came under their auspices. The sale of dressed chickens, geese and turkeys as well as butter in the local markets at Ledbury, Bromyard and Hereford provided useful (and indeed often the only) cash income available to them, as well as enjoyable social interaction. The prices they received or the quality of their produce are mostly the only times they are mentioned in the local press: Mrs Ann Smith of The Grove, Yarkhill, is recorded as selling produce at a special Christmas Show in Hereford market in 1851. The opening of the Hereford Butter Market in 1861 provided better opportunities for such activities. On occasion, the women kept the financial accounts.

Until after the Second World War virtually all farms kept at least one or more pigs for household consumption. The processing of the many pig products, a time-consuming activity, was normally the responsibility of the women.

On occasion widows played the major role in the organisation of the farm following the death of their husbands. One such woman was Maria Morris who is listed in the 1891 and 1901 censuses as the farmer of Felton Court.

It is clear that Maria was highly capable. In the 1861 census she, her husband, Edward, and her 10 children are recorded as living at Middle Court, Monkhide, Yarkhill, where Edward was farming 80 acres helped by two men and a boy. Life in Victorian England was uncertain and Edward died. However following his death she took over a larger rather than a smaller farm. In 1871 she and seven of her children were at the Farm, Much Cowarne, where she was farming 200 acres with the aid of two of her sons, Stephen 25 and William 20, described in the census as farmer's sons, and two of her daughters, Olive 29 and Lavinia 14, described as farmer's daughters. She was employing two men and a boy, and there was one living-in farmworker, Frederick Bufton 17. She was still at the Farm, Much Cowarne in 1881 but by that time was farming 231 acres. The household then consisted of two of her sons, William 30 and Henry 21, described as farmer's sons, her daughter, Jane 23, a granddaughter aged four and two living-in farm servants.

Maria's daughter-in-law, Mary Morris (née Sirrell), married to Stephen, seems to have been another resourceful woman. Stephen was killed in a pony trap accident leaving her with a young son, Stephen aged three and a daughter, Annette, who was born a few weeks after her father's death. This Mary Morris appears in the 1881 census as a miller at Much Cowarne. Perhaps her mother-in-law, the late Stephen's mother, with her large farm at Much Cowarne was able to assist her. Mary then moved to farm in the neighbouring parish of Ocle Pritchard. Annette grew up to marry Thomas Bowcott from another Much Cowarne farming family. From 1920 Annette and Thomas farmed at Felton Court and one of their daughters, Hilda, married Jack Price of Hynett Farm, Lugwardine. Hilda and Jack's daughter, Ann, together with her husband, Tom Nellist, have played a major role in the successful Trumpet and District Agricultural Society, which has been a feature of East Herefordshire farming life from 1944 onwards.

The second half of the 19th century

More reliable records

The first census of 1841 had listed the name, age, sex and occupation of every individual. In the censuses for 1851–1901 more detailed information is given, including how many workers a farmer was employing. It is notable that the numbers of full-time workers on the farms in Part III fell remarkably little even over the 90-year period between the census of 1851 and the Agricultural Census of June 1941. For example, Elizabeth Davies of Withington Court in 1851 was employing eight full-time workers. In 1941 William Farmer with approximately the same acreage was employing nine full-time farmworkers. He was also employing 11 part-time women and girls, probably mainly for that labour-intensive hop production.

The census records for 1851 and 1861 show that some permanent farmworkers continued to live in the farmhouse. This was especially so of Little Marcle. Thomas Bosley of Lower House Farm, Little Marcle in 1851 was employing two farmworkers, John King 16 and probably his sister Mary King, both living in the house. At Lillands in 1851, William Nutt was employing three live-in labourers. At Laddin Farm, Elizabeth Dobbs aged 78 was the farmer in 1851. Her son-in-law also resident was simply described as farmer's son, so there was no doubt who ran the farm. They employed three labourers, all three resident farm servants, William Farley aged 50, William Proternus aged 42, both born in Little Marcle, and Henry Barnett aged 71, born at Fownhope.

In contrast to Little Marcle, none of the 16 farm labourers working for William Apperley of Stone House Farm, Withington lived in in 1851. William Racster of Thinghill Court, Withington was employing 26 labourers in 1851 on his very large farm of 560 acres, but there were only three resident workers, George Jones 24 from Fownhope, John Mansell 22 from Sutton, and James Whitney 17, described as a groom, also from Sutton.

At the smaller Withington farm, Weston Corner Farm, John Godsall was employing another John Godsall aged 20 as a farmworker in 1851, but as there were several families of Godsalls resident in Withington at the time, including several Johns, it is difficult to trace the family connection. However, it appears that the practice of employing relatives as farmworkers continued at the beginning of the second half of the nineteenth century.

The census records show that the resident farmworkers were probably hired for the year and did not seem to stay very long on the same farm. None of the farmworkers described above was resident on the same farm in 1861 and had not been resident in 1841. In the few instances where the farmworker remained with the family this seems to have been where they were related or where the farmer was aged and an act of kindness may have been involved. The resident farmworkers were normally young people capable of earning money but not yet married. On occasion they could be very young, in a few instances only 10 or 12 years old, as compulsory education came in only in 1870.

The coming of the railways

The coming of the railways was an obvious benefit to the farming community. It permanently and radically improved contact between Herefordshire and other parts of the country. It also greatly assisted travelling within East Herefordshire. There were three stations between Hereford and Ledbury: Withington, Stoke Edith and Ashperton. These were only two to three miles apart and they were operational until 1963. No longer did the hops need to be transported by wagon to Worcester 20 miles away and the breeders of Hereford pedigree cattle could send their potentially prize animals easily to the important national agricultural shows, so promoting their breed. William

Taylor of Showle Court adopted this method of transport as a matter of policy, thus securing his place as a distinguished breeder. William Taylor's highly skilled herdsmen accompanying these prize animals would have seen parts of the country they never expected to get to know, increasing their knowledge of the outside world. For the more ambitious, travel within Herefordshire and beyond became much easier and cheaper, and it is notable that from the 1860s the populations of many of the East Herefordshire parishes fell.

It was no wonder that the coming of the railway to Hereford was met with typical Victorian festivities. On 6 December 1853, the day the first train from Newport arrived in Hereford, was declared a public holiday. Many of the farmers of East Herefordshire and their wives would have been among the 60,000 people estimated to have crowded in to Hereford that day. There was a huge banquet at the town hall at lunchtime, complete with champagne and a baron of beef. In the evening there was a grand ball at the Green Dragon Hotel for the gentry, with details of every dance given in the newspaper report. Lady Emily Foley herself led the dancing with the Mayor of Hereford. The lesser folk could attend a similar enjoyable dance at the town hall. Nor were the poor overlooked. All the children received a special tea. The inhabitants of the workhouse were given roast beef, plum pudding and ale, and the young workhouse boys were allowed to attend the firework display in the evening. Throughout the city various plays were performed. Nor were the navvies who had constructed the railways overlooked. A special fund was raised for them and 500 were entertained to a huge lunch comprising roast beef carved by 32 volunteer farmers, with vegetables, bread and two pints of beer each.

The ceremony for the completing of the Hereford to Worcester section was less extravagant but included a good meal for all those involved, once they had remembered to fetch the lady designated to open the section – Mrs Richards, the wife of the engineer, Edward Richards – who had inadvertently been left behind at Hereford.

The role of religion

The parish church played a particularly important role in the second half of the 19th century. In a period when there were limited social activities and virtually none on Sundays, churchgoing would be a social as well as religious activity. Many of the farmers were particularly involved as leading members of the congregations.

It was common for the larger farmers to be the churchwardens. Daniel Pope of Pixley Court was churchwarden from taking on the tenancy around 1850 until his death in 1886. John Sparkman of Brook Farm and Little Marcle Court was a churchwarden. Similarly

Thomas Davies of Claston Farm was churchwarden at Dormington in 1876 when the church was restored. Peter Davies has left a charming reminiscence of the churchwardens' duties when Lady Emily Foley graced Dormington Church with her presence.

> *She always notified my great-grandfather and he and his fellow churchwarden had to meet her at the church gate to escort her into church. When the collection was taken, she always put a velvet bag, containing five sovereigns, in the collection.*[5]

The completion of harvest has always been a time of festivity throughout the generations and indeed continues to be so right up to the present. Special harvest services came to be arranged from the 1850s onwards. An especially enjoyable occasion in Little Marcle involving the farmers and clergy was recorded in the *Hereford Times* of October 1861.

> ***Little Marcle.*** *There was an unusual excitement in this small parish on Thursday, the third instant, on the occasion of a festival to commemorate the ingathering of the harvest. The farmers gave a general holiday to their workmen, and the day commenced with morning prayers in the parish church, which was prettily decorated with corn, vine leaves, hops and fruit. The Reverend C. Smith of Cannington preached an excellent sermon to a full congregation from Isaiah IX part of third verse: they joy before thee according to the joy in harvest. After the service the labourers and their wives sat down to a substantial dinner of roast beef and plum pudding at the different farm houses, and by 3 o'clock assembled at the rectory for football and other games in which the clergy and gentlemen present heartily joined.*

Nor was this all. Afterwards there was an abundant supply of tea and cake laid out in the new schoolroom for the whole parish. The initiators of this excellent day seem to have been mainly the local clergy and the local farmers, especially their wives, as the report states that the ladies of the party were actively employed waiting on more than 200 guests. The clergy involved were said to be "the Rector and Mrs Fred Ward, the Reverend J. Lander and Mrs Lander of Dormington, the Rev. H. Hardy, the Rev. C. Smith, Mr and Mrs Firkin and friends. Farming families listed were "Mr and Miss Sparkman, Mrs Hartland, Mrs Dobbs and Miss Dobbs, Mr Truman, Mr E. Bosley". Thus of the farms described in Part III the families from Brook Farm, Little Marcle Court, Lillands, Laddin Farm and Baregains Farm all assisted in this occasion. Also present were a General Forster and the Misses Forster. One would like to have thought that they represented Earl Somers, the Little Marcle landowner, who otherwise was absent from the account.

From the 1880s the Western Deanery Newsletter provides further insight into parish entertainment. There were always requests for more men to join the choir, and some annual treat for the children, more often than not a tea and games. There was much planning for the Golden Jubilee celebrations and Lady Emily Foley ensured that the children really enjoyed the Queen's Golden Jubilee celebrations in June 1887.

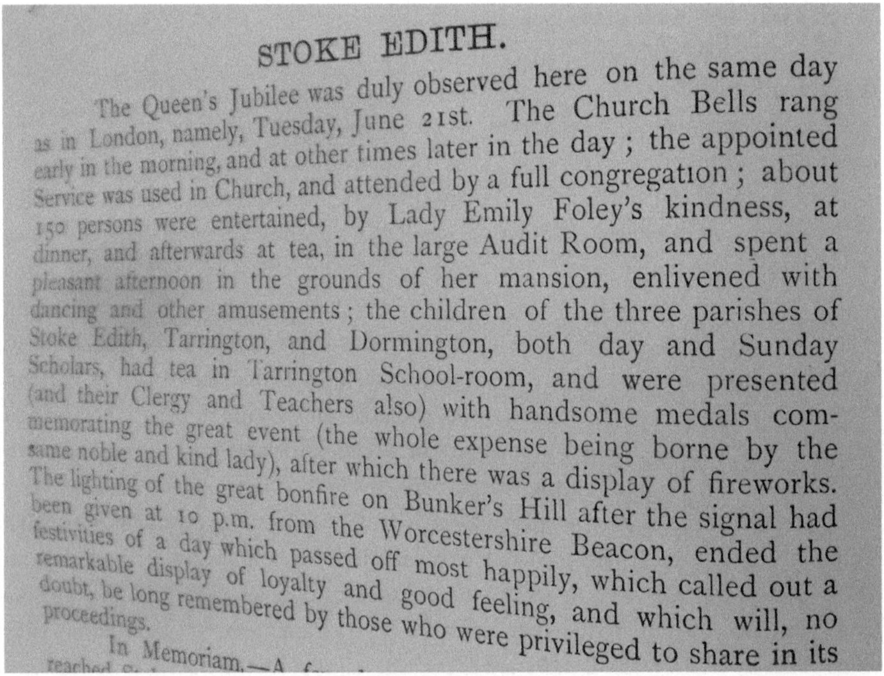

STOKE EDITH.

The Queen's Jubilee was duly observed here on the same day as in London, namely, Tuesday, June 21st. The Church Bells rang early in the morning, and at other times later in the day; the appointed Service was used in Church, and attended by a full congregation; about 150 persons were entertained, by Lady Emily Foley's kindness, at dinner, and afterwards at tea, in the large Audit Room, and spent a pleasant afternoon in the grounds of her mansion, enlivened with dancing and other amusements; the children of the three parishes of Stoke Edith, Tarrington, and Dormington, both day and Sunday Scholars, had tea in Tarrington School-room, and were presented (and their Clergy and Teachers also) with handsome medals commemorating the great event (the whole expense being borne by the same noble and kind lady), after which there was a display of fireworks. The lighting of the great bonfire on Bunker's Hill after the signal had been given at 10 p.m. from the Worcestershire Beacon, ended the festivities of a day which passed off most happily, which called out a remarkable display of loyalty and good feeling, and which will, no doubt, be long remembered by those who were privileged to share in its proceedings.

In Memoriam.—A

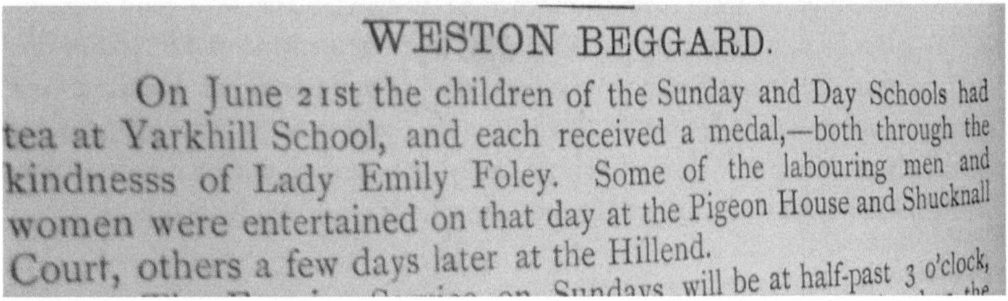

WESTON BEGGARD.

On June 21st the children of the Sunday and Day Schools had tea at Yarkhill School, and each received a medal,—both through the kindnesss of Lady Emily Foley. Some of the labouring men and women were entertained on that day at the Pigeon House and Shucknall Court, others a few days later at the Hillend.

Sundays will be at half-past 3 o'clock,

Fig. 8.8 Reports of the Gold Jubilee celebrations in Stoke Edith and Weston Beggard in June 1887

The Census of Religious Worship of 1851 shows that as well as the Church of England parish churches, most of the East Herefordshire parishes described in Part III had at least one nonconformist chapel and that they drew their congregation mainly from farmworkers. Of the farming families described in Part III, only the 19th-century Godsall family of Weston Corner Farm, Withington and Hynett Farm, Lugwardine, and the Price family of Hynett Farm were Baptists from quite early in the 19th century. The only other nonconformists were William and John Watkins from an established farming family in Radnorshire who took over tenancies in Woolhope in 1898. All played a very active role in the local Baptist community.

Early deaths

Even in prosperous times Victorian farming families could be ripped apart by unexpected deaths. Daniel Pope of Pixley Court had many children but he lost his first wife in childbirth and a little girl from this marriage. The wife of Edward Bosley of Baregains Farm similarly died within a few years of their marriage. Mr Goode of Felton Court lost his wife very young, also probably after childbirth.

On occasion it was the farmer who died unexpectedly. Abraham Pitt of Yare Farm, Woolhope died young in 1861. The family found enough money for a memorial in Woolhope church but had to give up the tenancy. John Taylor, the tenant at Claston Farm, Dormington between 1856 and 1866, had been granted the tenancy when he was only 21 and appeared as a judge for the prestigious Herefordshire Agricultural Society in that year. Sadly he died in 1866 and seems to have been too ill to farm from 1863.

One of the most poignant cases must surely be that of John Sparkman and his wife, Ann. John Sparkman farmed both Brook Farm and Little Marcle Court from around 1848–1873. When Ann died in 1869, John engaged a governess, Emily Hobbs, for his family and subsequently married her. After the birth of their son, Grant, relations with Ann's children deteriorated. Emily tried to prevent John's sons, the elder also called John aged 18 and Philip 17, from seeing him when he lay dying in May 1873. John overcame Emily's edict by seizing a ladder and climbing through the window. Emily then died in December that year. The boys tried to continue farming Brook Farm but were inexperienced and gave up in 1875. Both then emigrated to North America. John died when only 26. Philip travelled extensively, finally set up a small trading store in Rincon, California. Sadly he was murdered in 1907. He sounds a most interesting character.

He befriended the Carmilla Indians by whom he was greatly trusted. He spent his spare time over a period of the last eight years of his life, compiling a grammar of the

Luiseño Indian language which ran to 3 volumes and after his death it was acquired by the University of California.[6]

The South and North Herefordshire hunts

In 1869 the Herefordshire hunt was divided into two, South Herefordshire and North Herefordshire. It is from this time that hunting became a major recreational activity when the farming families felt that they could afford the time or the money. Many of the larger farmers described in Part III would have been subscribers to the North Herefordshire hunt from its inception. Especially keen were the Vevers of Yarkhill Court until around 1904. In addition to the meets a principal social activity right until the end of the 20th century was a hunt ball, and the annual steeplechase for each meet has continued to be a social event in the early 21st century. The hunt also attracted a lot of followers on foot (or bicycle when bicycles first came in). Mr Cooke of Old Court, Lugwardine was a keen follower from his youth at Stoke Edith at the end of the 19th century.

Agricultural shows

With better means of communication agricultural shows continued to prosper both at local and county level. Herefordshire never succeeded in attracting the Royal Agricultural Show to the county. However the old established Herefordshire Agricultural Society joined with the similar society in Worcester in 1894. Sadly the Withington Ploughing Match Association faded out in the 1870s but the Ledbury Agricultural Society remained an important event, joined by other smaller societies. One such was the Newtown Show near Yarkhill. Lady Emily Foley in her inimitable fashion instituted a Cottages Society with prizes for the best-kept cottages in seven parishes and dinner provided at the annual prize-giving, which must have been an enjoyable occasion for some of farmworkers.

Growing political importance of farmers

The Reform Act of 1832 and the Second Reform Act of 1867 probably had little impact on the Herefordshire rural community. It was the Third Reform Act of 1884 that gave the vote for the first time to male farmworkers. This was followed in 1888 by the Local Government Act which established elected County Councils. The councils took over many of the powers originally held by magistrates as well as newly designated powers. Some of the larger farmers in East Herefordshire were now elected to positions of immediate responsibility well beyond that of the parish. One of the earliest of such councillors was Mr Smith of Thinghill Court. The Local Government Act of 1894 created Rural District and Parish Councils. This extended the influence at local level of even the smaller farmers, but the position of farmworkers remained poor in country districts such as Herefordshire where there was little alternative employment.

The 20th century

Support for farmworkers and living standards

The provision of old age pensions from 1908 provided some support for the 'deserving poor' beyond the age of 70 and was administered by the Post Office rather than the poor law authorities.

In 1912 Sidney Box and some other farmworkers established the Herefordshire Agricultural Workers' Union with the intention of increasing wages from the very low level of the time. In his memoirs published in 1950 *The Good Old Days: Then and Now* he stated "In 1901 the average wage of Herefordshire agricultural workers was 13s 11d which had increased to 14s 2½ an increase of 3½d in 11 years. The hours of labourers were from 6 AM to 6 PM, one and a half hours for two meals, breakfast and dinner. Wagoners' hours were generally from 5 AM to 7 PM during the winter to enable the horses to be fed and cleaned ready for work at 7 AM." Wagoners were normally paid an extra shilling a week for the additional two hours worked each day. There were certain perquisites valued at two shillings. According to Sidney Box, in spring 1914 wages were finally increased but this happened only in the districts where there were branches of the union and the increase was given to keep the men out of the union. The wages and conditions requested by the union seem very modest when looked at with early 21st-century eyes. The union wanted general agricultural workers to be paid 18 shillings per week and wagoners more, with wagoners' hours reduced to 75 hours per week in the summer and 59 hours per week in the winter, including Sundays. A strike was called. The more humane employers, amongst them Mr H. W. Taylor of Showle Court, Yarkhill, increased agricultural workers' wages by two shillings a week.

Farming has always been a dangerous business. The *Hereford Journal* and *Hereford Times* include numerous examples of injuries including death to farmworkers throughout this and all the other periods examined. An element of Mr Box's work in the early 20th century was to press for adequate settlement of insurance in cases of accident. Even when insured, the farmer and his workers were at a disadvantage dealing with large wealthy insurance companies who often initially offered meagre compensation.

Farmworkers' cottages could be in a dismal state of repair at the beginning of the 20th century after so long a period of depression, with implications for the health and well-being of the inhabitants. However there was little Sidney Box could do to remedy this.

Some aspects of life improved in the interwar period, not least with the development of the Women's Institutes and the introduction of district nurses, but the hard struggles faced by the whole farming community, farmers as well as farmworkers and their wives, continued in the interwar period with the women, even the wives of the larger farmers, working at least as hard as the menfolk.

The standard of housing in rural Herefordshire remained exceptionally poor until the 1960s. The 1961 census includes information on housing. Over half the dwellings in rural Ledbury district lacked internal running water compared with only a quarter in rural areas of the country as a whole.

However with the introduction of electricity and then mains water all this rapidly changed. The post-war world saw a radical change in living standards in East Herefordshire as elsewhere. Farmers' incomes were at last commensurate with other sectors of the economy. The near full employment together with the safety net of unemployment benefits and state pensions aided the poorer groups. Proper secondary education opened opportunities for the children of farmworkers hitherto unknown. Holidays, even foreign holidays, were a possibility.

Community activities

Tom Bradstock gives a charming account of the farming life of the 1920s and 1930s in an unpublished reminiscence: "There was little machinery to worry about then and certainly no HSE – children soon learned to keep clear of horses' feet and not to get amongst cows and calves." He recalled the pleasures he had had ferreting with Sam Davies, from a farmworking family three generations of whom worked at Freetown, Ashperton.

There was enjoyment just in relaxing at that busy, but social time, of hop picking and harvest. Hop picking was not only important for farmworkers wives to raise money for winter clothing for the children, it was also an enjoyable event. For young Betty Hughes working for Mrs Powell of Hall Court, Much Marcle in the late 1920s the week's hop picking was her holiday – before the Second World War hop picking was a favoured opportunity for many of the farmworker families providing companionship as well as useful cash. Doris Prosser of Old Court Farm, Lugwardine describes the pleasures of the tea party round those busy groups of men bringing in the hay harvest or enjoying the farm cider together at the farmhouse when the corn was in. Ann Nellist, the daughter of John Price of Hynett Farm, Lugwardine remembers her mother cooking that special farmhouse cake around 1950 and driving down with the picnic basket to join Mr Price and the men cutting the hay two miles away at Eau Withington Lakes. Stephen Dale remembers the simple tea party in the apple orchard at Canwood Farm when the blossom was out.

Hunting remained a favoured leisure activity for those who could find the time and money. The Stedman family who took over Yarkhill Court from 1903 were keen supporters of the North Herefordshire hunt. Percy Bradstock and his wife kept hunters in their early married life whilst at Garford Farm, Yarkhill between 1906 and 1920. Mr Bird who purchased Showle Court after the Stoke Edith estate sale in 1919/1920 would invite the North Herefordshire hunt annually to sherry (or brandy) before they left to draw for the day. The annual hunt ball no doubt gave the same enjoyment. Those not favoured with participation in either of these would still enjoy the annual steeplechase meeting. All these activities continued throughout the 20th century. Tom Barnes of Showle Court, Yarkhill was president of the North Hereford Hunt as well as a county councillor.

The tradition of the farmer as churchwarden also continued. Long-standing churchwardens of the 20th century include Tom Bradstock of Freetown who was churchwarden at Tarrington for many years. Consequently the ecclesiastical parish of Tarrington was adjusted so that Freetown was included in that parish rather than in Ashperton.

The traditional annual village fête remained an important function in nearly all the parishes. Until the 1950s at least at the Lugwardine fête normally included a bowling competition for which the prize was a weaner pig donated by a local farmer. Only in the latter part of 20th century were the fêtes opened by 'a celebrity' rather than by a local landowner's wife.

The importance of agricultural shows was maintained and at a county level Gloucester joined up with Worcester and Herefordshire to found The Three Counties Agricultural Society in 1921. The annual Three Counties Show, a major social event as well as being one at which the prize animals and horticultural products could be proudly presented, rotated each year between the three different counties until 1958 when the permanent showground at Malvern was purchased by the Society.

However smaller agricultural competitions continued to take place at all levels, including the parish. The Western Deanery Newsletter for Tarrington in 1913 thanks Mr Foley of Stoke Edith for allowing a cottages flower and vegetable show to take place in Stoke Edith Park when Mr Bray of Dormington Court was one of the two farmers responsible for organising the event. The Withington Show with a large horticultural component as well as competitions for ponies was especially well known in the 1940s and 1950s.

1944 saw the birth of an important new agricultural society in East Herefordshire, one very much in keeping with the Herefordshire Agricultural Societies established from the 19th century.

The Trumpet and District Agricultural Society grew from a project of farmers engaged in home guard activities in a hut near the Trumpet Inn, Pixley, in 1944. Their first idea was a hedging competition, so important for livestock farming of that time. Like all good farmers they were passionate about skilled ploughing and from its inception this was an important part of the competition, with classes for different types of ploughs. The society grew in scope and in activities. In addition to the ploughing, competitions were introduced for hops as well as a horticultural section and competitions for jams, cooking, crafts and flower arrangements with special classes for children. The Annual Trumpet Ploughing Match rapidly became an important competition at national level and has continued to be so. The heart of the society remains the ploughing, with different tractors ranging from vintage to the latest models, but the most popular classes with the public are horse ploughing. A large area of land is needed for the ploughing. Farms described in Part III which have in different years hosted the annual event include Brooke Farm, Pixley Court, Freetown and Felton Court. A feature of the society has been the dedication of individual members to its success. Archie Cowell, a founder member, was secretary for 40 years and generations of the same East Herefordshire families have played an important role in the society. Tony Cotton, a long-term president, was the second generation of his family to be involved.

A special women's committee was formed in 1951 with Mrs R. F. Cotton as chairman from 1951 until 1962. It arranges special fundraising events during the year as well as organising judges for all the competitions (apart from the ploughing or hop sections) and provides excellent homemade refreshments on many occasions. Ann Nellist served as its secretary for over 20 years. Her husband, Tom, has undertaken the vital role of treasurer for even longer. He was first nominated as treasurer in 1962. There was a modest interregnum but now in 2018, well over 50 years later, he remains in this role.

The early 21st century

Many of the farmhouses described in the earlier centuries still remain although the inside of these houses may be radically changed. The farmers who farm the land are often the descendants of those who cared for it through the centuries. Herefordshire is no longer isolated from the rest of the country. The farming community may well visit the southern hemisphere as an excursion to learn about other farming methods. It is a far cry from the time when Oxford seemed so far to young John Powell. Many farm cottages have been totally renovated and are now lived in by prosperous incomers.

There is no longer that direct association with the farms but these newcomers often play important roles in the local community. Previously the cottages were in a deplorable state. Now there is a shortage of affordable housing. The roads may be better but public transport poor.

Woolhope each year has its August Bank Holiday Village Fête, attracting not just the local people but people from beyond the borders of Herefordshire.

In many ways the entertainment remains much the same. The Three Counties Show remains a major attraction in Malvern. There is still a small Ledbury Agricultural Society show. The Trumpet and District Agricultural Society continues to enjoy its national reputation with its Ploughing Match on the first Thursday in October.

Fig. 8.9 A Trumpet and District Agricultural Society Ploughing Match,
© www.trumpetanddistrictagriculturalsociety.co.uk

There are of course some changes. The Big Apple is now a special feature of the early 21st century in East Herefordshire with local producers exhibiting and selling their artisanal cider, perry and apple juices. In the 19th century, village entertainments could be in barns. Court Farm, Aylton is no longer a functioning farm but its remarkable manorial cruck barn, fully restored to its 16th-century glory, is in use for the Big Apple and other local celebrations.

In 1861 Little Marcle celebrated Harvest Festival with a party that included the entire village. In July 2017 the village turned out for the church fête, held at the Upper House just a hundred yards from Lower House Farm, the home of Thomas Bosley, one of the three accused of poaching in the 1836 court case. In 2017 it was a happy occasion. In 1836 the three pointer dogs were part of the evidence for the prosecution. In 2017 there were many dogs present as the event was advertised as a Joint Fête and Fun Dog Show. It seems appropriate to end Part II with a picture of this occasion showing that the rural community is still alive.

Fig. 8.9 Little Marcle Fête and Fun Dog Show 2017

Notes

[1] Reeves, Theodora, C. (November 1974). *The Powell, Stedman, Sparkman Family History*. By kind permission of David Powell.

[2] The Duke of Montrose. (1952). *My Ditty Box*. Jonathan Cape. pp. 21 & 22.

[3] Reeves, Theodora, C. (1972). *History of Little Marcle and Preston Parishes*. Gloucestershire Archives B146/36709G.

[4] By kind permission of Ann Nellist.

[5] Davies, Peter. (2007). *A Herefordshire Tale: Claston, Hops and the Davies family*. Peter Davies. p. 12.

[6] Reeves, Theodora, C. (1974). *The Powell, Stedman, Sparkman Family History*. By kind permission of David Powell.

JOURNEY 1: WITHINGTON AND FELTON PARISHES

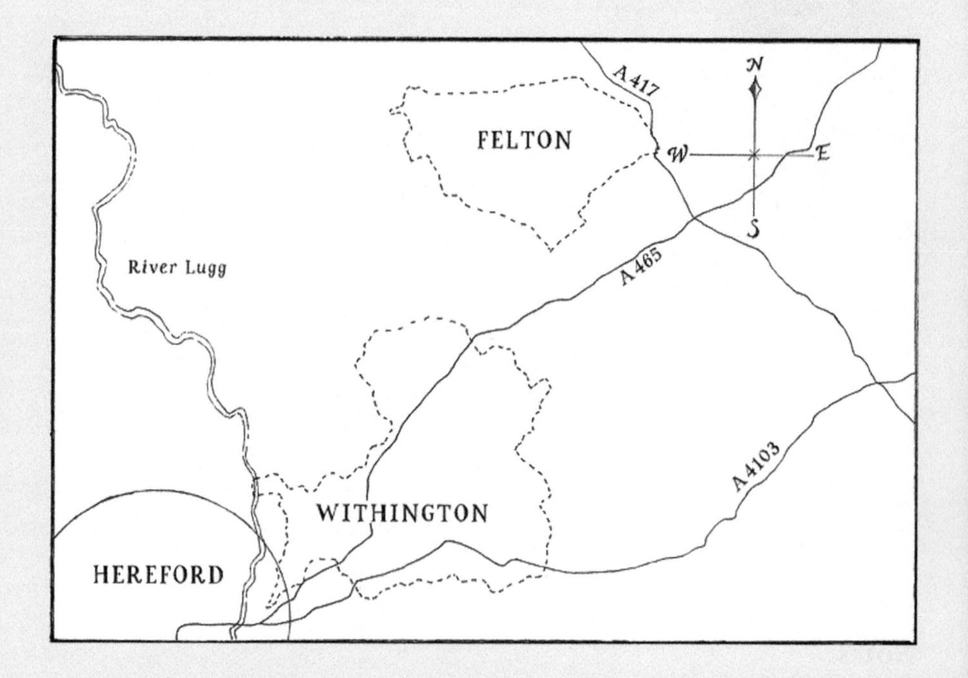

WITHINGTON PARISH

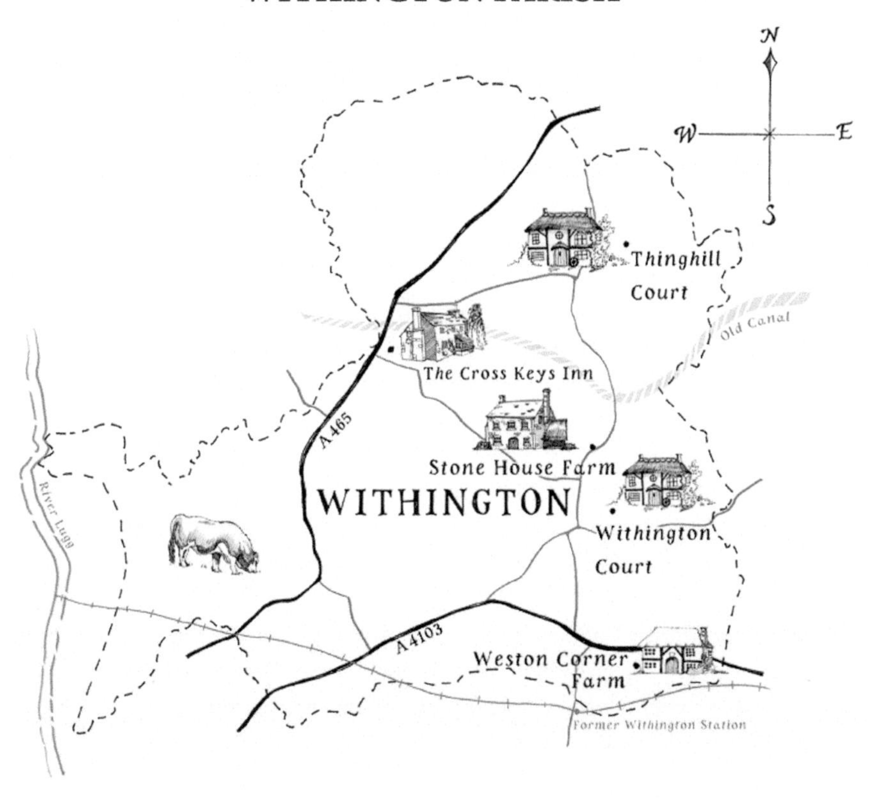

Withington is one of the largest of the parishes considered here. In the 18th and early 19th centuries it included also the parish of Preston Wynne. Withington parish itself (ignoring Preston Wynne) was 2,400 acres until the 1886 revisions. Since that time it has been 2,200 acres. The soil is generally heavy red sandstone. The River Lugg, which flows close to the parish (at one point forming the boundary), floods most winters, creating rich meadow land with interspersed gravel beds. Farmers sometimes either owned the meadow land or had separate grazing rights.

The earliest censuses are not very reliable but suggest a growth of population in the first half of the 19th century with the recorded population of 686 in 1811 rising to 817 in 1841 and increasing further to a peak of 881 in 1851. In common with most other parishes there was then a significant fall in the next 30 years with recorded populations of 772 in 1881 and 774 in 1891. The population in the first half of the 20th century oscillated between the censuses but varied relatively little. It was 757 in 1901, 756 in 1921 and 782 in 1951. From the latter years of the 20th century Withington has benefited from its proximity to Hereford and the planning strategy which permitted significant building in the parish. The population recorded in the 2001 census was 1,004 and this rose to 1,131 in 2011. In contrast with previous centuries very few of the households in 21st-century Withington have contacts with farming.

With the toll road passing through the parish in the 18th and 19th centuries, communications, though limited, were always better than in some other parts of East Herefordshire. The opening of the Withington Wharf on the Gloucester to Hereford canal in 1844 caused transport costs of farm produce and inputs to fall, and the opening of Withington railway station in 1861 provided a good outlet to the main urban markets, especially Birmingham, as well as access to more attractive employment for local people. A tile works built next to the station in 1863 provided welcome alternative employment to normal country farming activities until its closure in 1988.

Until the latter half of the 19th century much of the land in Withington was officially owned by Hereford Cathedral and let out to farmers on copyhold terms. Duncumb writing in 1804 distinguished no fewer than eight manors:

> *Withington, Church Withington, Withington parva, Eau Withington, Nunnington, Preston Wynne, Thinghill magna, and Thinghill parva. Of these, the first six continue in the possession of the church of Hereford; Withington forming part of the revenue annexed to the deanery.*[1]

The remaining two manors, Thinghill magna and Thinghill parva, had belonged since before the Norman Conquest to St Guthlac's Priory and had been sold off at the Reformation.

Duncumb pointed out that the six manors owned by Hereford Cathedral had long been successively leased out to leading families who, over generations, consequently acquired virtual freehold status. Of the four farms described below, Stone House Farm was originally part of the manor of Withington parva, Thinghill Court had been part of the manor of Thinghill magna and so in the hands of secular landowners since the Reformation, and Withington Court was originally part of the manor of Church Withington. All three farms played a major role in the development of pedigree Hereford cattle.

Over the course of time small acreages were spun off from the original eight manors. Throughout the 19th and first half of the 20th century Withington was characterised by seven exceptionally large farms (the eighth large farm was in Preston Wynne parish). In contrast there were no farms of intermediate size but an exceptionally large number of very small holdings of under 25 acres. This can be seen in the returns of the 1851 population census which asked for occupations and acreages. There were seven farms of 180 acres or more, the next largest farm was a mere 70 acres, there were only three of 50 or more acres, there were two farms between 25 and 49 acres and the remaining 16 smallholdings were under 25 acres. Nor had the situation changed greatly 90 years later at the time of the National Farm Survey of 1941–1943[2] when 23 separate holdings were identified. All seven large farms still existed, there were a few farms between 50–70 acres, but by far the greater number of farms were smallholdings under 25 acres.

Weston Corner Farm described below borders onto Weston Beggard parish and is an example of one of the more important of these smaller yeoman farms. It originally formed part of the manor of Church Withington and can be traced back to the 18th century.

Stone House Farm

Fig.WI 1 The Georgian front of Stone House

Stone House and outbuildings, on the W. side of the road, 250 yards N. of the church. The House is of rubble and was perhaps re-built early in the 18th century.

A chimney-stack on the N.E. side has the initials and date: W.A. 1714. The building has been much altered. Projecting to the W. of the house is an early 18th-century range of Outbuildings with a N. wing of stone and timber-framing. A large barn, N.E. of the house, is of the same period.[3]

Stone House belongs to Rachel Leake, the third generation of her family to have farmed here since 1919. Until 2009 the Leakes were tenants of the Apperley estate, and it was the Apperley family who owned and farmed this remarkable farm from the early 18th century until the early 20th century.

History of Stone House Farm

There is an early 17th-century reference to William Deem and the Deem family seem to have been associated with Stone House in the 17th and possibly very early 18th century. However, since then only two families apart from the Leakes have farmed here in the past 300 years: the Apperleys and the Yeomans.

Fig.WI 2 18th-century outbuildings at Stone House

The Apperley family: owners and farmers of Stone House c. 1690–1905

The Stone House estate, now the property of William Havard Apperley, was acquired, circa 1690, by William Apperley (d. 11 March, 1726 aet. 75) through his marriage with Eleanor, dau. of John Havard, and heir to her uncle, William Havard of Fownhope.[4]

It is not always easy to trace the Apperley family history owing to the habit, quite prevalent in Herefordshire, of using the same names for the succeeding generations. William Apperley (1684–1766) was succeeded by his son, the long-lived John Havard Apperley (1723–1812), named appropriately in grateful acknowledgement of the Havard family fortune. To confuse matters John Havard Apperley's son was also named John Havard Apperley and died in the same year as his long-lived father.

In their role as minor squires, members of the Apperley family played in a significant part in the establishment of the Herefordshire Agricultural Society, which was formed unusually early in 1797. As part of its enthusiasm for general improvement in agriculture, the society encouraged the development of the local cattle for meat rather than as oxen. The accounts of the society include prizes awarded to John Havard Apperley of Withington for his bull.

The Apperleys continued to be closely associated with the improved breeding of Hereford cattle throughout the first half of the 19th century and remained active members of the Herefordshire Agricultural Society. Together with other leading local farmers such as Matthew Goode of Felton Court, they were also instrumental in other farming initiatives, including the founding of a local Withington Ploughing Society in 1841 described in Chapter 2.

As a large farm, Stone House had clearly grown hops since well before 1841. One of the larger fields shown in the Tithe Map of 1841 is described as 'old hop yard'. In 1848, presumably at a time when the hops had failed, James Apperley was part of the nationwide delegation urging the government to postpone a proposed tax on hops which it believed could destroy many producers. However, the farm did not produce just cattle and hops. Arable farming was also important. The name of Mr Apperley appears on an advertisement in the *Hereford Times* in 1850 relating to the change of day for the Hereford Corn Market. He and other signatories would in future attend on Wednesdays rather than Saturdays.

The early Victorians made sure that any public occasion, small or large, was marked with an excellent dinner and the *Hereford Times* notes the attendance of the Apperleys at such functions. Meetings of the Withington Ploughing Society, for instance, invariably culminated in a really good dinner at the local Cross Keys Inn. At the important social occasion of the marriage of Queen Victoria to Albert, Mr W. H.

Apperley acted as one of the stewards at the celebratory ball at the City Arms Hotel in Hereford. On 10 January 1856 it was James Apperley who was the steward at a Card and Dancing Assembly at the City Arms. Mr Ballard was the guest of honour at a dinner to celebrate the completion of the canal as far as Withington Wharf in 1844, and naturally Mr W. H. Apperley was one of the organisers. On a more cultural front, Mr W. H. Apperley was a member of the Herefordshire Philosophical Society, which predated the more famous Woolhope Naturalists' Field Club.

Stone House also went through difficult times in this period. To the great grief of the family, John, the eldest son of W. H. Apperley, died at the early age of 27 on 30 May 1843. There then seem to have been some problems after the death of W. H. Apperley in 1851, possibly associated with his will, and in September 1859 the farm and land was put up for sale. The items listed included the herd of 67 white-faced Hereford cattle, all bred on the farm. Fortunately the situation seems to have been resolved and in the latter half of the 19th century it was William Apperley and then after him James Apperley who were farming at Stone House. From time to time mention was made of farming activities at Stone House in the *Hereford Times* and *Hereford Journal*, including the sale of farmhouse cider and perry.

James seems to have married late as at the time of the census of 1901 he was 73 but the household comprised his much younger sister Lucy aged 53 and daughter Edith 23. He died in 1901, three months after the census was taken, and it was four years later that the Apperleys ceased to farm Stone House themselves.

J. H. Yeomans: tenant of Stone House Farm 1905–1920

From 1905–1920 J. H. Yeomans was the tenant of Stone House Farm and the 1910 valuation documents show that J. H. Yeomans had rented the farm with 251 acres from H. W. Apperley, Apperley and Brown, Cathedral Close. In his early career John Yeomans had been a remarkably successful breeder of Herefords and indeed was renowned in Hereford breeding circles for having exported virtually his entire herd to the United States for a record price in 1882 at the peak of the demand. Prior generations of Yeomans and of John Yeoman's wife's family, the Haywoods of Blakemere, had played a very significant role in the history of Hereford pedigree cattle. It was John's great-grandfather, also John Yeomans, who experimented with breeding as early as the 1780s when a tenant of Thinghill Court.

In the census of 1911 the household comprised John Yeomans aged 59, his wife, Rebecca aged 57, and three of their four children: Haywood aged 19, Jane aged 16 and Walter aged 14. Presumably their younger daughter, Honor, was away at school. Ironically, given the future war, the children had a German governess. As a modern farmer, Mr

Yeomans' household also contained a farm pupil, George Edward Gunning, as well as the normal two indoor maids. A family friend, Ronald Palethorpe, was staying at the time.

The Yeomans family was smitten with tragedy in the succeeding 1914–1918 war. Haywood, a talented young man at Oxford when the war started, volunteered and was killed in October 1917. His younger brother, Walter, did not even have those few enjoyable adult years: he had been killed a few months earlier in April 1917.

Occasional references in the *Hereford Times* indicate the role John Yeomans played in supporting the war effort by contributing to various funds. (Funds at that time specified contributors and the amount contributed.) Records of a tribunal of 26 February 1916 show that John Yeoman requested to be permitted to keep his wagoner, W. G. Smith, as his two sons and six farmworkers had already enlisted. The request was turned down.[5] Following the death of his sons John Yeomans gave up the farm in 1919 and died soon afterwards. His widow and daughters then moved to Woodfield, Weston Beggard where they lived for the rest of their lives. For Jane and Honor, Stone House always had a special place in their hearts and their happiest times were spent here.

The Leake family at Stone House Farm: 1919–present

J. M. Leake farmed at Stone House from 1919 and officially took over the tenancy in 1920. The Leake family had previously farmed in Moreton Jefferies and were already breeders of pedigree Hereford cattle and members of the Hereford Herd Book. The traditional importance of Hereford cattle at Stone House from the early 19th century was therefore maintained. Mr Leake was a highly educated and innovative man who designed his own telescope.

Stone House in the Second World War

The National Farm Survey of 1941–1943 and the annual Agricultural Census of June 1941 together provide a picture of the farm at this period. At 284 acres plus nine acres of meadowland in Eau Withington, Stone House was one of the larger Herefordshire farms. Mr Leake received an A grading for competence. Exceptionally for the time, the farmhouse, buildings and four farm cottages were all in a good state of repair, as were the farm roads, hedges, ditches, and field drainage. There was mains electricity and well water, plus roof water supplied to the house and buildings.

It was a quintessentially mixed farm with both pastoral and arable land. Following the urgent need to increase arable production to feed the population, under the County War Agricultural Executive Committee (CWAEC) instructions the area under approved crops had recently been increased by 12½ acres for the 1940 harvest and a further 16½ acres ploughed up specifically for wheat for the 1941 harvest. Consequently by June 1941, there were 50 acres under cereals, principally wheat, a further five and a half acres under potatoes, also considered of strategic importance for feeding the population, whilst the remaining seven and a half acres were under root crops intended mainly for animal fodder (turnips, swedes and mangolds). This still left 165 acres under permanent or temporary grass. The farm's rich soil supported a hop quota of 25 acres and there were no fewer than 40 acres of orchards. By modern standards the number of cattle seems low, but a herd of 104 beef cattle was substantial at the time (41 cows in milk or calf, two bulls, 30 calves under a year old and the remaining animals between one and two years old). The farm had a flock of 53 sheep including its own ram and the lambs yet to be sold. There were three piglets between two and five months old and a modest flock of 50 chickens. Unlike most of his smaller neighbours who remained dependent upon horse power, Mr Leake had a 20-horsepower Massey-Harris tractor, although the farm still had no fewer than five working horses. Considerable labour was needed and the farm employed nine full-time men and 12 part-time workers, of whom 11 were women. The farm owned four cottages of which two were used for employees.

Stone House after the Second World War

The farm has seen quite remarkable changes in output since the 1950s. In the early post-war period the emphasis was on cider apples and indeed the farm produced its own commercial bottled cider. There was then a radical switch to hop production: a change made possible by hop machines replacing the original hand-picking of hops. The orchards were grubbed up and no fewer than 150 acres, over half the entire acreage of the farm, were put down to hops. These in their turn were grubbed up in the late 1980s to be replaced by arable.

Fig. WI 3 The Stone House herd of pedigree Hereford cattle[6]

Fig. WI 4 A Stone House prize-winning Ryeland lamb[6]

Rachel Leake, the present owner, has run the farm since 2004, first in partnership with her mother and then from 2011 on her own. The Apperley estate sold the farm to the Leake family in 2009. Throughout their years at Stone House and indeed before that time, the Leake family have always reared pedigree Herefords. Currently the herd comprises 50 cows plus their offspring. Since 2004 the farm has also reared the historic Herefordshire Ryeland sheep, once widespread in East Herefordshire but now considered a rare breed. Stone House is however a mixed farm of 250 acres with 137 acres of mixed arable (wheat, barley and oilseed rape). There are no full-time employees but as is common in the 21st century, some considerable use is made of contractors, especially for the arable land.

Fig.WI 5 Thinghill Court with more recent additions on the right

Thinghill Court

Thinghill Court has always been a large farm by the standards of East Herefordshire. From before the Norman Conquest until the dissolution of the monasteries, Thinghill Magna, of which Thinghill Court land forms the major part, was owned by St Guthlac's Priory of Hereford.

In the late 18th and in the early and mid-19th centuries Thinghill Court was the location for the early development of pedigree Hereford cattle and has always been at the forefront of farming – not least in the present day. James Hawkins is the fourth generation of the Hawkins family to farm at Thinghill Court. Dedicated to farming from boyhood, he lost his father Stuart when only 18 and took over the responsibility of the farm businesses from his mother, Sheila, at the early age of 23. His great-grandfather Thomas Hawkins officially purchased the farm in 1920 following the death of his maternal uncle Mr T. Smith, who had farmed Thinghill Court and Thinghill Grange land from around 1877. The census records for 1911 show Thomas Hawkins as a farm student at Thinghill Court and Kelly's Directories suggest that he resided there from that time. Consequently Thinghill Court has been in the same family for almost 150 years.

History of Thinghill Court

In the Middle Ages the land surrounding Thinghill Court formed part of the manor of Thinghill Magna and belonged to the Benedictine Priory of St Guthlac's of Hereford. According to Duncumb:

> *At the dissolution of religious houses Thinghill was granted to Sir John Pryce, and remained in his family during several generations, as detailed in the account of Felton. Being alienated by one of his descendants near the close of the seventeenth century, one portion was held by the Burghill family, and the other by a Mr. Carwardine. In the year 1700, General — Cornewall purchased the two parts, and left the whole to a female relative, who married William Moore, esq. who was succeeded in this property by his son William, who sold it A.D. 1799, to Francis Glossop, of London, esq.*[7]

There are references in the Withington Church baptism records to the Moore family in the 18th century who seem to have lived at Thinghill Court for at least part of the time. At the time of its sale by auction in November 1798 Thinghill Court was advertised as 534 acres, virtually the same as the acreage of 522 acres recorded in the National Farm Survey of 1941–1943, over 140 years later.

However the advertisement of late 1798 speaks of two farmhouses. Almost certainly the other farmhouse was the historic Thinghill Grange which partially dates back to the 15th century. Thinghill Grange, which in the 20th century had around 200 acres, was still owned by Thinghill Court in 1941, although farmed separately. Thinghill Court was rented out to Mr Henry Williams for £320 per year until 1808, a fairly low rent with the inflated rents obtainable during the Napoleonic Wars. It had, moreover, the important advantage of being of being tithe free, a historical anomaly harking back to the time when the land belonged to St Guthlac's Priory.

Historic links with Hereford pedigree cattle

Thinghill Court had many early associations with the development of pedigree Hereford cattle. According to James McDonald in his authoritative book *History of Hereford Cattle* first published in 1885 and revised by James Sinclair in 1909, John Yeomans, one of the earliest pioneers of selective breeding of Herefords, left Thinghill Court for Howton Court in 1785 with three breeding cows[8], the earliest record of the Yeomans family's long-term association with the breed. His great-grandson, also John Yeomans, was president of the Hereford Herd Book in the early 20th century and as indicated above, farmed Stone House Farm, Withington between 1905 and 1920.

This early association with Herefords was maintained. Mr H. Williams, who succeeded Mr Yeomans as tenant of Thinghill Court, was a leading member of the Herefordshire Agricultural Society, winning several prizes for his cattle. At the sale of his cattle in 1814, 52 breeding animals, including young calves, fetched an average price of £32, quite remarkable for the time, with the highest price of £76 paid for the cow, Prettymaid, and her heifer calf. There were close family links with the famous Tomkins family, also renowned for their effective breeding of Hereford cattle. Mr H. Williams' brother, Mr John Williams, who died in 1815, was married to a sister of Mr Benjamin Tomkins, the younger. Mr William Taylor, whose son, another William Taylor, would be renowned for his pedigree Herefords at Showle Court, Yarkhill, was also stated to have commenced his own herd at Thinghill Court around 1820[9].

From at least 1841 Mr William Racster was renting Thinghill Court with his sister as his housekeeper. The census records for 1851 show him to be farming 560 acres and employing 26 labourers. He was a progressive farmer and as described in Chapter 2, he was one of the initiators of the Withington Ploughing Match Society in 1841. He appears in the second edition of the Hereford Herd book as owning Hereford cattle. Around 1856 he left Thinghill Court for the important but smaller farm of Withington Court. Confusingly the next tenant at Thinghill Court was yet another Mr William Taylor. There is evidence that he was closely related to William Taylor of Showle Court but the exact relationship is not clear. From the age of his children it would appear that he had taken up the tenancy in 1858 as his young son Alfred aged three was the first of the family to be born in Withington. According to the census of 1861 this Mr Taylor was farming 566 acres and employing 19 men and four boys. The Rev. Charles Robinson writing in 1872 stated that Thinghill Court belonged to Francis H. Newland Glossop of Silver Hall, Isleworth, the grandson of the Francis Glossop who had bought it in 1799[10].

John Smith purchased at least part of the combined Thinghill Court and Thinghill Grange estates in 1877. Initially he seems to have farmed both estates while living at

Thinghill Grange. He is shown to be resident there in the directories of 1877 and is described as a hop grower. He also purchased a herd of pedigree cattle in 1877 from the executors of William Taylor:

> *The herd belonging to Mr John W. Smith at Thinghill Court was founded in 1877, purchases having been made from the late Mr W. Taylor.*[11]

By 1881 he had moved to Thinghill Court and in the 1881 census he is shown as farming a remarkable 804 acres and employing no fewer than 30 men.

The Local Government Act established elected county councils in 1888 and John Smith became a leading man of the county: a County Councillor, an Alderman and a JP. In the 1901 census he was listed as a 'gentleman farmer' and he appears to have been growing soft fruit in the early 1900s. John Smith was invariably described as a landowner in *Kelly's Directories* and in the 1910 land valuation he is listed as the owner of Thinghill Grange. However, the 1910 land valuation shows the Rev. Glossop as the landowner of Thinghill Court with John Smith as his agent, so some land seems to have remained in the ownership of the Glossop family.

John Smith's nephew, Mr. T. J. Hawkins, was living at Thinghill Court from at least 1911. He purchased Thinghill Court following the death of his uncle in 1920 and also owned Thinghill Grange. He played an important role in local government in his turn, for which he received an OBE. The pedigree herd was sold and Thinghill reverted to mixed farming: beef, dairy, soft fruit and, of course, the hops for which Herefordshire was so long famed.

Thinghill Court in the Second World War

The National Farm Survey of 1941–1943 and the annual Agricultural Census of June 1941 confirm Thinghill Court's position as one of the leading farms of Herefordshire at that time. Mr T. J. Hawkins was recorded as farming and owning 522 acres and was given an A grading. Mains electricity was not generally available in Withington until the 1940s, but in collaboration with a few other major farms, including Shucknall Court and Hill End in the parish of Weston Beggard, Thinghill Court had paid to have public electricity installed in the 1930s. There were 12 service cottages. The farm had no fewer than three Fordson tractors at a time when many farms had none and very few had more than one. Nevertheless it is worth noting that the farm still had 11 heavy horses and one other horse.

The farm was highly diversified. Around one-third of the acreage was under arable, a higher proportion than in most other farms. Of this some 22% was under corn (47 acres of wheat, 39 acres of oats and 23 acres of mixed corn). In addition there were 16½ acres of potatoes and 33 acres were given over to turnips, swedes and mangolds. Both wheat and potatoes were considered vital strategic crops and of the area under wheat, 15½ acres of the wheat had been ploughed up under the instructions of the CWAEC for the 1940 harvest with a further 12½ acres of wheat for the 1941 harvest. Thinghill Court had long been a major hop producer and was entitled to 41¾ statute acres of hops (rather than hop acres, each of which equalled about two-thirds of a hop acre). It was also a major producer of fruit with 12% of the acreage, some 60½ acres, under orchards. Rare for East Herefordshire at the time, no fewer than 22 acres were devoted to soft fruit.

Even with this diversification 215½ acres were under permanent grass either for mowing or grazing, and a further 24 acres were under clover. Consequently Thinghill Court supported a herd of 160 beef cattle, nearly all bullocks or heifers between one and two years old, although the farm was also self-supporting in milk products with three cows or heifers either in milk or in calf. Unusually there were no sheep, but there were eight pigs over eight months, and a small flock of 51 poultry (ducks and chickens). Such a big enterprise needed very substantial labour input. In June 1941 Mr Hawkins had a workforce of 20: 17 full-time workers of whom 14 were men and three were women, and a further three part-time workers, all men.

Thinghill Court after the Second World War

John Hawkins, Thomas Hawkins' son, took over the farm. From around 1964 John farmed together with his son Stuart, with Stuart undertaking most of the decision-making as John was also a hop factor and so away in London during the week.

Always responsive to new ideas, in addition to running Thinghill Court as a major mixed and hop farm, Stuart pioneered from the late 1960s growing 'instant trees', collaborating with John Williamson of the then newly established Wyevale Nurseries of Hereford. These trees were in great demand for urban planners at the time and continue to be produced at Thinghill Court until the 21st century. At the time of publication some trees are still containerised on Thinghill Court land although Thinghill Court has no longer any connection with Wyevale Nurseries.

In the 1970s dairying could be a profitable enterprise. Stuart developed a large and successful dairy unit in 1976 based on Holstein-Friesian cattle. Following Stuart's death in 1988 the farm, including the dairying enterprise, was run by Stuart's widow, Sheila, until 1995 and then for a few years in partnership with their eldest son, James, before he took over. The dairy enterprise itself was retained until 2010 when the conditions made it no longer practicable. In 2002 James and his wife, Sandra, moved into Thinghill Court. Their two sons in their turn are interested in farming.

Many of the large farms are now specialists; not so Thinghill Court. It is still associated with some traditional occupations but approaches these in an innovative way appropriate to the 21st century. Thinghill Court continues to grow hops, retains a very old cider orchard and some land remains in arable, supporting its beef herd. However, it is also a major producer of free-range eggs with some 32,000 birds, and many of its strawberries are to be found in the major supermarkets. The farm now also grows both garlic and asparagus and produces lawn turf under the company name of Easylawn. Different enterprises need different regimes and James's brother, Paul, is in charge of some of them. Some are produced as partnerships, some through Thinghill Court company. Some are produced on land belonging to Thinghill Court, some on rented land, some on different leasing arrangements. In its hop enterprises, all of which grow dwarf hops, Thinghill Court collaborates with other large farms in the area, including Claston Farm, Dormington and Pixley Court.

Fig. WI 6 Hops at Thinghill Court 2016

Weston Corner Farm

With its 50–60 acres Weston Corner was until the second half of the 20th century a much more modest-sized farm than the other three Withington farms considered here, and more typical of an average family farm in East Herefordshire. From before 1841 until 1966 it had belonged to only one family, the Godsalls. The other three farms in Withington described in this section were the successors of medieval manor houses and owned by important families. In contrast, from early on Weston Corner was a yeoman establishment carved out from part of the manor of Church Withington.

Fig.WI 7 Weston Corner Farm[12]

History of Weston Corner Farm

Part of the current house and farm buildings date back to the 18th century.

The earliest reference to Weston Corner was in 1780 when the *Hereford Journal* of October of that year included the announcement that the executors of Richard Waring, Clerk, were to sell by auction on 7 November 1780 land in Withington including:

> *Lot one. All that stone built messuage or dwellinghouse situate in Weston Corner with barn, Mill house, garden, two orchards, and a piece of arable land thereto adjoining containing by estimation 6 acres.*
>
> *Also all those two orchards and a small coppice situated at a place called Whitestone containing by estimation two acres and a half.*
>
> *The above premises are now in the possession of Mr Morris as tenant from year to year at a rent of 12L.*

Fig.WI 8 18th century barn at Weston Corner Farm

Weston Corner was put up for sale again some 35 years later in April 1815. The farm comprised 20 statute acres and belonged to Mr Barnes of Putley but was occupied by a Mr Head on an annual tenancy. It was fully equipped for mixed farming with a stable, barn, cider mill, fold and outbuildings.

At the time of the 1841 census Mr John Godsall (1812–1886) was living at Weston Corner and was stated to be farming 50 acres. The Tithe Map of 1841 shows him to own 20 acres in Church Withington and he was also farming fields close to the River Lugg. He came from a family who had lived in Withington since the latter part of the 18th century. His father, James Godsall (1780–1835), was baptised and buried at Withington. His mother, Alice (née Tranter), also came from a Withington family, but his grandfather, Thomas Godsall, was born in Much Cowarne. It is possible that there is a family link with the Godsalls of Showle Court, but the relationship is very distant. John Godsall seems to have been an effective farmer and by 1861 he was farming 60 acres. He was a signatory to a petition in 1854 from hop growers supporting a market for hops in Hereford so was producing hops by this time. In 1861 the household comprised his wife, Ann, two daughters (Alice aged 19 and Mary aged 16), and two sons (John aged 19 and James aged 13). An indication of the success of John Godsall was revealed by the changes in the farmhouse itself. Sale particulars of 2015 mention a substantial Victorian extension.

The Godsalls differ in an important respect from the farmers at the three other Withington farms described here. Whereas the larger farmers were frequently churchwardens of the Church of England, the Godsalls were nonconformists, supporters and indeed probably among the founders of Whitestone Baptist Chapel, which was built in 1821. All the Godsalls are buried in the little churchyard there and their contacts would have been mainly with the other worshippers at the chapel.

In the 1870s John Godsall's eldest son, also called John Godsall (1841–1912), married Anne Tranter who was living in London, but who had been brought up by her grandparents at Castle Farm, Aylton. The young couple moved to Hynett Farm, Lugwardine with its then 106 acres, which John farmed with the aid of a man and a boy. There they reared a large family. Following the death of John Godsall senior the family moved back to Weston Corner. After this John Godsall's death in 1912, Weston Corner continued to be in the possession of the family. Two of John and Anne's sons moved to other well-known East Hereford farms. William Godsall farmed Hoar Farm (later called Underhill) in Woolhope from the early 1900s until about 1960. Charles Harold Godsall farmed Moor Court, Stretton Grandison, where his descendants still farm.

Fig. WI 9 The Godsall family in front of Weston Corner Farm probably around 1890[12]

The connection with Hynett Farm also continued. Editha, John and Anne's elder daughter, married Reuben Price, a fellow member of Whitestone Baptist Chapel. Before moving to Hynett Farm, Reuben had previously been farming with his brother at West Lydiatt Farm, Withington. The history of Hynett Farm including the Price family is described in the section on Lugwardine parish. Editha, the longest living member of the family died only in 1970 at the great age of 97. She was to be the last of the family to be buried in that lovely little chapel at Whitestone.

Weston Corner in the Second World War

At the time of the Second World War Weston Corner was farmed by Joseph Godsall, the second youngest of John and Anne's sons. The CWAEC thought he was not active enough and only gave him a B grade. The farm of 46 acres had good medium soil and the fences, ditches and drainage were in a good state of repair. Three and a half acres of oats had been ploughed up for the 1940 harvest and of the total holding of 34½ acres was down to grass with an additional six acres of orchards. Three-quarters of an acre was down to potatoes and the remaining one and a quarter acres to root crops. There was no electricity. There were 14 cattle, mainly store cattle, but no sheep and only a modest flock of 67 poultry and two piglets. They were two farm horses.

Weston Corner after the Second World War

Joseph Godsall married late in life. He and his wife Queenie had two children, and his elder sister, Nellie, lived with them for many years. In 1966 this small farm was sold to Arthur Gittoes who then sold off part of the land in 1982. In 1998 Weston Corner effectively became a private residence when it was sold to Alan and Julie Densley with around 13 acres of land.

Weston Corner was purchased in 2015 by Tania Blonder and her mother, Jane Pasquill, who wish to use the outbuildings and land for sustainable rural activities. The 18th century barn mentioned in the sale of 1815 is still there. Jane is an artist and her work includes specialised geometric wall hangings using different textiles. She is also part of a group that promotes the revival of hemp growing to provide the fibres for a cottage industry.

Fig.WI 10 John Dent outside Withington Court

Withington Court

> *Withington Court,* 170 yards E.S.E. of the church, is of two storeys with cellars and attics; the walls are of rubble and the roofs are covered with slates and tiles. It was built probably in the 16th century, but was remodelled in the second half of the 18th century and has later additions on the N. side. The W. wing and the adjoining block on the S. are probably 17th-century additions. The E. end has an original stone window of two lights with elliptical heads; there is a similar window of three lights in the gable, and on the gable is the stump of a pinnacle. In the garden is a gable-pinnacle with ranges of shallow trefoil-headed panelling. Inside the building are some chamfered ceiling-beams and some 17th-century panelling; one panelled partition [...] on the first floor, has a frieze of carved scrolls. The roof of the main block is of collar-beam type with slightly curved braces.[3]

Although the Royal Commission on Historical Monuments thought some 16th century remains could be detected in Withington Court, Kelly's Directories satisfactorily dodged the question through many editions stretching from the latter part of the 19th century right until 1941 by describing it as 'an ancient Gothic stone mansion pleasantly situated near the church'.

Architecturally, Withington Court is probably one of the most interesting of the buildings discussed in Part III. As indicated in the section on Withington parish above, Church Withington was a separate manor attached to one of the prebends of Hereford Cathedral back in medieval times. There would therefore always been a house on the site since that time.

Withington Court has been in the same family since 1946. It was purchased after the Second World War by Daniel Hess, a northern businessman, as part of an aim to diversify his capital. When his young daughter Elizabeth came to live at Withington Court, she was entranced by Herefordshire and the farming environment. In 1959 Elizabeth married John Dent, descended from several generations of well-known Herefordshire farming families. Following the practice for many large Herefordshire farms, Withington Court is now a company with Elizabeth and John's children and grandchildren involved.

History of Withington Court

There are records of Withington Court dating back to the early 17th century. The Withington Church registers record that Hugh Taylor of Withington Court was buried on 7 January 1633.

The Philips and Broome families

Withington Court perhaps reached its highest distinction in the late 17th and early to mid-18th centuries when the Philips family were the principal copyholders and Withington Court was their residence. Duncumb devotes four pages to information on the Philips family and the family with whom they intermarried, the Broome family of Eau Withington Court.

The most distinguished member of the Philips family, John Philips, poet and composer of Cyder, the earliest eulogy to this famous Herefordshire drink, died in 1708 and probably never lived at Withington Court. His great-grandfather, and presumably the source of the Philips fortune, was a clothier in Ledbury. His grandfather was a Residentiary Canon of the Cathedral as well as Vicar of Lugwardine. Since the Dean and Chapter owned the freehold of the manor of Church Withington, disposing of it periodically on copyhold terms for a certain number of lives, this would have been useful. Stephen Philips, gentleman, died at Withington Court in 1754 and Robert Philips in 1760.

It was probably with the death of Robert's widow Anne in 1763 that the copyhold ownership moved to the Broome family as a result of intermarriage. The Hereford Cathedral Archive records for 28 September 1763 (D541) state that Withington Court was then leased by William Williams, the Cathedral Prebend of the Withington, to James Broome for 21 years for a most modest annual rent, even by the standards of the time, of £13. The Broome family may well have continued to live at Eau Withington Court, rather than at Withington Court.

Further changes of ownership

The Broome family of the late 18th century had no heirs. Duncumb records that their possessions (presumably Eau Withington Court and Withington Court) were left to Thomas Griffiths, Clerk, and after his decease to John Lilly, Clerk of New Court, Lugwardine. In 1832 Thomas Hill of Blaenavon took over the copyhold lease which was renewed for 21 years with the annual rent still at £13. (Thomas Hill was the heir to the Blaenavon iron works but preferred the life of a Herefordshire squire. In 1842 he had moved first to Penygraig near Ross-On-Wye and then to Rudhall also near Ross-On-Wye.) In the 1841 Tithe Map records, Thomas Hill was listed as the owner of Withington Court and its 153 acres, as well as of Eau Withington Court. (He was also the owner of Felton Court in Felton parish.) In 1868 all these farms were put up for sale. Withington Court was bought by a Mr Mark Clarke. However all was not well; in August 1880 Withington Court with 275 acres, together with the 10-acre smallholding of Banks Farm, was sold by mortgagees of Mrs Clarke. It would appear to have been very run-down at this time. It was purchased by Joseph Myers and remained in the Myers family until 1913 as a Mrs Myers is described as the owner in the valuation records of 1910.

Mainly a rented farm from the late 18th century until 1913

Apart from the ill-fated time of the Clarke family in the 1870s, Withington Court was a rented farm associated with a number of farming families from at least the late 18th century until it was purchased by Mr W. Farmer in 1913. In the early 19th century the farmer seems to have been a Mr John Legeyt as the church records for baptisms records the birth of a Frances Legeyt, daughter of John and Elizabeth Legeyt of Withington Court in 1813, another daughter, Caroline, in 1815 and a son, William Edwin, in 1817. By the time of the first census in 1841, the tenant was Joseph Davies and his family. The Davies family clearly experienced considerable troubles. By 1851 Joseph was dead and it was his daughter, Elizabeth Davies, who was the farmer. It seems that Joseph's sons were not able to fulfil this role since according to the 1851 census she was assisted by one brother as the bailiff and another brother described as a farmworker. By 1856 the struggle had been too much and the *Hereford Times* of 11 January announced that the remaining livestock, equipment and all the household furniture were to be auctioned on 14 and 15 February. Poor Elizabeth Davies appears to have been bankrupt.

In 1861 Mr W. Racster was living at Withington Court, having presumably moved there from Thinghill Court. He was still there at the time of the census of 1871 now aged 77 but employing 13 workers and three boys. His sister had died and he had 'a lady housekeeper'. In the 1870s it was occupied by the owner Mr Mark Clarke and then by his widow, Elizabeth Clarke. At the time of the census in 1881 it was lived in by a bailiff. From the late 1880s until 1913 Withington Court was farmed by Joseph Elliott. Mr Elliott seems to have been an innovative and effective farmer at a difficult time for farming which included the great agricultural depression. He was a hop grower on a significant scale and from 1885 onwards he also introduced soft fruit. A map of 1902 shows the location of both raspberries and strawberries. According to the 1910 valuation, the farm at this time had 238 acres.

W. Farmer: owner occupier of Withington Court 1913–1946

In 1913 the farm was purchased by Mr Willie Farmer. A lifetime bachelor, he farmed with the aid of a bailiff and had the reputation of being an academic, having read mathematics at Cambridge University (academic links were unusual in the farming community of Herefordshire at that time). He was a hop grower and on one dramatic occasion which merited publicity by the *Hereford Times* in the early 1920s, the hop kilns caught fire and nearly set fire to the house itself. He was also a very successful farmer and breeder of Hereford cattle, building up his herd by purchasing some of the best bulls from well-known breeders. In 1925 his bull, Aldersend Non-Such by Aldersend Wilton, was reserve male champion at the Royal Agricultural Show in Chester.

Withington Court in the Second World War

Willie Farmer received in an A grading for his competence. Unlike many farms at this period, Withington Court hedges, ditches and drainage were all in a good state. The farm also had electricity. Despite some switch to arable in 1940 and 1941 as part of the war effort, Withington Court was largely a pastoral and hop farm in 1941. Of its 273 acres, 166 were grass and clover and 30 statute acres were hops. 27 acres had however already been given over to wheat with a further 14 acres of oats and six and a half acres to potatoes – all very important strategic crops the time. There were also 20 acres of orchards, but unlike Thinghill Court, the farm did not produce soft fruit. Mr Farmer maintained a herd of 69 cattle and presumably nearly all of these would have been his Hereford pedigree herd. The lambs throughout East Herefordshire were still with the ewes in June 1941 so the total flock of 84 consisted mainly of lambs but included 34 ewes and a single ram. There were no pigs and only 25 poultry, just enough to provide for the needs of the farm itself. To run the farm Mr Farmer employed nine full-time male workers and 11 part-time women and girls. Unlike many farmers he had tractors, but nevertheless the farm still had five working farm horses.

Withington Court: family owned since 1946

Withington Court continued to be run as a mixed farm after Daniel Hess purchased the farm in 1946 and Willie Farmer's herd of pedigree Hereford cattle. In addition to livestock and hops, Withington Court produced cider apples, wheat and root crops.

Following the marriage of Daniel's daughter, Elizabeth, to John Dent in 1959, Elizabeth and John took over the running of Withington Court. In the 1950s the hop-picking machine replaced the seasonal labour in the hop fields, but some labour was still needed which was supplied by friends of the Dent children. Up until the 1960s the farm needed a substantial workforce as well as seasonal labour, and almost all the nine cottages attached to the farm contained farm labourers. The farm ceased to grow hops in 1990 and now most of the cottages have been sold and renovated to the extent which would have astonished the original occupiers. There are only now only two fulltime workers and their work is very different from that of their predecessors.

Modern capital-intensive farming requires more acreage. Elizabeth and John purchased another farm, White House, Ocle Pritchard. Withington Court is now lived in by one of their sons, Malcolm and his family, whilst Elizabeth and John live in the converted barn. Their other son, Simon, and his family live at the White House, Ocle Pritchard. As part of general diversification Malcolm has developed an organic peat-free compost company, Fertile Fibre Limited, based on imported coconut fibre with its head office at Withington Court. This enterprise has grown over the past 12 years to be one of the leaders in its field.

Modern farming is so different from the farming of previous generations. The Dents no longer have a flock of Ryeland sheep, a breed traditionally associated with Herefordshire which they sustained throughout most of their long married life when it shrank from being the main type of Hereford sheep to being a rare breed. Yet there is still continuity at Withington Court as both Elizabeth and John are firm supporters

Fig.WI 11 The Withington Court herd of pedigree Hereford cattle in the organic orchard

of Hereford cattle. Members of John's family, including his grandfather, H. J. Dent, who farmed Perton Court, have been distinguished breeders of pedigree Herefords for generations as was his uncle, H. C. Dent (see Eastwood Farm, Tarrington). There therefore continues to be a long bloodline of Herefords at Withington Court.

FELTON PARISH

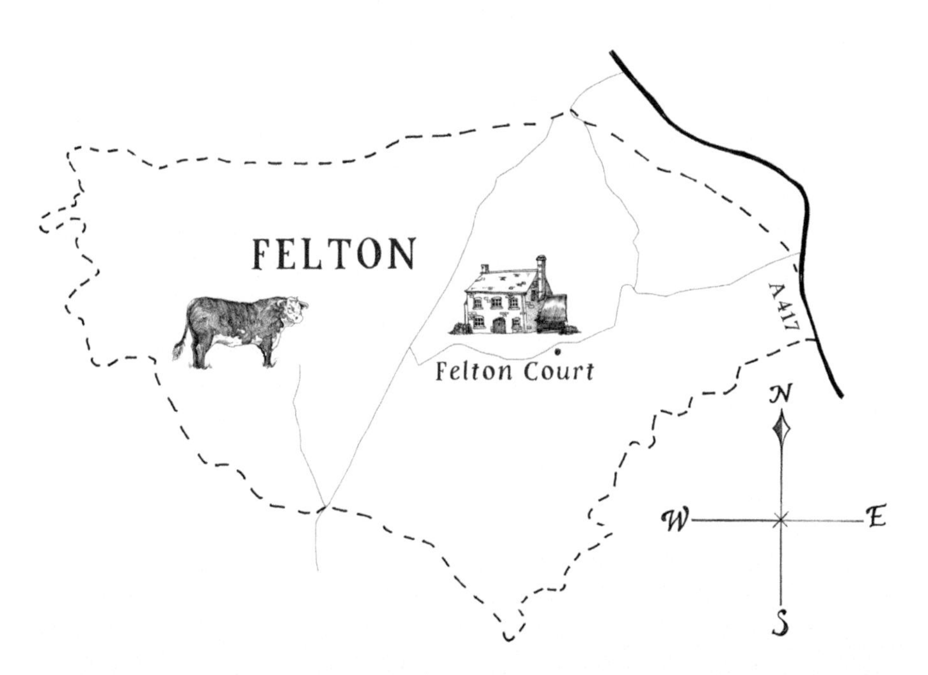

Felton is one of the smaller as well as one of the more isolated parishes of East Herefordshire tucked away as it is some two miles on the west side of the A 465 Hereford to Bromyard road. It is approached by country lanes, denied as much as a B grading and hazardous to modern traffic. The population of this parish has always been small. In 1851 the population was 112 and the acreage 1,800. Boundaries shrank with the 1886 nationwide adjustments and in 1901 the acreage was 1,149 with the population in the civil parish 85 and in the ecclesiastical 117. Population fell throughout the 20th century and in 2011 was a mere 58. However the richness of the heavy soil has always sustained important farms.

The rich land of Felton and the neighbouring parishes was owned in the 13th century by St Guthlac's Priory. When the priory was dissolved in 1539, Felton, along with a number of other parishes, was granted by letters patent to Sir John Pryce and his heirs. Sir John Pryce's son, George, married Mary the daughter of Sir Humphrey Coningsby of Hampton Court. Duncumb, writing in 1804, records that George's great-grandson, another John:

> *[…] died without surviving male issue, but left one daughter, Mary, who married Thomas Hayton, esq. whose son Thomas Chute Hayton, esq. […] sold Felton to*

> *Thomas Griffiths, Clerk, who dying A. D. 1800, left them to John Lilly, of New Court, in the Parish of Lugwardine, Clerk [...]*[13]

Besides owning the freehold of Felton Thomas Griffiths had also been the principal copyhold owner of Withington Court and Eau Withington Court. The combined ownership passed to John Lilly, then to Thomas Hill in 1838. It was sold to the Hampton Court estate in 1868 and then resold by the estate after the First World War.

As in most other East Herefordshire parishes there was considerable continuity in the names and size of farms throughout the 19th and first half of the 20th century. The 1851 census listed four large farm households and two smallholdings, and gave the acreage. The National Farm Survey of 1941–194314 90 years later listed four large farms and one smallholding. The acreage of three of the four larger farms was only moderately different. Felton Court was 236 acres in 1851 and 261 acres in 1941, Green Farm was 230 acres in 1851 and 229 acres in 1941, Hinton Farm was 233 acres in 1851 and 208½ acres in 1941. The only significant change was in Rosemaund Farm which had been 231 acres in 1851 and 420 acres in 1941 (part of which was outside the parish). All these four farms can be identified also in the land tax records of the 18th century. Two smallholdings were listed in 1851, one of 10 acres and not named, the other, Westfields, of 44 acres. The 1941 National Farm Survey listed only one smallholding, Stonehouse Farm of 23 acres. The major change was in land ownership. All four principal farms were tenanted in 1851 but were owner occupied in 1941.

Unusually all four of the major farms were still functioning at the time of publication albeit they have further expanded their acreage into the neighbouring parishes. The history one of these farms, Felton Court, is described below. Rosemaund Farm has become well known for its Chase distillery producing 'own mark' vodka and gin from its own produce. Green Farm, which was jointly owned with Felton Court in the 18th and early 19th century, remains in the hands of the Simcock family who purchased it from the Hampton Court estate in 1920. The smallholding of Stonehouse only ceased to be a farm at the beginning of the 21st century.

Felton Court

> Felton Court, 720 yards s.s.w. of the church, is of two storeys with cellars and attics; the walls are ashlar-faced and the roofs are slate-covered. it was built early in the 17th century, but has a modern n. range and other modern alterations. inside the building are some exposed ceiling-beams.[15]

Fig. F1 Felton Court

Felton Court is farmed by Richard and Clare Edwards. It was purchased in 1920 by Thomas William Bowcott 1879–1949, one of Richard's maternal great-grandfathers, who had previously been farming in the adjacent parish of Morton Jefferies.

The Bowcott association with Felton Court preceded 1920 as Thomas William Bowcott married Annette Morris in 1903, who was a granddaughter of the previous tenant of Felton Court. Thomas William and Annette had five children: three girls, Vera, Doris and Hilda, and two sons, Leslie and Thomas Ernest Morris. Hilda married Jack Price of Hynetts Farm, Lugwardine, Leslie later farmed at Monksbury Court, Yarkhill and Thomas Ernest Morris Bowcott (1909–1975) took over the farm after his father's death. He married Alice, the sister of Jack Price of Hynetts Farm. The connection between these different farms illustrates the close links of the farming families of East Herefordshire and their association over time with many of the farms in the area.

Felton Court was bought by the Edwards family of Collington in 1963 when their son, Robert, married Joy Bowcott, one of the two daughters of Thomas Ernest Morris

Bowcott. (The Edwards family had three sons and wished to provide a farm for each son.) Richard is Robert and Joy's son. Around 260 acres attached to the farm has remained virtually unchanged since the mid-19th century.

Fig. F2 Clare and Richard Edwards in the Felton Court kitchen

History of Felton Court

Owners of Felton Court

In the late 18th century, Felton Court, in conjunction with Eau Withington Court and Withington Court in Withington parish, and Green Farm, Felton, was owned by Thomas Griffiths of New Court, Lugwardine and then by John Lilly when Thomas Griffiths died. In 1832 the ownership passed to Thomas Hill of Blaenavon. When the farms were put up for sale in 1868 the acreage of Felton Court given as 255. Felton was then purchased by the Hampton Court estate, owned at that time by the Arkwright family.

Tenant farmers of Felton Court

Like most farms between the late 18th and late 19th centuries, Felton Court was rented out throughout this period. The *Hereford Journal* of 21 March 1827 lists the sad death from croup of Mr Samuel Goode of Felton Court's two little sons, Francis aged eight and Joseph aged three. From the 1830s until his death in 1868, Mr Matthew Goode was the tenant at Felton Court. He was a pioneer and successful breeder of Hereford cattle. His bulls were registered from the first edition of the Hereford Herd Book in 1848 and he played an active role in local agricultural societies of the time. In 1842 he was, for instance, one of the three judges at the newly established Withington ploughing match. It was a modest affair with only two classes, one for living-in ploughmen under 21 and one for those over that age. Matthew Goode's own employee received second prize for those under 21.

In addition to being a breeder of pedigree cattle, Matthew Goode was a hop grower. At the time of the sale of Felton Court in 1868, 17 acres were under hops, quite a significant acreage for the time. There were also 20 acres under orchard, including pasture orchards. Other crops and farm activities are not known, but the sale lists:

Substantially built FARM HOUSE and Premises, together with three Barns, two Hop Kilns, roomy Cow Houses, Cart and Hack Stables.

Fig. F3 Old hop kiln at Felton Court

Matthew Goode and his wife, Frances (née Colebatch), had four daughters, of whom one, Anne, died as a child, but no sons. Frances died aged only 33 in February 1838 and Matthew never remarried. The census records show that in addition to his family, many of the farmworkers lived as part of the household. In 1861, for instance, as well as his three surviving daughters (Mary Elizabeth aged 30, Fanny 28 and Susanna 24), his sister, Sarah 42, and a housekeeper, Mary Hill, there were five farmworkers living in: James Green 47, farm labourer; Alfred Matthew 24, carter; Andrew Jauncey 19, cowman; John Davies 17, carter's boy; Charles Bevan 14, agricultural labourer. All had been born in parishes two miles or less from Felton Court. Similarly in 1861 five of the farm labourers were living in.

Matthew Goode's successor at Felton Court, William George, was also a farmer in the 'high farming' tradition. In July 1878, together with other major breeders of Hereford cattle, he attended a sale of the Broadward herd near Bromyard which had been smitten by foot-and-mouth in 1875 and 1876 and purchased a heifer there costing him 39 guineas. He also attended important sales of Shropshire ewes. Unlike Matthew Goode's household, none of William George's farmworkers lived in. William had retired by 1891 and was recorded in the census of that year as living modestly in Edgar Street, Hereford. His wife died in 1891 but William himself lived to be over 90.

The census of 1891 shows the next tenant at Felton Court to be a woman, Maria Morris, a widow of 75. She was assisted by her son, Henry, aged 28. Besides Henry, the household comprised Maria's two daughters, Anna and Laura, and a granddaughter, Elizabeth. There was no living-in servant but one living-in farmworker, Charles Brooks aged 16. The 1890s were a time of agricultural depression. Hops were somewhat less affected than other crops, but still demand was faltering and prices lower. However, Maria was still recorded as the farmer in the 1901 census when she was 85 years old and was helped by two other daughters, Sarah listed as housekeeper and Susanna described simply as 'worker', as well as her granddaughter, Elizabeth. There was also a grandson, Sidney aged 19, listed as stockman.

Tracing the history of women farmers is fraught with difficulty. Yet it is clear that Maria must have been a remarkably resourceful and able person. She appears in the census of 1861 as the mother of 10 children, living at Middle Court, Monkhide, Yarkhill where her husband, Edward, farmed 80 acres with the aid of two men and a boy. After the death of her husband, she is recorded in the 1871 census as tenant of another farm owned by the Arkwright family, simply called the Farm, Much Cowarne, with seven children, farming 200 acres and employing two men and a boy. Two of her sons, Stephen 25 and William 20, described as farmer's sons, were no doubt working hard, as probably were two of her daughters, Olive 29 and Lavinia 14, both described as farmer's daughters. There was one living-in worker, Frederick Bufton aged 17. Maria was farming 231 acres at the Farm, Much Cowarne in 1881. As she grew older, she obviously became accustomed to managing larger and larger farms.

Fig. F4 The Bowcott family in the 1930s: Thomas William in the deckchair with his daughters Norah and Hilda seated to his right and his son Tom standing immediately behind him (the others are unknown)[16]

When Thomas William Bowcott married Annette, a granddaughter of Maria Morris in 1903, they were initially tenants of the Farm, Morton Jefferies. It was a William Evans and his wife, Clara, both from South Herefordshire, who took over the tenancy of Felton Court around 1903. Two of their workers, a cowman and a groom were living in the household in 1911. Mr Evans farmed there until the Hampton Court estate sold its land in Felton in 1920 when it was purchased by Thomas Bowcott.

Between the two World Wars, Felton Court was a typical Herefordshire mixed farm with hops, cattle and orchards. Thomas William had been born in Much Cowarne, the son of another Thomas Bowcott, who was farming an 80-acre holding. His grandfather did not have a farm at the time of the 1851 census and so was listed as a farm labourer. However the 18th century land tax records for Felton parish list a Thomas Bowcott as paying land tax for a substantial farm, which would appear to have been Felton Court. There may well have been a very long connection between the Bowcott family and Felton Court.

Felton Court in the Second World War

In that grim period early in the Second World War, the acreage of Felton Court was 261½, virtually the same as at present. In June 1941 farming was highly labour intensive, and the farm employed 10 men and two women, including three members of the family. There was a herd of 71 cattle and a flock of 72 sheep, of which 30 were ewes and the rest lambs about to go to market. It had, compared with most of the other East Hereford farms described, a substantial flock of poultry of 330 chickens. There were also five weanling pigs of two to five months old.

Like other East Hereford farms of this size there had already been a significant response to the war effort with pastureland ploughed up. There were 25 acres of hops, 20 acres of orchards and 86 acres of pasture and clover, but around half of the farm had already been put down to some form of arable production: 73½ acres were under the all important cereals of which 32½ acres were wheat. Farmers had also been urged to increase the production of potatoes and Felton Court seems to have planted five acres. Although the farm had an unusually large number of tractors – three plus a stationary machine – it was still dependent upon horses, with three carthorses and a further unbroken horse. For nearly all East Hereford farms the 1930s had been a time of struggle, and money, even on farms lucky enough to have a hop quota, was very scarce. Although the drainage at Felton Court was in a good state, as were the farm buildings and three farm cottages, the fences and ditches were stated to be only in fair condition. As was common throughout most of Herefordshire there was no mains electricity in the parish of Felton. However Felton Court together with Rosemaund Farm had installed private electricity, even though initially this was purely used for lighting purposes at Felton Court.

Felton Court after the Second World War

A hop picking machine was purchased shortly after the war. After Thomas William Bowcott's death in 1949, Felton Court was farmed by his son, Thomas Morris Bowcott. Before mains electricity came to Felton in 1956, the farm made use of its own generators for power. Indeed Thomas M. Bowcott, a practical man like most farmers, considered that the farm generators worked better than the mains electricity in the first year that mains electricity was available.

When Robert and Joy Edwards took over the farm in 1963, Felton Court still had nine farmworkers, but with the growth in machinery, together with Robert's skill in operating them, the number of farmworkers fell sharply.

Felton Court is situated in an area famed for its hops and its hop kilns are still clearly visible. In 1962 one of these hop kilns was listed as 18th century. However like so many other farms, the prevalence of wilt and the decline in prices meant that Felton Court ceased to produce hops in 1986 after probably growing hops for over 200 years.

Felton Court continues to be a mixed farm but produces for the consumer demands of the 21st century. About 50 acres is given up to potatoes, grown on contract for Tyrrells. It produces free-range eggs from a flock of no fewer than 12,000 birds. The Edwards also maintain a herd of around 120 beef cattle, purchased as suckling calves and reared until slaughter at around 20 months. Although historically Felton Court was famed for pedigree Hereford cattle, currently continental breeds are preferred. The farm also maintains a rotation of arable crops: oilseed rape, wheat and spring beans.

Modern farming depends almost exclusively on expensive machinery replacing those valued and greatly skilled, though underpaid, farmworkers of previous generations A part-time woman assists with the free-range eggs, but otherwise this mixed enterprise is farmed entirely by Richard and Clare Edwards and their family.

NOTES

[1] Duncumb, John. (1804). *Collections Towards the History and Antiquities of the County of Hereford*, Volume 1. E. G. Wright. p. 350.

[2] The National Archives, National Farm Survey of England and Wales 1941–1943: Withington MAF 32/27/129.

[3] 'Withington', in *An Inventory of the Historical Monuments in Herefordshire*, Volume 2, East (London, 1932), pp. 216–219.

[4] Robinson, Rev, Charles J. (1872). *A History of the Mansions and Manors of Herefordshire.* Longman and Co. p. 308.

[5] Laws, Bill. (2016). *Herefordshire's Home Front in the First World War.* Logaston Press. p. 62.

[6] By kind permission of Rachel Leake.

[7] Duncumb, John. (1812). *Collections Towards the History and Antiquities of the County of Hereford.* Volume 2, Part 1. E. G. Wright. p.251.

[8] Macdonald, James, & Sinclair, James. (1909). *History of Hereford Cattle.* London: Vinton & Company Ltd.

[9] Macdonald, James, & Sinclair, James. *op. cit.*

[10] Robinson, Rev, Charles J. *op. cit.* p. 308.

[11] Macdonald, James, & Sinclair, James. *op. cit.*

[12] By kind permission of Tania Blonder.

[13] Duncumb, John. (1812). *op. cit.* pp.111–112.

[14] The National Archives, National Farm Survey of England and Wales 1941–1943: Felton MAF 32/9/19.

[15] 'Felton', in *An Inventory of the Historical Monuments in Herefordshire*, Volume 2, East (London, 1932), pp. 79–80.

[16] By kind permission of Ann Nellist.

JOURNEY 2: WESTON BEGGARD AND YARKHILL PARISHES

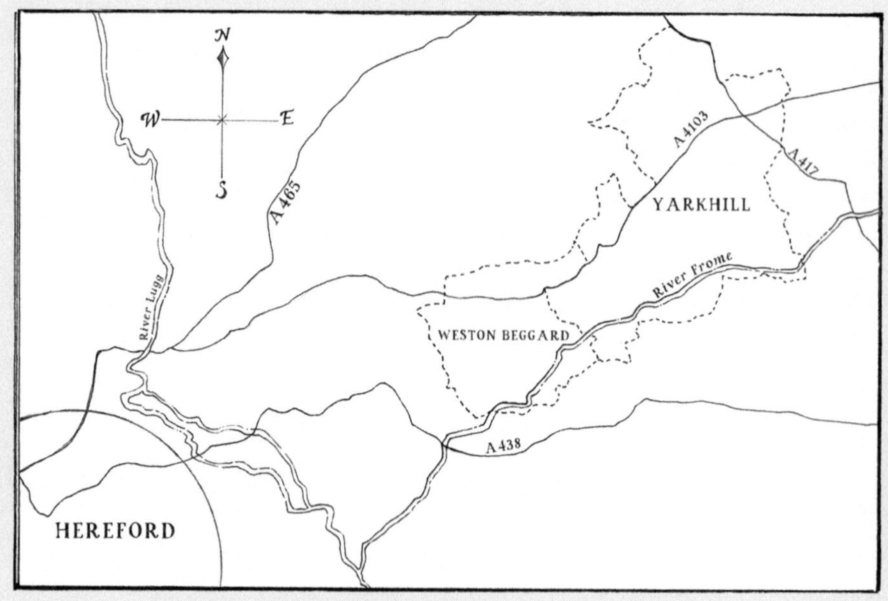

Journey 2 map and individual parish maps by Heather Colbert

WESTON BEGGARD PARISH

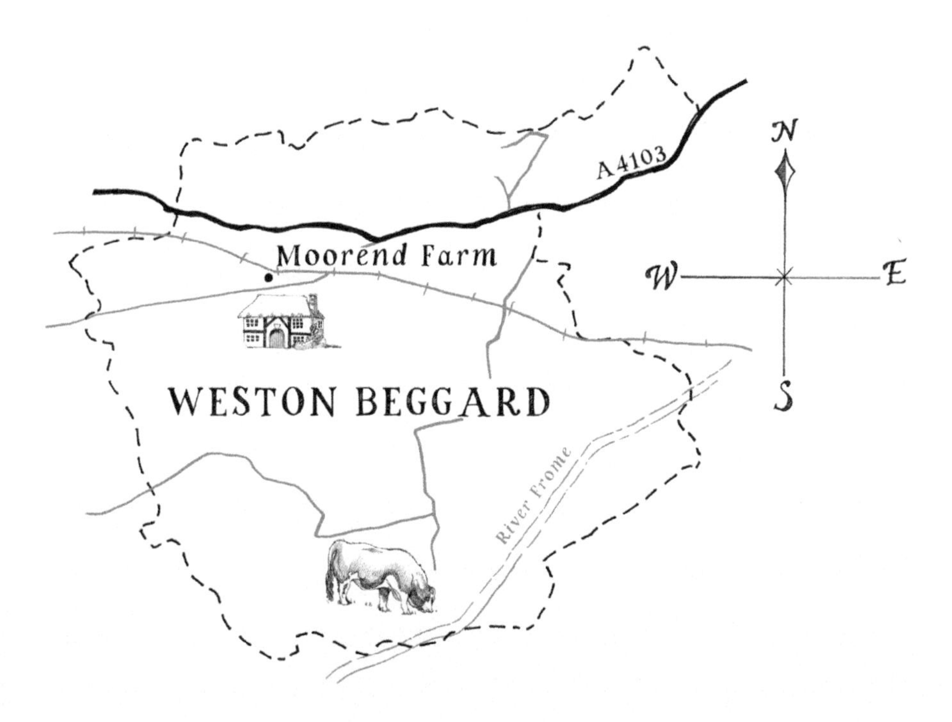

The small parish of Weston Beggard is around five miles from Hereford. It lies mainly on the rich red sandstone of the south side of the A 4103 Hereford to Worcester road but encompasses a small part of Shucknall Hill, which rises sharply above the plain to reveal that remarkable Silurian limestone. Throughout most of its history Shucknall Hill was the home of poor labourers and quarry workers, but is now transformed into desirable residences enjoying modern conveniences and a superb view. The farms are mainly on the sandstone.

Weston Beggard has always been a small parish. In 1835 it was 1,100 acres but it was then reduced to 935 acres and from 1886 it was reduced further to 925 acres. The 1841 census gave the population as 300. The population then fell somewhat before reaching a peak of 314 in 1891. In 1911 it fell to 244 and to 210 in 1961. It was still at this level in 2011.

Weston Beggard was part of the domain of the De Lacy family after 1066. By the early 18th century most of the land was owned by the Foley estate. The Foley holdings were further increased in the parishes of Weston Beggard, Yarkhill and Dormington following the Enclosure Act of 1798. However St Katherine's Hospital, Ledbury owned an important manor here from early medieval times and two farms in the parish, Church House Farm and Friars Court, remained in church hands until after the Second World War.

In East Herefordshire generally there was considerable continuity in the number and size of farms throughout the 19th and indeed right until the last quarter of the 20th century. Weston Beggard is unusual though in that only four separate farms (Shucknall Court, Hillend Farm with 300 acres, Pigeon House Farm with 200 acres and Purlbrook Farm) and two smallholdings of under 10 acres were recorded in 1851, whereas the National Farm Survey in 1941–19431 lists seven separate farms and one smallholding. The largest farm at the time of the National Farm Survey was the moated Shucknall Court with 280 acres. The remaining farms were Hillend Farm with 179 acres, Church House Farm with 138 acres and Pigeon House Farm 108 acres, Friars Court 74½ acres, Purlbrook Farm 89 acres, Moorend Farm 142½ acres and a smallholding of fewer than 15 acres, confusingly called Weston Corner like the farm of the same name in Withington parish. The smaller acreage recorded for Hillend Farm and Pigeon House Farm in the National Farm Survey can possibly be explained by the inclusion of Church House Farm, Friars Court and Moorend Farm land in the acreage for these two farms in 1851.

Shucknall Court ceased to be a farm late in the 20th century and Hillend Farm at the turn of the 21st century. Friars Court merged with Church House Farm and Purlbrook Farm land was sold off in 2017.

Moorend Farm

The first records of Moorend Farm date back to the early 1800s. The farm formed part of the Foley estate in the 19th and early 20th century and during this long period saw both exceptionally good and exceptionally hard times. Moorend has been farmed by five generations of the Bayliss family since 1907 when Clement Thomas Bayliss (1861–1929) took over the tenancy and then purchased the freehold at the great Foley sale of 1919/1920. Moorend is now farmed by Keith Bayliss, great-great-grandson of Clement Bayliss, and Keith's wife, Marie.

History of Moorend Farm

1835: the bankruptcy of James Morris Pritchard

The first newspaper reference to Moorend is a sad one. An advertisement in the *Hereford Journal* of November 1835 advertises the sale of both farm effects and household goods consequent upon the bankruptcy of the then tenant farmer, Mr James

Fig. WE1 The original buildings of Moorend Farm lie back from the old Roman Road leading from Stretton Grandison to Kenchester

Morris Pritchard. The advertisement makes it clear that Moorend at this time was a mixed farm with peas and barley in the lofts and a rick each of hay, clover and beans. (Owing to lack of storage, beans, like hay, were often make into ricks and thatched.) Potatoes had only been introduced as a field crop at the beginning of the 19th century. Mr Pritchard had three acres given over to potatoes yet to be harvested. Like virtually all farms in the area of this period, Moorend was a significant producer of cider. Was it perhaps investment in hops that had proved Mr Pritchard's downfall? Hops, though often profitable, were a risky crop, subject both to failure in production and oscillating demand, and the early 1830s had proved bad times. The *Hereford Times* of 1835 speaks of the disease which affected hops and Mr Pritchard seems to have had a considerable acreage of hops, with 10,000 poles included in the sale.

The Pritchard family seem to have been associated with Weston Beggard, but probably not with Moorend, some 40 years before. In 1797 a James Pritchard was farming a holding owned by John Halloween Esq. and paying only £2 1s 6d annual land tax, so it was not a large holding. James Pritchard was also paying land tax of £3 0s 0d for the tithe land of the Rev. William Barry bringing the area he farmed to perhaps 100 acres.

An indication of the probable size of Moorend after the Enclosure Act of 1798 can be found in a land tax record of the 1820s. Elizabeth Pritchard, possibly the widow of late 18th-century James Pritchard and the mother of the hapless James Morris Pritchard, was paying £10 16s 6d for a farm in Weston Beggard. It is known that when Moorend was rented out in 1860 it was around 280 acres and the 1820s land tax is appropriate to that size of farm. Families at that time were closely related. The widow Elizabeth Pritchard may have been the daughter of James Morris of Shucknall Court, giving her son the second name Morris, in addition to the name of his father, James Pritchard.

1860s–1880s: the Davies family

In contrast, by the mid-1850s farming had started to enter the prosperous age of 'high farming' and Moorend was to see considerable prosperity in the later 19th century. The next glimpse of Moorend can be found in the 1861 census. Thomas Henry Davies, a highly competent farmer who also farmed other Foley estate farms in Weston Beggard and Dormington, had moved his family to Moorend by this time. Surprisingly in 1871 his 14-year-old son John Charles was recorded in the census of that year as living at Moorend, described as 'head of household' and accompanied only by his sister Louisa aged 23. John Charles was later to become a successful businessman and farmer who rented and then purchased Pixley Court and Aylton Court, amongst other farms, for his sons.

Placing relatively young sons in charge of the farm seems to have been a regular practice of Thomas Henry Davies. In 1881 William H. Davies, his youngest son, was living at Moorend aged 20, and described as farming 525 acres. Louisa was still present at the farm aged 33.

1890s–1900s: farm labourers

In 1891 and 1901, Moorend was lived in by farmworkers, although the land was probably still farmed by the Davies family. It was quite common at the end of the 19th century to find farmhouses lived in by farm labourers and was probably indicative of the difficulties of farming at the time; the labourers did not stay long. In 1891 the farmhouse was occupied by Joseph Williams with his wife ,Susan aged 25, and two small boys aged four and two. Joseph came from the parish of Burghill and both children had been born there, so they were recent arrivals. In 1901 another farm labouring family was living in Moorend, Thomas Henry James with his wife, Emma, and five children, all of whom had been born in Lugwardine.

1907: the arrival of the Bayliss family

The Bayliss family of this period are an example of resourceful small farmers who worked hard and effectively to be in a position to take over the tenancy of a farm.

LOT 5
(Coloured Yellow on Plan No. 1)

A Mixed Farm

KNOWN AS

MORE-END

Capitally served by highways and extending to an area of about

144 a. 3 r. 21 p.

Situate in the Parish of WESTON BEGGARD.
Let to Mr. C. T. Bayliss, on a Yearly Tenancy, expiring 1st January, 1920

LANDLORD'S OUTGOINGS:—

Commuted Tithe Rent Charge—Vicarial	... ...	£18 4 11
Impropriate	...	5 15 2
Extraordinary	...	1 12 10
		£25 12 11

THE HOUSE

Mainly brick and tiled, contains:—Three Sitting Rooms, Kitchen, Scullery Pantry, Dairy, Wash-house, and Eight Bedrooms.

The Farm Buildings

Mainly brick and tiled, comprise:—Two Hop Kilns, Cider Mill and Press, Granary, Cellar and Bagging Room.

Nag Stable for three, Coach-house, Cook-house, Cart-horse Stable for five, Harness Room, Cow-house and Range for seven, Bull Stall, large Fold Yard and Shedding, and Root-house.

Stone, timber and tiled Chaff-house, Machine-house, Two-bay Barns, Floor, and Wain-house, iron Wain-house and French Barn, Pig Cot, and Poultry-house.

Enclosure 83 on Plan contains a half-timbered and thatched COTTAGE, also a Loose Box, Fold, and Shedding.

SCHEDULE

No. on Plan	Tenant	Description	Acres	Total Acres
	PARISH	OF WESTON BEGGARD.		
64	C. T. Bayliss	Arable	2·705	
65		Grass	9·455	
67		Orchard	3·620	
74		Grass	15·437	
75		Orchard	7·157	
77		Do.	·742	
78		Grass	20·135	
82		Do.	4·396	
83		Cottage, etc.	·281	
84		House, Buildings, &c. ...	2·058	
85		Orchard	6·236	
88		Grass	1.181	
108		Arable	11·313	
109		Do.	9·720	
110		Do.	8·657	
179		Do.	14·401	
187		Hop Yard and Arable ...	13·777	
190		Arable	13·610	
				144·881
		Total A.		144·881

This Lot is sold subject to a Right-of-Way for all purposes, including the haulage of stone and timber, between points A, B and C on Plan.
Timber valuation, £286 3s. 10d.

— 16 —

Fig. WE2 Moorend Farm: lot 5 in the Foley sale catalogue of December 1919

Clement Bayliss had had experience of working with his father and later as a farm bailiff before he took over Moorend in 1907. He and his wife, Eliza Jane, suffered a terrible blow in the First World War when their only son, Reginald, was killed at the age of 32. Clement bought Moorend in the Foley sale of 1919/1920 when the sale particulars advertised Moorend as a mixed farm of just under 145 acres, with two acres taken up by the farmhouse, farm buildings and garden, around 60 acres of arable, around 13 acres of hop land, 17 acres under three orchards and the remaining 53 acres under grass.

Moorend Farm between the two World Wars

Farming was difficult in the 1920s and even more so in the early 1930s. The resourcefulness that had already been shown by Clement and Eliza Jane was certainly required.

Clement died in 1929. Eliza Jane and her grandson, Charles Reginald – Reginald's son who had been born in 1905 – then took over the management of the farm.

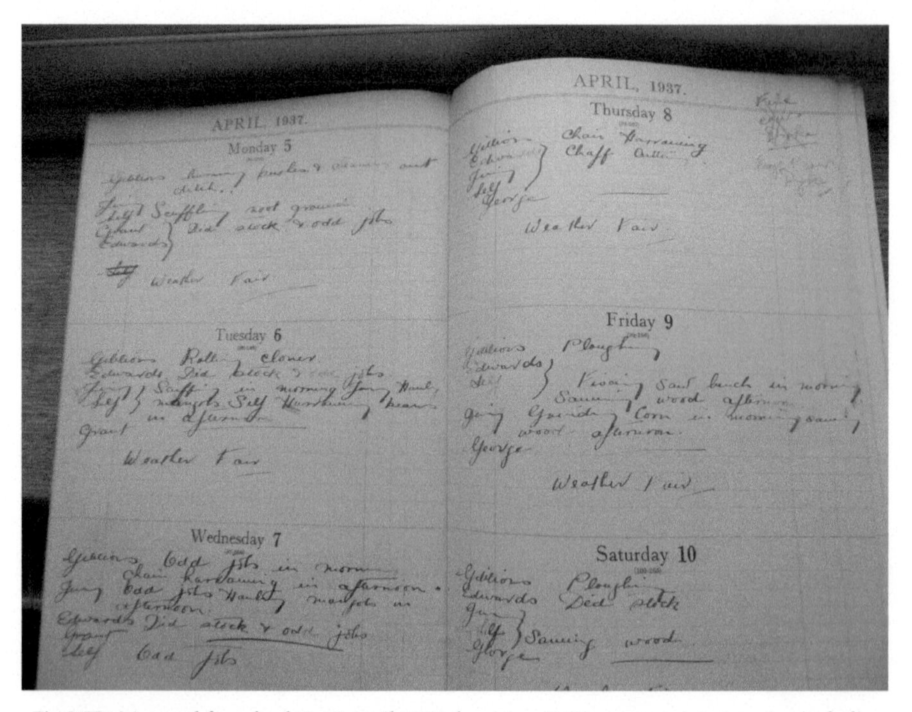

APRIL, 1937.

Monday 5

Weather Fair

Tuesday 6

Weather Fair

Wednesday 7

APRIL, 1937.

Thursday 8

Weather Fair

Friday 9

Weather Fair

Saturday 10

Fig. WE3 Moorend farm book 5–10 April 1937 showing activities appropriate to spring including ploughing and rolling the clover as well as normal stock management[2]

It is possible to deduce the Bayliss' resourceful response to the difficulties of the time from the changes in acreage under different crops between the two World Wars. There were very hard times for hops in the late 1920s and early 1930s before the establishment of the Hop Marketing Board in 1932. In 1930 hops were virtually unsaleable and were expensive to harvest. Reg Bayliss, Clement's great-grandson, can recall that the farm had no fewer than two seasons' hops stored at the farm at this time. Consequently, Moorend gave up hop production from 1930.

The area under orchards remained approximately the same between the First and Second World Wars. However, a comparison between the 60 acres of arable specified in the Foley sale of 1919/1920 and the 56 acres recorded in June 1941, which included 31 acres that had been ploughed up for the war effort, shows that the arable acreage had been significantly reduced by 1938. It seems that there was a switch from arable towards livestock. According to Reg, the farm concentrated on beef.

Moorend was very well run. Many East Hereford farms, struggling with the difficulties at the time, kept going during the interwar period by allowing the drainage and fences to deteriorate. Not so at Moorend. In keeping with good practice a farm book was kept. This, and other such documents, provide an insight not only to farming but also to the weather. The example from this book for the week 5–10 April 1937 shows that the farm employed three men, Gibbons, Edwards and Grant. Gibbons appears to have been the stockman.

Moorend Farm in the Second World War

The National Farm Survey of 1941–1943 lists Mrs Bayliss as the owner and farmer. The farm was given an A grading. Like most of the farms in East Herefordshire at this time there was no electricity. The hedges and drainage were in a good state of repair with only the ditches designated as fair. The farm comprised 142½ acres. A further seven acres were rented out.

The Bayliss family had already responded to the urgent wartime need to increase cereal production. Out of a total of 56 acres of arable in 1941, 44 acres were given up to cereals of which no fewer than 31 acres of cereals had been specifically planted under the CWAEC schemes. It is not possible to say whether the two acres of arable devoted to potatoes had been a similar response to the war effort or were part of normal pre-war production. The Bayliss family also at this time devoted 10 acres of arable to peas, mangolds and turnips, presumably all as fodder for their own livestock. As with many other East Hereford farms, cider apples remained a significant source of cash income with 15 acres given to orchards.

Despite the switch to arable, livestock production remained very important during the war. In June 1941 there were 43 cattle including the two bulls of which 18 were cows or heifers either in milk or in calf and 17 were calves for rearing under a year old with the remaining five cattle between one and two years old. Reg Bayliss remembers that in 1943 the farm switched to dairying and remained a dairy farm until 2010. Like most neighbouring farms, Moorend maintained a small flock of 58 sheep, including 22 lambs yet to be sold. There were four piglets of two to five months old which would have included at least one or two pigs for home curing. There was a flock of 58 poultry. The farm had one tractor, but much of the farm work was done with the aid of horses. Charlie Bayliss was very fond of horses and the Baylisses had seven of which, unusually, three were unbroken. (Possibly the farm made some money from the sale of these young horses.) The farm had a tractor and there were three full-time employees. Like some of the other farms in Part III, the farmworkers often had long associations with the farm. Charlie Hince from Shucknall Hill worked at Moorend until his retirement in 1960. He succeeded his uncle, Jim, who was a similar long-term employee.

Moorend Farm after the Second World War

Reginald's son Charles continued to farm Moorend in the post-war period in partnership with his two sons, Harry and Reg, and their wives, Janet and Muriel. As was common with farming generally, the main changes were associated with increased mechanisation and the decline in the number of agricultural workers. Reg won prizes for his skill in mechanisation and was even chosen to be the representative of the West Midlands Young Farmers' Clubs at the Royal Show in 1949.

Harry and Reg continued to farm after their father's death in 1976. Moorend ceased to have agricultural workers when Keith, Harry's son, left school in 1980. The dairy herd was only given up in 2010 and replaced with a Limousin cross beef herd. Reg continued to help on the farm for some time after his own retirement.

Moorend continues to be a mixed farm with mainly pasture for its large herd of beef cattle and flock of several hundred Mules sheep (a cross of Welsh Mountain sheep with Bluefaced Leicester). There is also some arable. The acreage of the farm has been increased with the addition of around 70 acres of land previously belonging to Hillend Farm, Weston Beggard. The farm also makes use of fields in the ancient pastureland in Eau Withington, partly owned and partly rented. Like other farms it now relies on family labour supplemented by help from neighbours at peak times of the year.

YARKHILL PARISH

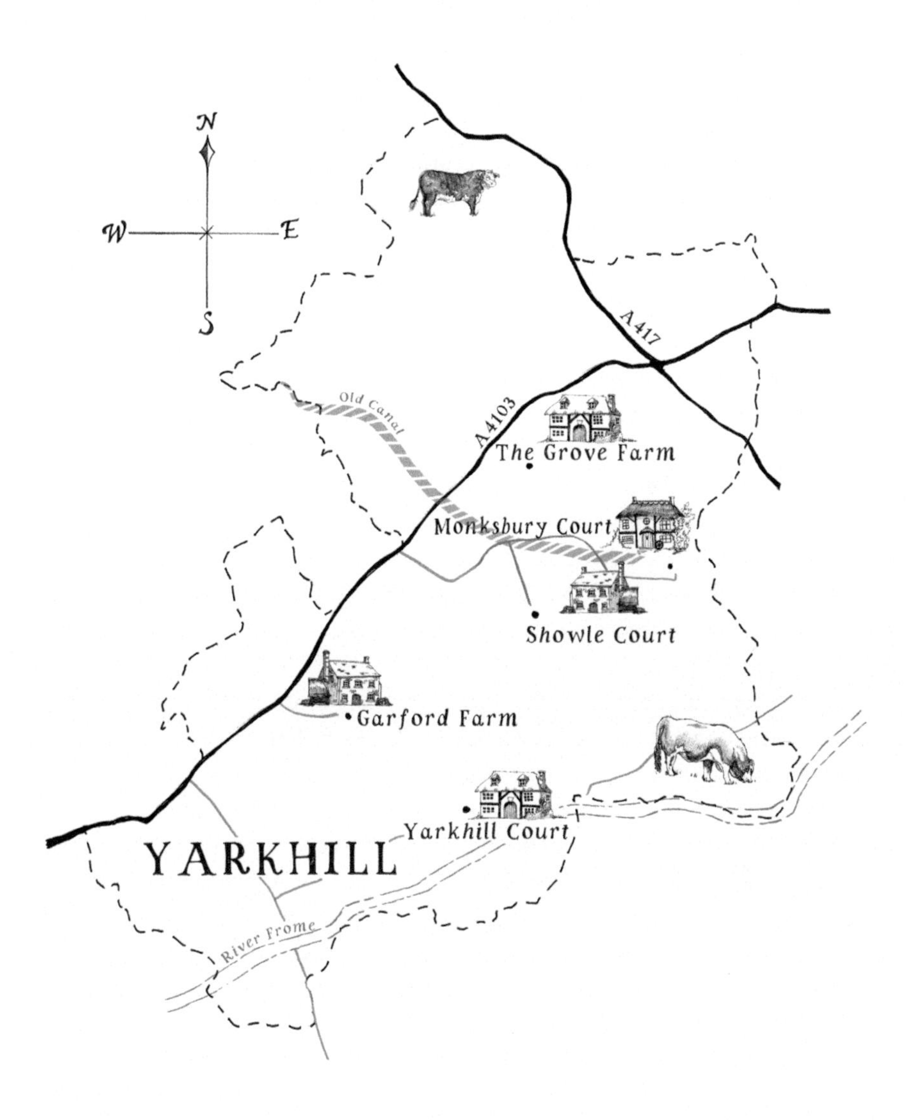

Yarkhill is situated between the A 4103 Hereford to Worcester road and the River Frome in an elongated triangle. It contains some of the most famous and oldest of East Herefordshire farms. During the period 1831–1886 the acreage of the parish was around 1,649. As part of the national changes in 1886, the acreage rose to 2,302 with the incorporation of areas on the north side of the A 465 close to Shucknall Hill and Whitwick Manor. It has remained this size ever since.

The earliest censuses indicate that the population rose in the first half of the 19th century. The recorded figure for 1811 was 365 compared with 432 in 1841. In 1851 the population was 547 but this incorporated the workers on the new railway. For the rest of the century a consistent fall was recorded in each census period and by 1881 the population had fallen back to 443, approximately the same as it had been 40 years previously and only rose to 470 even in the considerably larger area covered by the parish in 1891. There was a small temporary rise in 1921 but by 1931 the population had fallen to 435 and by 1961 it had fallen further to 330, about the same as the 2011 figure of 325.

The occupations of the modern inhabitants of Yarkhill though are very different from that of their predecessors. Until the First World War more than a third of the population of Yarkhill would have been children under 14. Until at least the Second World War most of the male adult population would have had some contact with agriculture, most would have left school at 14 and would have been manual workers. In contrast Yarkhill, like other East Herefordshire country parishes of the early 21st century, attracts the better off. In 2011 19.3% of those in employment came under the highest employment category of 'Managers, Directors and Senior Officials' compared with 11.6% under this category in Herefordshire and 10.9% in England as a whole. The proportion in agriculture is still higher than elsewhere but at 10.5% is well below other activities, even though it compares favourably with 5% in Herefordshire and under 1% in the country as a whole.[3]

Until the Enclosure Act of 1798 a significant proportion of the land in Yarkhill was common land. From the 18th until the end of the 20th century the parish with its rich soil was specially famed for hop production as well as for its cider. Even today hop kilns can be seen from the road although most of these are no longer active. At the time of the Tithe Map of 1841, 8% of all the fields were classified as hop fields and 21% as orchards.[4] In the late 19th and early 20th century Yarkhill farms also played a major role in the development of pedigree Hereford cattle.

Most of the farms that are still extant are owned by their farmers but until after the 20th century the parish was a prize possession of local landowners. In the Domesday Book Yarkhill was listed as part of the possessions of the De Lacy family. It was then inherited by Petronilla de Thong, who also held two hides of land in Stoke Edith, possibly Showle Court land. Writing in 1872 in *A History of the Mansions and Manors of Herefordshire* the Rev. Charles J. Robinson states:

... in the reign of Henry III Petronilla de Thong held four hides of land here of the heirs of Walter de Laci. The manor came subsequently to the Duchy of Lancaster and was granted by James I in 1607 to Robert, Earl of Salisbury, whose son sold it in 1614 to Richard Dobins, William Brydges, and others. From then it passed to the Bodenhams, and in 1652 Roger Bodenham of Rotherwas was its owner. His descendant sold it to the Foleys, and it is now part of the Stoke Edith estate.[5]

The land was sold off by the Foley family after the First World War when prices were very still very high causing considerable worry to those who had to repay their mortgages at a time of agricultural depression.

Of the four farms described below, three – Garford Farm, Showle Court and Yarkhill Court – originally formed part of the Stoke Edith estate. However the Foleys were not the only landowners. St Katherine's Hospital, Ledbury held land here from early medieval times.[6] This church land included The Grove Farm, the third farm discussed below, which was not sold off by the Ecclesiastical Commissioners until after the Second World War. Similarly, Whitwick Manor was never owned by the Foley estate.

No fewer than 21 holdings were recorded in the National Farm Survey of 1941–1943[7]. Apart from Garford Farm, Showle Court, The Grove Farm and Yarkhill Court they included five other important farms: Castle Farm, Little Yarkhill Court with 90 acres owned and farmed by A. Spencer, Monksbury Court with 211 acres tenanted by Beran and Turner, Whitwick Manor with 437 acres owned and farmed by Mrs Woodward and Woodmanton Farm. The other farms were mainly smallholdings of under 50 acres.

Garford Farm

Garford Farm, house, ½ m. N.W. of the church, is of two storeys with cellars and attics. It is of T-shaped plan with the cross-wing at the N.E. end and modern additions on the N.W. side.[8]

Garford Farm is a highly successful arable enterprise owned by James Parker and his wife, Helen, and is also renowned as one of the very best bed-and-breakfast farms in Herefordshire. Many of its clientele are return visitors attracted to this beautiful and peaceful place with its warm welcome.

History of Garford Farm

One wing of Garford Farm dates back to the early 17th century so it was certainly a farm before the 18th century. In the 17th and early 18th centuries Garford Farm

Fig. Y1 Garford Farm hop kilns, barn, 17th-century farmhouse and cider mill

formed part of the Bodenham estates, with a Thomas Beale of Yarkhill signing a new lease from Sir Roger Bodenham on 30 June 1710 for both Garford Farm and Yarkhill Court. The ownership of Garford Farm then moved from the Bodenhams of Rotherwas to the Foleys of Stoke Edith before the end of the 18th century.

Long tenancy of the Hall family

During the 18th and 19th centuries, it was common for farms to continue to be farmed by generations of the same family. This was true of Garford Farm, which, although owned by the Foley estate, was tenanted by generations of the Hall family for well over 100 years and quite possibly for over 150 years. According to a land tax record a John Hall was paying £13 9s 4d for Garford Farm in 1789. This was a relatively high tax and suggests that Garford Farm was around 200 acres, a large farm for the period. John had been born in Yarkhill in 1750 so quite probably his father was farming Garford Farm before 1750. In the 1841 census, John's son, another John Hall, born in 1777 (but erroneously described in the census as 60 years old), was a widower farming Garford Farm with his son, George. In 1861 George Hall was farming 275 acres and employing eight men and three boys. The acreage had expanded by 1871 when he was farming 350 acres with 10 labourers, three boys and five women.

George Hall lived at the time of 'high farming' and would have considered himself a progressive and scientific farmer. In 1854 he won the prize for the best large farm on the Foley estate. Consequently, following the usual Foley estate tradition, in the following year 1855 he and his wife, Alicia, had the honour of entertaining to lunch the entire band of the larger Foley estate tenants. (It was the practice of the tenants to spend the prize-giving day riding round the estate farms.) Lady Emily Foley certainly expected her tenants to maintain a high standard and George Hall is shown in 1861 as having a farm pupil. A further indication of George's status is the fact that the farm pupil's name was William Vevers. This name is rare, and would suggest that there was some family connection with the Vevers of Yarkhill Court. In 1871 another resident farm pupil, James Douglas, was recorded. In 1879 George Hall suffered the terrible financial blow of the loss of his entire flock of sheep from liver rot, a reflection of the poor weather in the latter half of the 1870s. By 1891 George Hall had given up the tenancy and was living with his son, Henry Scott Hall, at Dormington Court. Sadly, in 1903, after George's death, his son was to go bankrupt having overextended himself with new hop yards.

Yarkhill contained some of the best land of East Herefordshire. Overseas sales of the best pedigree Herefords and, in the more prosperous urban areas of the United Kingdom, increasing markets for soft and orchard fruit could help sustain incomes of some of the larger farmers in the more difficult times of the late 19th and early 20th century. However even East Herefordshire was not immune to those low prices in what came to be termed the Great Agricultural Depression of 1885–1895.

In 1891 Garford Farm was lived in by an agricultural labourer and the Garford land was farmed by Samuel Smith, the tenant of Woodmanton Farm. Samuel was the eldest brother of Albert Smith of The Grove Farm, Yarkhill.

Percy Bradstock commences his successful pedigree Hereford herd

In 1906 the young Percy Bradstock moved from his uncle H. W. Taylor's farm, Showle Court, and took over the tenancy of Garford Farm, taking with him his first few pedigree animals. These formed the foundation of the famous Freetown line of Herefords described under Ashperton parish. By this time, the acreage attached to Garford Farm was much lower, a mere 134 acres.

In 1919/1920 the Foley sale of Garford Farm included 41 acres of arable land attached to Castle Farm bringing the total acreage of Garford Farm to 175. The sale particulars show that the acreage at Garford Farm attached to hops was quite high with no fewer than 34 acres of hops, whilst the area of 15 acres given over to orchards was relatively modest.

Fig. Y2 Garford Farm buildings

Garford purchased by Mr Harry Stedman in 1920

Percy Bradstock then moved to the much larger farm of Freetown (see Ashperton parish) and it was a son of Mr Harry Stedman of Yarkhill Court, also confusingly called Harry Stedman, who purchased Garford Farm in 1920. *Kelly's Directories* for the period between the two World Wars and indeed right up to 1941 list a Mr Shelley Stedman as the farmer at Garford. It seems that this was to distinguish father from son as Harry Stedman junior's full name was Harry Shelley Stedman.

Garford Farm in the Second World War

The National Farm Survey of 1941–1943 erroneously lists Garford Farm as being in the parish of Tarrington. Its 174 acres were owned and farmed by Mr H. Stedman. The soil was heavy but good and the farm had mains electricity. Unlike many other farms of this time all fences, ditches and drainage were in a good state of repair, as were the two cottages. 20½ acres of wheat had been ploughed up under CWAEC instructions for the 1940 harvest and a further 31 acres were given over to approved crops for the 1941 harvest, bringing the total acreage under crops or fallow in June 1941 to 109 acres. Of this, 20 acres were devoted to hops, 17 to orchards, 55 to cereals (with 37 acres given over to wheat) and nine acres of potatoes, that other strategically important crop, leaving eight acres for other arable crops. The farm had a modest herd of 48 cattle, mostly calves or store animals. There was also a flock of 48 sheep of which 23 were lambs. Unusually there were neither pigs nor poultry. There were two tractors: one 20-horsepower Fordson and one 12-horsepower Austin. Consequently the numbers of farm horses was quite low for the period – only three. In addition there were two riding horses. To run this farm there were 16 farmworkers – five men full-time and five men and six women part-time.

Garford Farm after the Second World War

One of the few references to Garford Farm in the newspapers immediately after the end of the Second World War refers to a tragedy of October 1945. A contractor grubbing up an orchard was felled by a tree and died. Farming has always been a risky profession and many of the farms reviewed have experienced at least one such tragedy over the course of their history. The farmer at Garford Farm who gave evidence at the time was a Mr Beale.

Around 1950 Garford Farm was bought by Trevor Parker, originally with a business associate, but this share was later purchased by the Parker family. It is now owned by Trevor's son, James, and his wife, Helen. For the first two or three decades after the war it was a mixed farm with rather more arable than would have been the case before the Second World War, but with a significant acreage of hops and also cattle and sheep. The combination of the winding up of the Hop Marketing Board in 1982, together with the growing problems of wilt led to the end of hop growing which had provided such useful income for the larger farmers of East Herefordshire for at least 100 years.

Garford Farm is now an exclusively arable enterprise. To obtain the necessary advantages of scale the Parkers have taken over land originally belonging to Woodmanton Farm. The arable crops grown vary according to prices. At one time potatoes were highly profitable but in recent years the demand for potatoes has fallen and the main crops are wheat and barley. Whereas in the past the farm was a major employer, in the last 30 years production has been highly mechanised.

Fig. Y3 Showle Court, the remains of the moat, the old hop kiln and modern barn with hay for the organic herd of dairy cattle

Showle Court

Showle Court, house, outbuilding and moat, 1,160 yards N.N.E. of the church. The House is of two storeys with cellars; the walls are timber-framed and partly faced with brick and the roofs are tiled. It was built early in the 17th century on an H-shaped plan with the cross-wings at the N.W. and S.E. ends. There are 18th-century and modern additions on the N. and N.W. Inside the building are some exposed ceiling-beams.

The Outbuilding, N.W. of the house, is timber-framed, with a thatched roof. It was built in the 17th and extended in the 18th century.

The Moat, S.E. of the house, formerly enclosed a roughly rectangular island, but is now fragmentary.[8]

The famous Herefordshire farm of Showle Court has been owned by the Clay family since 1983. Tom Clay comes from a family in the adjacent county of Shropshire who have been farming there since the late 1700s. His wife, Harvey, comes from Hertfordshire, where her father, G. W. Cooke, was engaged in important work at Rothamsted, aimed at increasing agricultural production in the Second World War.

In the 19th and early 20th centuries Showle Court was especially famed for the role it played in the breeding of prize-winning pedigree Hereford cattle for which the county is so well known. The Clays run Showle Court as a specialised farm; one of the very few local major producers of organic milk. The milk is produced partly from Friesian cattle but also from the old established British breed of Shorthorns. The Clays breed their own replacement animals and produce all the fodder on the farm itself.

History of Showle Court

Hints of medieval and 17th-century Showle Court

Showle Court was a significant manor from early medieval times. Part of the present house dates back to the early 17th century and the puzzling arrangement of the building could possibly imply that within the original building remains a secret priest's hideout. The moated site of Showle Court denotes a nearby medieval manor house, and a book on Hereford Jews includes a reference to William Showle of Showle Court who owed money to Aaron II le Blund, the leader of Hereford's Jewish community in 1275.[9] Could Showle Court possibly be the successor to the early medieval holding of Petronella de Thong, one wonders? Despite its location, until 1886 Showle Court was included in the Stoke Edith parish, the home parish for the Stoke Edith estate of the Lingens in the mid-17th century and the Foleys from the late 17th century.

Farmed by the Godsall family in the 18th century

Although owned by the Bodeham estate of Rotherwas, in the late 17th and early 18th centuries Showle Court was farmed by the Godsall family. The inventory of Walter Godsall, who died in 1705, provides a picture of the farming of the period. Walter was not a literate man – his will was signed with a cross – but he was a farmer on a significant scale. From the baptism records of Yarkhill parish it would seem he was born about 1637 so was around 68 years old at the time of his death – quite an age for the period.

The inventory of 1705 lists substantial numbers of livestock. On the heavy soil of Showle Court, ploughing would be mainly, or exclusively, by oxen. Walter left 10 oxen with a total valuation of £40. He had eight cows and a bull worth £29, also six two-year-olds, and nine one-year-olds (the type of animal is unspecified but they were presumably cattle), worth £12 and £13 0s 6d respectively. Other livestock included a flock of 80 sheep. There were 17 large pigs worth £10, 10 store pigs worth £2 10s and 12 suckling pigs worth 14s. There were an unknown number of horses, colts and mares worth in total £30 6s 8d so part of the farm work was clearly done by horses.

Arable was an important source of income as the wheat and barley in the house and the barn were worth £90. There were significant quantities of cider in the cellars worth in total £33 19s. In the cheese house was cheese worth £4 0s 6d.

Further generations of Godsalls were probably associated with Showle Court throughout the 18th century. One of Walter's sons, Anthony, farmed Monksbury Court, Yarkhill, as did Anthony's son, also called Anthony. The daughter of the younger Anthony, Margaret Godsall, married John Vevers of Yarkhill Court in 1779.

Showle Court famed for pedigree Hereford cattle in the 19th and early 20th centuries

William Taylor, who farmed at Thinghill Court in around 1820 had purchased 'modern' Hereford cattle at the sale of breeding animals belonging Mr Williams of Thinghill Court, Withington in 1814. His son, also William Taylor, was already farming at Showle Court in 1841 and animals from his father's herd formed the basis of the Showle Court herd which he founded. A glance at the census records shows the exceptional importance of William Taylor's farming enterprise at Showle Court. By 1851 he was already farming 565 acres, probably including his second farm, Lower Hope Farm in Ocle Pychard, and employing 20 men. In 1871 he was farming 587 acres and employing 23 men, four boys and nine women. At the age of 70 in 1881 he was recorded as farming 737 acres employing 22 men, 13 women and four boys. William Taylor's bull Tredegar won first prizes at the Royal Agricultural Society of England's shows of 1874, 1875, 1876 and 1877. His cattle were exported to Australia, the United States, Canada and South America.[10] He was not only renowned for outstanding prize bulls, he also had a shrewd sense of publicity and made sure that his pedigree Herefords were well represented at important national agricultural shows of the time.

Although famed for its pedigree cattle, Showle Court was a mixed farm, and William Taylor was also a significant hop grower. He was the only Herefordshire hop grower to give evidence to the House of Commons Select Committee on Hop Duties in 1856. At that time he was growing 23 acres of hops at Showle Court and Lower Hope Farm.

William Taylor's son, Henry William Taylor, took over Showle Court after William's death and continued the family tradition as a successful breeder of Hereford cattle. An early success was the celebrated bull Maidstone who, according to the Hereford Herd Book, was 'one of the best of his time'.

In the difficult period before the First World War when prices could be quite low, Henry Taylor's bull Quarto was both first in his class and Royal Show Champion at the Royal Agricultural Society of England 1913 show. Quarto was subsequently exported to the Argentine, no doubt very lucratively.

Fig. Y4 Maidstone as illustrated in the Hereford Herd Book

In *Kelly's Directory* of 1900 Mr H. W. Taylor was described, unusually and somewhat ungrammatically, as "farmer & hop and cider grower, cattlebreeder and landowner". As indicated in the description of Garford Farm above, he was Percy Bradstock's uncle and provided some of his cattle as the basis of Percy Bradstock's herd. Mr Taylor gave up the tenancy following the major Foley sale of 1919/1920.

Showle Court purchased by Mr John Bird

Most farms in the 1919/1920 sale were purchased, albeit at high prices and somewhat unwillingly, by the farming tenants. Unusually, this was not the case with Showle Court. Mr John Bird came from a well-established professional family connected by marriage to Ballard, the great railway engineer who played a major role in the development of the Hereford–Worcester railway. In the 1920s it was farmed by Mr Bird. However by the later 1930s it was a tenanted farm.

Showle Court in the Second World War

With the onset of the Second World War, farming was seen to play a vital role in the war effort. In 1941 the tenant, Mr Bishop, was farming 273 acres with 13 acres of hops and 15½ of orchards. There had already been a response to the call for more arable so that for the 1940 harvest five acres had been ploughed up for wheat. This been followed for the 1941 harvest with a further 22 acres of wheat and 20½ acres of oats. Consequently, in June 1941 74 acres were under cereals and three under potatoes. Of the 72 cattle, 49 were bull calves under a year old. The farm had its own bull and there were 22 cows and heifers in milk or in calf. Of the flock of 220 sheep, 104 were lambs ready to be sold. There were 133 poultry, two pigs over five months old, presumably for household use, and eight horses, of which five were young unbroken geldings. Surprisingly, there were only four full-time workers on this large farm.

The difficult farming years of the 1930s had been a time of struggle for all farmers. When the quality of Showle Court's tenant was called into question, young Tom Barnes, who had married a daughter of John Bird, took over the farm by early 1942. He was given an A grading for competence but, probably because of earlier neglect, the farm buildings were in a bad state of repair and the roads, hedges, ditches, field drainage, farm cottages only merited a 'fair' classification. There was no electricity.

Showle Court after the Second World War

The Barnes family: 1945–1983

Tom Barnes continued to farm Showle Court after the Second World War and much of the post-war period was a period of great prosperity. This was the time of the tennis party and Showle Court boasted a hard rather than a grass court. In a recent private reminiscence, Christopher Barnes, one of Tom and Barbara's four sons, commented:

> *Life was a bonus, my brothers and I were indulged. We always had a shotgun, a fly fishing rod or horse to go hunting on and a car, which were even replaced when we crashed them.*[11]

Tom Barnes took an active part in Herefordshire public life as chairman of Herefordshire County Council, chairman of the West Mercia Constabulary amongst many other responsibilities and chairman for many years of the North Herefordshire hunt. He was also a hard-working and successful farmer. According to Christopher Barnes:

> *The farm was productive and mixed, with main crops of grain, fruit, cider apples and hops, plus a herd of Hereford commercial cattle.*[12]

Robert, another of Tom's sons, remembers the chicken farm. Rather than the few hundred hens which had been normal in the pre-Second World War era, Showle Court had, for many years, some thousands under the watchful eye of a specialised female chicken farmer.

Sadly in 1983 the Barnes family suffered a blow in the tragic death in a motorcar accident of Tom's son, Bill, together with his mother-in-law. In family-owned farms when land prices are high it is sometimes difficult for one member of the family to buy out the others. The Barnes sold the farm in 1983 when they retired to Australia and enjoyed many years of retirement. Indeed Barbara was to die only in 2013 at the great age of 99.

The Clay family: 1983–present

To ensure a successful enterprise as a specialised organic milk producer in the modern era requires a considerable acreage of land. It is far from easy to obtain such land in the surrounding neighbourhood. However in the mid 1990s, when land became available in the aftermath of difficult farming conditions, the Clays were able to expand Showle Court from 400 to 500 acres.

Like other farms Showle Court needs to be highly mechanised and presents a very different picture from the labour-intensive enterprises of the past. The Clays manage the farm with the aid of only one full-time and one part-time assistant.

The farming fraternity has always needed to have practical skills. The specialised milking parlour, critical to this enterprise, was especially designed by Roger Clay, Tom's brother. The cows enter a circular parlour and then step off when the milking is complete.

Fig. Y5 Feeding the Showle Court calves

Although the farm is highly specialised the Clays also breed Shropshire sheep. These are specially suitable for grazing under orchards and in Christmas tree plantations. They also have a few Jacob sheep.

Fig. Y6 Showle Court Jacob sheep with the remains of the original moat in the background

The Grove Farm

Mr and Mrs Williams, both from local farming families, purchased the old established farm of The Grove in 1957, immediately after their marriage. They are now semi-retired and the farm buildings comprising the original 18th-century house and hop kiln have been turned into family accommodation for three generations of the Williams family.

History of The Grove Farm

Most of the land historically associated with The Grove belonged for many hundreds of years to St Katherine's Hospital, Ledbury. By an anomaly St Katherine's Hospital, unlike many other such institutions, was not dissolved at the Reformation.[13] For most of the 19th century The Grove was tenanted by the Smith family, a junior branch of the Smith family of Huntleys Farm, Much Marcle, who had owned the smallholding

Fig. Y7 The Williams's daughters, Vivien and Valerie, outside The Grove hop kiln and part of the original farmhouse

of Hillfield in Putley since the early 18th century. Hillfield was mortgaged throughout much of the 19th century, presumably to provide the capital necessary for this larger farm which was tenanted until after the Second World War.

From at least the 1790s John Smith was renting some land in Yarkhill, probably part of The Grove Farm. His grandson, Thomas Smith, married Ann Nokes from a Yarkhill family in Yarkhill Church in 1825 and seems to have moved to The Grove at that time. He was certainly already living in Yarkhill the late 1820s and growing hops amongst his crops. He was one of the 550 signatories of Herefordshire hop growers of a petition in 1831 to the Treasury complaining that the 1831 price was so low that it had never exceeded 90s per 4 cwt and that in the previous two years:

> *[...] the Crops of Hops were so deficient as scarcely to be sufficient for payment of Parish rates and Taxes leaving the Planters at the loss of the Greater Part of the Rent, Tithes, Labour and Interest of Capital.*

Thomas Smith is shown in the 1851 census as a farmer of 100 acres, employing two men. He was living in modest style with his wife, Ann, and five of their children: two boys, Samuel aged 18 and Albert 5, and three girls, Sarah 24, Catherine 13 and Jane aged 10. There was a live-in maidservant and a farm servant. The Smiths' other sons, William, Charles and John seemed to have been living elsewhere. It was normal for farmers' wives to sell poultry, especially at the Christmas markets. There is a reference to Mrs Smith in the local press coverage of a special Christmas Show in Hereford market in 1851. In 1854 Thomas Smith was one of the signatories supporting the establishment of a new hop market from 27 September 1854.

Thomas died in 1855 aged only 55. Ann seems to have successfully taken over as the farmer. In the 1861 census at the age of 60 she is recorded as farming 100 acres and employing six men. Her son, Charles aged 22, is described as a miller and his younger brother, John aged 18, as farmer's son and so is presumably working on the farm. Albert is still a scholar. On 2 July 1867 James Chamberlain was charged with stealing a chicken from Albert Smith of The Grove and sentenced to 21 days' hard labour. In the 1871 census, Sarah, Albert and Jane Smith were all recorded as staying at the large farm of their brother, John Smith, who was farming 358 acres at Birchend Farm, Castle Frome. In the 1881 census, the family were mainly back at The Grove. Ann Smith now aged 80 had reduced the farm size to 80 acres which she was farming with the aid of three men and a boy. John aged 40, widower, and Albert 35, unmarried, were both described as annuitants and their two unmarried sisters, Sarah aged 49 and Catherine (Kate) aged 40, were also part of the household. In 1891 it was Albert who was described as the farmer, married now to Ann aged 44. Living in were a female servant, Ellen Jaunsey aged 16, and two farm servants, a wagoner and a cowman. Albert does not appear to have been a very efficient farmer. In the 1901 census there are two households living at The Grove and Albert is described simply as a bailiff living with his wife and daughter. Also living there was his elder sister, Sarah, who was described as the farmer.

In 1905 William Court was the tenant farmer. He was not a local man and had been born in Birmingham. However he seemed an efficient farmer and remained there through the difficult times until the Second World War.

The Grove Farm in the Second World War

At the time of the 1941–1943 National Farm Survey The Grove was 72 acres and owned by the Ecclesiastical Commissioners, the successors to the former owners, St Katherine's Hospital, Ledbury. The Grove was farmed by W. J. Court who had been there for 36 years. In 1941 he was paying £135 14s rent and was employing three full-time male workers and three women. He received an A grade for his quality as a farmer. The roads, ditches, hedges and drainage were all in a good state as were the two cottages. The land was good and it was deemed to be heavy soil. The house and the buildings were served by a well. There was no electricity and two cottages were let on service tenancies. There were three carthorses and no tractor. Of the total acreage, 39 acres were under either temporary or permanent grass, there were eight acres of hops and eight of orchards. Mr Court had not been required to plough up any land for the war effort but of the acres under arable, five acres were under potatoes, an unusually high acreage at the time, with a further five under wheat, also a high priority crop.

The Grove Farm after the Second World War

When Mr and Mrs Williams bought The Grove in 1957, the farm was around 64 acres. The subsequent sale of family land in Holme Lacy enabled them to expand the farm and they purchased additional land around Monkhide, including a cider orchard. In the early years after their marriage, they still retained a small acreage of hops and kept a small dairy herd, like many other smaller farms in the area. Around the 1970s the milk lorry was reluctant to hazard at the lane leading to the house. The Williamses then switched to rearing suckling calves – four to one cow – and also built up from an original purchase of 12 ewes a modest flock of sheep. Like so many other Herefordshire farms The Grove was struck by the terrible foot-and-mouth outbreak of 2001 when all the cattle and sheep had to be destroyed. They were not replaced.

Fig. Y8 Orchard Grove preserves and jams on sale at Hereford Farmers' Market 2016

Part of the land belonging to The Grove is now rented out, but although semi-retired, Mr and Mrs Williams still produce and sell cider apples to Westons Cider of Much Marcle, assisted by their son, Neil, and daughter, Valerie. Neil works at Westons when not engaged on the farm. Their other daughter, Vivien, of Orchard Grove Preserves can be seen at the Farmers' Market in Hereford and other markets and venues in the locality with a wide array of delicious preserves and jams.

Fig. Y9 Yarkhill Court 2017

Yarkhill Court

The imposing farmhouse built in mid-Victorian times gives a false impression of the antiquity of Yarkhill Court. References to the farm date back well into the 17th century and the present house supersedes a much older building.

Yarkhill Court was one of the possessions of the Bodenham family from the 17th until sometime in the 18th century. From then until 1920 it was owned by the Foley family of Stoke Edith. Yarkhill Court is situated next to Yarkhill Church on the old Roman Road close to the River Frome – a stretch of road called with justification Watery Lane. Close by, on the opposite side of the road is an ancient moated site. The location then is suggestive of Yarkhill Court's medieval origin.

Although until 1920 a tenanted farm, Yarkhill Court was associated for some 250 years with only two families – the Vevers from the second half of the 18th century until the beginning of the 20th century, and the Stedmans and Leigh families from the beginning of the 20th century until 2009 when Yarkhill Court ceased to be a farm.

Yarkhill Court is no longer one of the more important farms of East Herefordshire, a role it played for so many hundreds of years. However, its illustrious past is not forgotten and Yarkhill Court still promotes East Herefordshire farming. The large Victorian house and the surrounding land on the opposite side of the road, including the moated site, has been owned by the Day family since 2009. For the past four years the field has been the location of The Field to Fork Festival. This is a unique combination of Farmers' Market, Village Fête and Evening Musical Event. Farms taking part include Pixley Court promoting Pixley berries and Thinghill Court, Withington promoting its strawberries and free-range eggs. Other farms promote their asparagus and their artisanal cider. Excellent food of all types made with local produce is available. In addition there are entertainments for children, the obligatory cream teas and homemade cakes. In the evening the tent is given up to local bands so all tastes and all ages are provided for. The festival raises money for local charity and community projects within Yarkhill village. It is truly a memorable event and always much looked forward to.

Fig. Y10 Yarkhill Court Field to Fork Festival on Yarkhill Court land with Yarkhill Church in the background

History of Yarkhill Court

Yarkhill Court, like Garford Farm, was owned by the Bodenham family in the 17th century. On 30 June 1710 Sir Roger Bodenham granted a new lease for both Garford and Yarkhill Court to Thomas Beale of Yarkhill. By the latter 18th century ownership had passed to the Foley estate.

The Vevers family: tenant farmers of Yarkhill Court from the later 18th to the early 20th century

When John Vevers (1750–1835) married Margaret Godsall in Yarkhill Church in 1779 he was already the tenant at Yarkhill Court. He came from a landed gentry family associated with Scholes Park, Leeds. The area around Scholes Park contained coal and it is possible that some of the income from this had trickled down to John Vevers as a junior branch of the family. The acreage attached to Yarkhill Court must have been very substantial at this time as John Vevers was paying £30 14s 6d land tax in 1789, well over double the land tax charge for Garford Farm and more than the land tax for any other farm reviewed in this book. Yarkhill Court could well have been over 400 acres at that time.

Other farms in Yarkhill are associated with pedigree Hereford cattle and hops. Although Yarkhill Court did indeed have both cattle and hops, the earlier Vevers were associated more with successful horseracing. This followed the example of the 18th century Vevers of Leeds, whose horses were regular winners at the racecourses of York and Wakefield. It was John and Margaret's younger son, William Vevers of Dormington Court, who was the most distinguished breeder of horses for flat racing and steeplechasing. It is not known whether John Vevers or his eldest son, another John (1781–1845) also bred racehorses.

The third decade of the 19th century saw yet another generation of John Vevers at Yarkhill Court. However this John Vevers (1811–1877) was the eldest son of William Vevers of Dormington Court, presumably because his uncle, John, did not have any male heirs. This generation of the family were certainly interested in breeding improved Hereford cattle as a Mr Vevers purchased stock at the Miss Tomkins disposal sale in 1840. Unfortunately the report in the *Hereford Journal* does not give the purchaser's Christian name so it is not clear whether it was William Vevers of Dormington Court or his eldest son, John Vevers of Yarkhill Court.

It is clear however that William Vevers' son, John, farmed Yarkhill Court to the highest standards known at the time. John Vevers won the prize for the best large farm at Lady Emily Foley's Annual Farm Inspection described in Chapter 3 no fewer than three times (1851, 1855 and again in 1859). He was invited to join the Hereford Farmers' Club and was present at the evening when a leading chemist of the period gave his findings on the qualities of the different lime quarries of Herefordshire. As a major hop grower, John Vevers signed his name to an advertisement in the *Hereford Times* supporting the establishment of a new hop market in Hereford in 1852.

A farm of the size of Yarkhill Court could only be run with a substantial number of workers. In 1861 John Vevers was described as farming 280 acres and employing 10 men and five boys. In 1871, the acreage had gone up to 320 and Yarkhill Court was farmed with the aid of 10 men, two boys and two women. The permanent staff was of course supplemented by seasonal labour, especially at harvest time.

By 1881 there was yet another John Vevers at Yarkhill Court farming 325 acres with the aid of 10 men and two boys. This John Vevers had been born in 1851 and married Emily Hobbs from Buckinghamshire in 1873. John and Emily had four children. Sadly Emily died in childbirth on 17 September 1886 aged only 32. Poignantly her infant daughter, Emily, was baptised two days after her mother's death. In 1893 John married Lucy Armstrong, the daughter of a civil engineer, and the couple had one daughter. The last record of this Vevers is in the *Kelly's Directory* of 1901 where he is described as "John Edward Vevers landowner & farmer and hop grower". John Edward Vevers suffered a major blow in the death of his eldest son, John Aubrey Hobbs, in South Africa in 1897. Maybe it was because of this that the Vevers dynasty came to an end at Yarkhill Court. John Edward Vevers himself died in 1906.

The Stedman family: tenant farmers and then owners of Yarkhill Court c. 1904–2009

By 1904, after at least a century and a quarter, Yarkhill Court had passed out of the hands of the Vevers family and for the first half of the 20th century, Harry T. Stedman was the farmer and hop grower. A distant ancestor in the 17th century, Francis Stedman, had been the vicar at Yarkhill and the father of Fabian Stedman, the great campanologist who is reputed to have been born in Yarkhill in 1640.

Harry Stedman, though, came from a Shropshire family. He seems to have wanted to recruit at least some staff from his former locality as he advertised in the *Wellington Journal* of 1905, firstly for a ploughboy and then secondly, rather more significantly, for a specialised groom to accompany his high-quality carthorse stallion as it moved around the county. The Stedmans too had an interest in horses.

The farm Harry Stedman took over was smaller than the acreage farmed by the Vevers. The Land Registry of 1910 shows him as renting 209 acres in Yarkhill with the land valuation of £269 per year. The Foley sale catalogue of 1919 provides more detail. In total, including a modest acreage under grass in Tarrington parish, the total holding came to 236 acres of which just over three acres comprised the house and gardens. There were 38 acres of hops and arable, a further 33 acres under soft fruit, and 19 acres of orchards. There were only 11 acres specified as arable with the remaining 132 acres specified as grass.

Fig. Y11 Yarkhill Court from the 1919 Foley sale catalogue showing the extensive farm buildings

Because of shortages, farming had revived during the First World War and immediately afterwards, but generally farming was difficult both during the pre-1914 period and in the interwar period after Harry Stedman bought the farm in 1920.

As described in Chapter 4, hops went through very difficult times in the latter 1920s with the nadir in 1930 when they were virtually unsaleable. They revived somewhat with the establishment of the Hop Marketing Board in 1932, but there were always problems associated with hop pickers, who were sometimes considered a necessary evil rather than a pleasure. In 1932 Harry Stedman prosecuted two hop pickers for stealing 23lbs of apples from his orchard. The prosecuting counsel asked that specially severe penalties should be imposed as farmers had to engage a nightwatchman in order to avoid losing as much as a quarter of their crop. However, the court doesn't seem to have been very impressed and the hop pickers were fined £1 each.

Yarkhill Court in the Second World War

Birmingham and Gloucester newspapers show Harry Stedman to be advertising for hop pickers in the fateful year of 1939, specifying that the accommodation would be good and that all costs would be covered. Possibly hop pickers were more difficult to obtain in the first month of the Second World War. Harry Stedman retired early in the war and was succeeded by his son, Raymond, who was away fighting in the Second World War. St Mary's School of Hampstead took over the large Yarkhill Court farmhouse for the whole six-year period, catering for small boys as well as for girls. Some of the pupils were boarded in neighbouring houses and a few local children also attended the school.

The National Farm Survey of June 1941–1943 gave the acreage of Yarkhill Court as 240½, owned and farmed by Mr J. R. Stedman who was given an A grading. It was heavy soil: 50 % good quality and 50% fair. It had mains electricity giving light and power. The farm and buildings were supplied by well water. The ditches and drainage were only in a fair state of repair reflecting the difficult times of the 1930s but the hedges were good. No grassland had been ploughed up under the CWAEC schemes of 1940 and 1941. The farm had three acres of hops and five acres were under orchards, with an additional 12 orchards with soft fruit below the trees. The major arable crop was wheat with 39 acres. A further 10 acres was under mixed corn and 10 under beans. 131 acres were under grass. Of the 70 cattle, 68 were beef cows who were two years old or more. There were several working horses and four other horses presumably for pleasure. There was a flock of 146 sheep of which 86 were lambs. There were no pigs or poultry. Although Raymond Stedman is given as the resident farmer in 1941, for most of the war Yarkhill Court was farmed by Raymond's brother at Garford Farm, Harry Shelley Stedman.

Yarkhill Court after the Second World War

Raymond Stedman had a distinguished army career during the Second World War and only took over Yarkhill Court from his brother after he retired from the Army in 1950. The period 1950 to 1983 saw a transformation of production from the pasture, hops and soft fruit combinations of the earlier 20th century to cereals, hops and soft fruit.

During this period, and in contrast to the depressed conditions prevalent prior to the Second World War, arable could be highly profitable. In 1983, slightly over half of the 274-acre farm was down to cereals with around 108 acres under wheat and a further 30 acres under barley. Although modest in terms of acreage, soft fruit remained an important crop with 12½ acres under blackcurrants and three acres under gooseberries. There were 40 acres under hops with the varieties grown mostly Northdown or Challenger, but with four and a half acres under the old-fashioned Fuggle variety.

Michael Leigh inherited Yarkhill Court from his stepfather Raymond Stedman in 1983 and he and his wife, Gilla, farmed Yarkhill Court from 1986, the year he retired from the Army, until 2009. The abolition of the Hop Marketing Board in 1982 and the prevalence of wilt in the 1980s made hop growing impracticable and the Leighs ceased also to produce soft fruit. Some of the land was rented out but cider apples remained an important crop and the Leighs maintained a herd of cattle.

In 2009 more than 200 acres of land were sold off. Part of this land is now farmed by Thinghill Court, Withington. The fine and extensive farm buildings were converted into residential accommodation. The hop kilns which show that Yarkhill Court was a major hop producer, probably from early times, can still be seen, but they are now separate houses.

Over its long history Yarkhill Court was known for its horses and pedigree Hereford cattle. On the remaining modest acreage the Day family now host the Field to Fork Festival and graze their alpacas.

Fig. Y12 Yarkhill Court showing the alpacas grazing on the field used for the annual Field to Fork festival[14]

Notes

[1] The National Archives, National Farm Survey of England and Wales 1941–1943: Weston Beggard MAF 32/26/128.

[2] By kind permission of Reginald Bayliss.

[3] Yarkhill Draft Neighbourhood Development Plan 2017–2031 accessed 27 November 2017 www.herefordshire.gov.uk

[4] White, Paul & Ray, Keith, Ed. (2011). The Frome Valley Herefordshire: Archaeology, Landscape Change and Conservation. Herefordshire Archaeology. pp. 80–81.

[5] Robinson, Rev., Charles J. (1872). *A History of the Mansions and Manors of Herefordshire.* Longman and Co. pp. 315–316.

[6] Hillaby, Joe. (2003). *St Katherine's Hospital, Ledbury c.1230–1540.* Logaston Press. pp. 42–43.

[7] The National Archives, National Farm Survey of England and Wales 1941–1943: Yarkhill MAF32/27/168.

[8] 'Yarkhill', in *An Inventory of the Historical Monuments in Herefordshire, Volume 2, East* (London, 1932) pp. 223–225.

[9] Hillaby, Joe & Hillaby, Caroline. (2013). *The Palgrave Dictionary of Medieval Anglo-Jewish History.* Palgrave Macmillan UK. p. 163.

[10] Heath-Agnew, E. (1983). *A History of Hereford Cattle and Their Breeders.* Duckworth. p. 85.

[11] Barnes, Christopher. (2007). *Pure Nostalgia.* Christopher Barnes.

[12] Barnes, Christopher. *ob. cit.*

[13] Hillaby, Joe. (2003). *op. cit.* pp. 131–132.

[14] By kind permission of Fiona Day.

JOURNEY 3: LUGWARDINE, DORMINGTON, STOKE EDITH, TARRINGTON AND ASHPERTON PARISHES

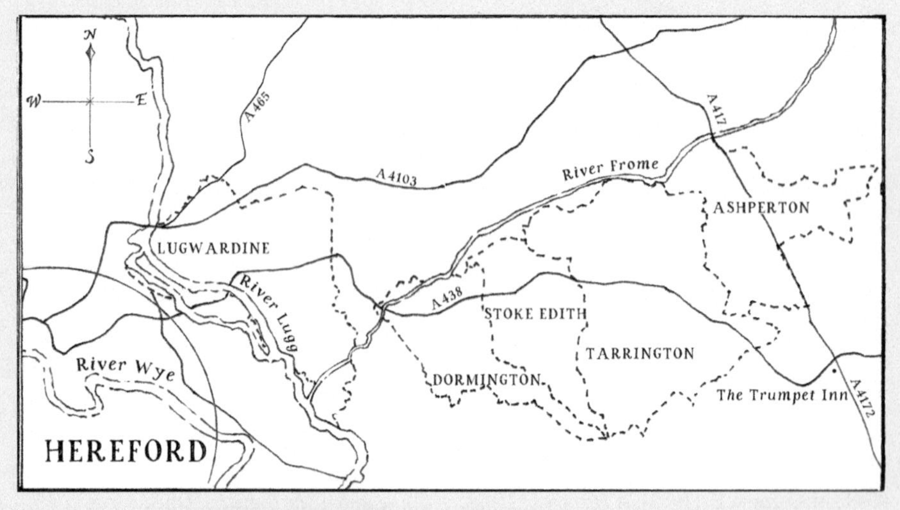

Journey 3 map and individual parish maps by Heather Colbert

LUGWARDINE PARISH

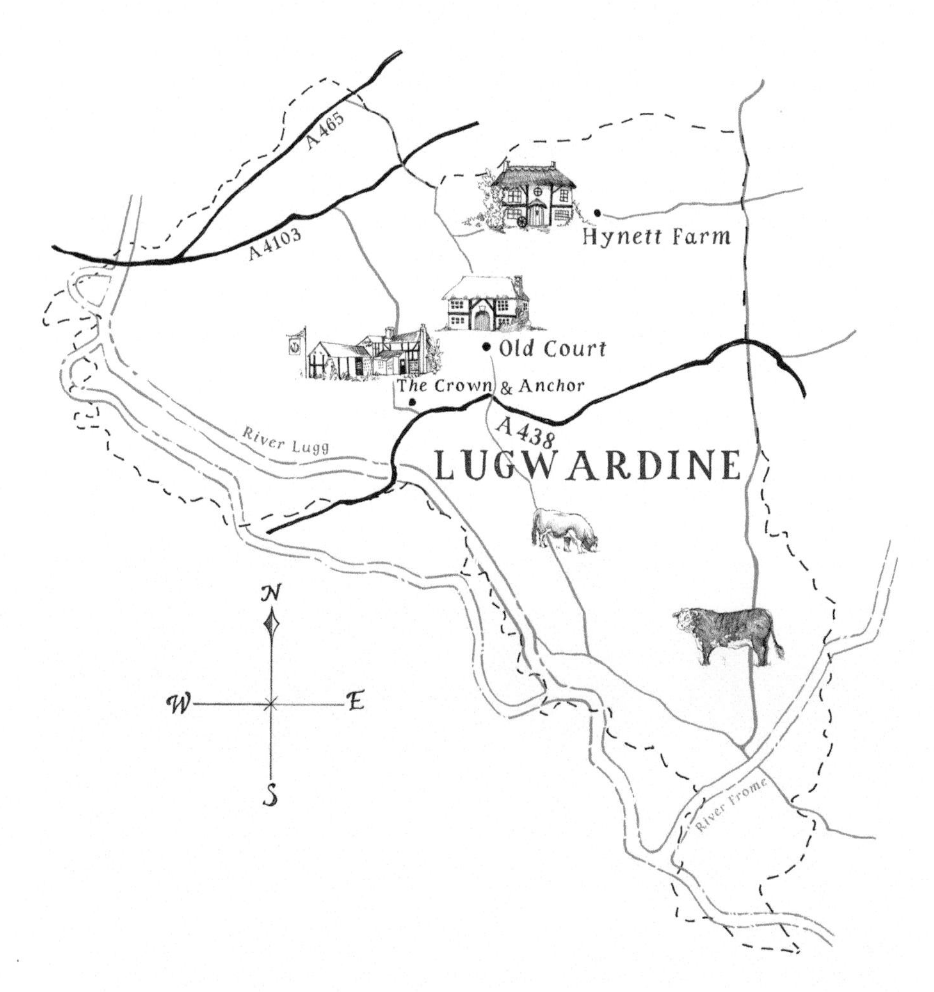

Lugwardine is a large parish starting some three miles from Hereford and continuing on that road for another mile and a half with land on both sides. It now effectively includes the tiny parish of Bartestree with its mere 420 acres. Despite small adjustments over time the area of the parish has hardly altered over the last centuries. It was 2,097 acres in 1851 and 2,116 in 1961. It adjoins the parish of Withington to the north, Weston Beggard to the north-east and, beyond Bartestree, Dormington to the east.

Despite its location so close to Hereford itself, Lugwardine was a rural agricultural community until the last quarter of the 20th century. The population recorded as 690 in 1841 rose to 755 in 1881 before falling back again to 686 in 1921 and 660 in 1961. The population of Bartestree was a mere 98 in 1871 but the rising numbers in the Roman Catholic convent, which had been constructed in the parish in 1863, caused the population to increase to 278 in 1911.

However Lugwardine and Bartestree were designated in the last decades of the 20th century as one of the areas in Herefordshire suitable for major expansion. Consequently the numbers and character of the population are now radically different. The convent was closed in 1992 and the buildings converted to attractive apartments and houses. The population of Lugwardine in 2011 was 1,700 and that of the tiny parish of Bartestree had risen to 330.

Fig. L1 Lugg Meadows by Brian Hatton, 1906, © Hereford Museum Service

Meadows by the River Lugg have been used throughout the centuries by farmers in Withington and Weston Beggard parishes as well as by those in Lugwardine parish. The ownership of the Lugwardine Lugg Meadow is divided between different farms who typically use this for the cutting of their entitlement to hay. Most unusually the meadow is open for common grazing from 1 August (Lammas Day).

At the time of the Doomsday Book and indeed until 1265 Lugwardine manor was owned by the King. The manor of Bartestree was included in the lands of Nigel the physician.

In the latter 16th century New Court and its manor were in the possession of the Reed family and at least three generations of the Reeds lived in the parish. There is a fine monument to William Reed who died in 1634 in the entrance to Lugwardine church. He is shown leaning on an arm with his family mourning him – one wonders if he got pins and needles. The Reed family seems to have been an intellectual one. A later member, possibly William Reed's grandson, was making recommendations on beekeeping in correspondence with the Royal Society.

In the late 18th century and throughout most of the 19th, New Court was owned by the Griffiths family before passing New Court on to relatives, the Burdens.

A number of other landowners are associated with Lugwardine. From the latter Middle Ages a branch of the Walwyn family owned Longworth Manor and Old Court. Longworth Manor was sold to the Philipps family in 1800 and Old Court was sold in 1805. Following the death of Robert Biddulph Philipps in 1855 Longworth Manor was sold to a Mr Hutchison and then repurchased by the county family of Barnaby associated with Brockhampton Court and related to the Philipps. The family let and eventually sold Longworth Hall itself but retained the majority of the estate throughout most of the 20th century whilst living at Sheepcote, Bartestree. Early in the Second World War 100 acres of the Sheepcote land was tented by Mr Dent of Eastwood Farm, Tarrington. Later in the war it was rented by Philip Davies of Claston Farm, Dormington and after the war bought by him. No doubt partially attracted by Lugwardine's location close to Hereford Sir Herbert Croft from the family associated with Croft Castle in north Herefordshire purchased Lugwardine Court and its land, including Old Court, in the 1860s and the Crofts were associated with Lugwardine until after the Second World War. A succession of landowners were also associated with Wilcroft House, Bartestree from the late 18th century.

Despite its proximity to Hereford the population of Lugwardine at the time of the Second World War was closely involved with agriculture. In this large parish no fewer than 25 farms filled in the National Farm Survey of 1941–1943[1] covering holdings of five or more acres.

Only two farms were over 150 acres: Mr L. Greenow of Cotts Farm with 168 acres and P. G. Meredith of Lugg Bridge Farm with 151 acres. Four farms had more than 100 acres: Captain Burden of New Court with 114 acres, Mr Tidmarsh who was farming

Stalls Farm on behalf of the owner of Hagley Hall, Miss Hopton, Jack Price of Hynett Farm with 106 acres and his friend Bill Ballinger of Upper House Farm with 105½ acres. A non-resident farmer, Mr H. C. Dent of Eastwood Farm, Tarrington was farming 100 acres of Sheepcote land owned by the Barnaby family. Seven farms were between 50–99 acres: Mr H. Philipps of Rock Farm with 97 acres, Mr Dyke of Castle Farm, Blackhole Lane with 93 acres, Mr Walter Carver of Hagley, the local butcher with 75½ acres, Mr Jack Jones of Tidnor Farm with 68½ acres, E. Perkins of Lugwardine Court with 67 acres, Mr A. J. Cooke of New Rents Farm with 55 acres, Mr Cooke of Old Court with 50 acres. Of the remaining holdings of between five and 49 acres, only one, farmed by Mr Watkins of Homelands Farm, was over 20 acres and almost of those listed supplemented farming with other activities. The elderly Mrs Hall had 18 acres at Bennetts Hill, Mr Watkins of Bridge House with 14 acres was a part-time butcher, Mr C. Philipps farming 12 acres at Wilcroft was an agricultural mechanic, Mr Hughes of the Mill, Lugwardine Bridge was a baker, Mr G. Adams with 10 acres at Tidnor Mill worked in the munition factory and also had a milk round.

In addition a remarkable 40 completed the annual Agricultural Census of June 1941, supposedly compulsory for holdings of more than two and a half acres, thus indicating that a significant number of holdings under five acres received at least part of their income from some farming activity at this time.

The farmers of Lugwardine and Bartestree were all traditional mixed farms and all had cattle with a mixture of beef but a predominance of dairy. As *Kelly's Directory* of 1940 points out, in contrast to most parishes in East Herefordshire, electricity was available in Lugwardine. However what *Kelly's Directory* does not point out was the expense involved in installing it. It is astonishing to discover how many of the farms, including Cotts Farm, Hynett Farm, Old Court and Tidnor Farm, were without electricity, a reflection of the difficulties faced by farming in the 1930s.

The Agricultural Census of June 1941 shows that around half the farmers in Lugwardine had sheep. Pigs were of little commercial importance but most farms kept at least one presumably for household needs, selling excess piglets. All the farmers kept poultry but in numbers considered very small by modern standards.

The number of farms has now greatly diminished although a few such as Hynett Farm described below, now the nucleus of an important 21st-century agricultural enterprise, still exist. The remaining farms are much bigger and some land is farmed by those resident elsewhere. Much of the land close to the A 438 has been developed for housing – land belonging to Old Court also described below was sold for development in the 1980s – and very few of the current residents are associated with farming.

Fig. L2 Hynett farmhouse 2017

Hynett Farm

Hynett Farm is located nearly a mile from Lugwardine Church in Blackhole Lane, which forms part of the old Roman Road between Stretton Grandisson and Kenchester. It is a working farm with 80 acres but forms part of a much larger enterprise of some 500 acres. It has been owned by the Gibbs family since 1964. As is common with many other Herefordshire farms a small part of this old farmhouse dates back to very early times, possibly even medieval. It was however missed from the 1932 inventory of the historical monuments in Herefordshire. The farmhouse was sold a number of years ago and the Gibbs family live in the renovated farm buildings. The farm owes its name to the nearby common field, Hynett Field, which was subject, as was the case in much of Lugwardine, to a fairly late enclosure.

History of Hynett Farm

The first written record of Hynett Farm was in 1813 when the *Hereford Journal* advertised the sale of a messuage or tenement called Hynet. At this time Hynett Farm was a copyhold premise of Lugwardine manor and the occupier was George Butcher. It comprised 12 acres and contained “a barn, stable, cider mill, fold and garden”. In addition “there were several closes or parcels of good meadow pasture arable land and orcharding”.

In 1841 the census shows John Phillipps aged 40 as farming Hynett Farm with his wife, Phoebe, and three children, Charlotte, Louise and Mary. In 1851 William Powell, described as a farm labourer, lived at Hynett Farm and was farming 83 acres. In 1861 John Powell was at Hynett Farm farming 49 acres with the aid of one man and one boy.

By 1871 John Godsall, whose father, also called John Godsall, owned and farmed Weston Corner, Withington, was farming Hynett Farm. He was at this time unmarried. His sister, Alice, was living with him as his housekeeper and they were assisted by one farm servant, William Arrowsmith aged 15, from Lugwardine. By the time of the 1881 census John had married Anne Tranter and they had started to rear their large family at Hynett Farm. The Godsalls were unusual in being nonconformist Baptists rather than Anglicans and leading members of the Baptist Chapel at Whitestone.

Fig. L3 Reuben Price in the early 1920s [2]

By 1891 John and Anne Godsall and their family had moved back to Weston Corner and Hynett Farm was farmed by two brothers, John and Reuben Price. Reuben was also a member of the Baptist congregation at Withington and married in 1893 Editha Godsall, John's daughter. Reuben died in 1925 but his widow lived until 1970. They are both buried in the chapel at Whitestone. One entertaining tale still recalled relates to the Baptist minister of the early 20th century. Sometime whilst he was bicycling down Blackhole Lane he saw Reuben turning his head round whilst ploughing. The minister's sermon the next Sunday was based on the biblical text "No man who puts his hand to the plough and looketh back is fit for the kingdom of heaven".

Reuben and Editha had three daughters: Nell who emigrated to Australia, Alice who organised the dairy before she married and Ina who trained as a nurse before marrying a farmer from Bredenbury. John Price, their only son was born in 1892 at Hynett Farm and was always known as Jack. He fought in and survived the First World War, and took over the farm following his father's death in 1925. He married Hilda Bowcott, the daughter of Thomas Bowcott of Felton Court. His sister, Alice, married Hilda's brother, Thomas Bowcott, an example of the close links between Herefordshire farming families.

Hynett Farm in the Second World War

Jack Price was the farmer at Hynett Farm and its 106 acres at the time of the National Farm Survey of 1941–1943 and the annual Agricultural Census of June 1941. He was paying rent of £28 10s for 18 acres and owned the remaining land. The holding included grazing on Lugg Meadows.

The farm was predominantly pasture with around 70% down to permanent or temporary grass. There were however 17 acres down to cereals of which 12 were of wheat and the remainder barley or oats, mostly planted as a response to the war effort.

Mr Price concentrated on dairying; of his total herd of 28 cattle no fewer than 16 were dairy cows or heifers, most of the remainder were weaner calves. Poultry was another important activity with 270 chickens, the second highest number in

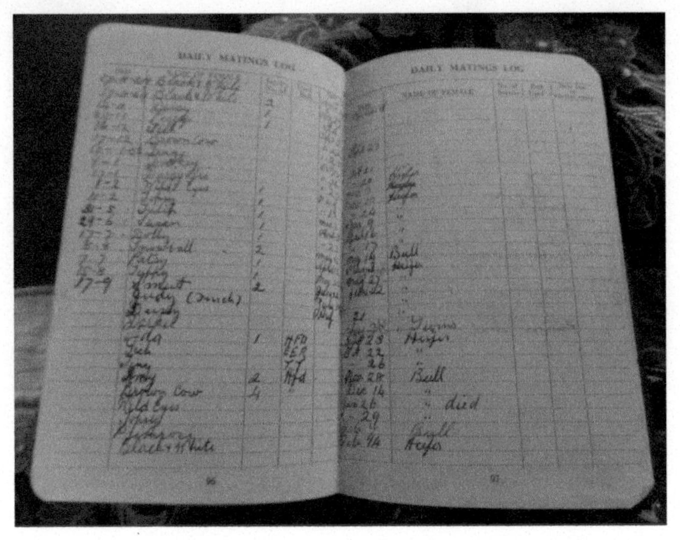

Fig. L4 Jack Price's dairy record for 1950 showing servicing and calving[3]

Lugwardine. There were only nine ewes with a further nine lambs. There were eight acres of orchards – as was common in Herefordshire, Mr Price produced his own cider. There were three farm horses plus an unbroken horse. He employed two male workers. Electricity was not installed.

Hynett Farm after the Second World War

Until 1964 when Jack Price retired, Hynett Farm continued to be a mixed farm with a concentration on dairying. As was common at the time all the cows had names.

Jack and Hilda Price's only daughter, Ann, and her husband, Tom Nellist, play major roles in the Trumpet and District Agricultural Society, a society established in 1944 by local farmers enrolled in the Home Guard (see Chapter 8). On Jack Price's retirement the farm with its 100 acres was sold to Mr Gibbs from a local farming family and is now owned and farmed by his son, Geoffrey, and his wife, Donna. Until near the end of the 20th century it remained a mixed farm but with beef rather than dairy cattle. It is now an arable farm of 80 acres run in conjunction with other land totalling 500 acres. Each year 200 acres are devoted to potatoes. Most of these are sold on contract to McCain, but Mr Gibbs also sells direct to the public.

Fig. L5 Geoffrey Gibbs with his potato harvest of 2017

Fig. L6 Old Court, now a private house

Old Court

Old Court is just a short distance from Lugwardine Church. Some 50 yards from the farmhouse is the moat which must originally have surrounded the medieval manor house denoted by the farm's name. The farmhouse with its old barn did not attain a mention in the 1932 inventory of the historical monuments in Herefordshire although parts of the existing farmhouse probably date back to at least the 18th century.

Old Court was owned by the Cooke family from 1921 until April 1988. Following the death of their father, George, in 1959 and their mother, Ann, nine months later, it was farmed by Percy Cooke and his sister, Doris Prosser (née Cooke). Mrs Prosser wrote a remarkable account of farming at Old Court over this long period of 67 years, giving a vivid description of Herefordshire life and families which have now passed into history.[4]

History of Old Court

The land tax records of the 18th century show the Walwyn family as owning Old Court. At this time it was an important farm. In 1786 Mr Jones was farming Old Court and paying land tax of £9 10s which suggests that the farm may have been as much as 150 acres. In 1792 William Pritchard was the tenant of Old Court and was farming on a large scale as in addition to the £9 10s for Old Court he was also paying land tax of £4 19s for part of the nearby Upper House Farm. At the autumn meeting of the Herefordshire Agricultural Society on 20 October 1800 one guinea was given to John Davis of Lugwardine for 31 years' service in Mr Pritchard's family. In 1800 the Walwyn family sold the Longworth estate to Mr Philipps and then sold Old Court in 1805.

Is not possible to identify the owners of Old Court in the subsequent land tax records. At the time of the Tithe Map in 1839 a considerable part of the acreage of Lugwardine was still divided up into strips just as the common fields had been in medieval times, but the map shows that Old Court had been more successful than other farms in enclosing some of the surrounding land.

Old Court seems to have been farmed by tenant farmers from 1805 until it was sold to the Cooke family in late 1920. The decennial census records from 1841 onwards provide information on these farmers. In 1841 Old Court was farmed by John Preece aged 25 with his wife, Charlotte aged 30. In 1851 he had been replaced by John Malley aged 56. Mr Malley had been born in the nearby parish of Hampton Bishop, as had his 19-year-old son, Samuel. By this time Old Court had only around half the acreage of the 18th century as the census records that the farm was 80 acres and Mr Malley was only employing one man, Thomas Jones, who was living in the household. Mr Malley seems to have moved from Hampton Bishop to Tarrington where four of his younger children were born, but his youngest child, Elizabeth aged four in 1851, had been born in Lugwardine, so presumably the family had moved to Old Court by 1847. John Malley was still at Old Court in 1861 farming the same acreage employing one worker. By 1871 Old Court was lived in by James Atwood, a farm bailiff aged 33 with his wife and children of two and one, both of whom had been born in Lugwardine. The census records show that from 1880 until after 1911 it was farmed by Caleb Barnes, the son of a farmer with 96 acres from Churcham in Gloucestershire. At the time of the land valuation of 1910 it was owned by the Croft family of Lugwardine Court and farmed by Caleb Barnes. The acreage had sunk to 50 acres. In 1920 the tenant farmers were called Williams and had six grown-up children – three girls and three boys.

Old Court, originally a copyhold farm, came up for sale in 1920 and seems to have been fairly run-down at this time. Land prices had risen during the First World War and remained high immediately afterwards so the Cookes had to pay a high price, £3,750, for this 50-acre farm and struggled with mortgage payments for most of their time there.

George and Ann Cooke, Doris Prosser's parents, had previously run the New Inn, a pub at Hentland in South Herefordshire from 1904 to 1920 before purchasing Old Court. Ann Cooke (née Bayliss) kept poultry and a few cows, and sold dressed chickens and butter at Hereford butter market. Ann was the sister of Eliza Bayliss of Moorend Farm, Weston Beggard.

In her first booklet, Doris describes taking over the farm. It exemplifies the remarkable resourcefulness of the family in building up their farm that Percy Cooke, then aged only 16, Doris's younger brother, had to walk the family's four cows 14 miles to their new home. The Cookes then gradually built up their milking herd from these animals. Doris was given a Ryeland pedigree ewe by her mother's younger brother, Reginald. She built up a small flock of Ryelands from this one animal (although a few other Ryeland sheep were purchased by her parents) and for quite a number of years the family could not afford the fee to register them as pedigree. Doris also built up a flock of poultry, including White Orpingtons, which received a 'highly recommended' at a London show. George Cooke planted two orchards, skilfully grafting many of the fruit trees himself so that they could be easily picked. It proved a success and subsequently the family normally sent 20 tons of apples to Bulmers factory in Hereford each year.

The hay was cut from the 20 acres owned by Old Court in Lugg Meadows. The expression 'make hay whilst the sun shines' was certainly relevant to the timing problems of haymaking before the Second World War. More than once the whole crop could be lost if there were unseasonable floods. In her first booklet Doris states:

I have seen a sea-like flood all over those meadows and the hay implements sticking up out of it ... And if one got caught in a heavy shower down there there was no place to shelter. I have known our folks get under the wagon of hay to shelter and as the hay was loose in those days and not baled it would go straight through and soak them. It [haymaking] was all done with horses. Percy used to go down at 4 a.m. to cut the grass before it got hot, and again in the evening. He started in June and, if the season was good, it could be done in 10 days. Now I have known it take four days with all those modern improvements in farming.

Not only was the hay brought back loose at this time but the haystack had to be thatched with straw to keep it dry. George Cooke was skilled in this remarkable art. Doris's second booklet includes a faded picture of her father in 1939 when he was 80, just distinguishable standing beside the rick he has thatched.

Evidently though, neighbours were there to play a hand: a change from the full employment and television entertainment days of the 1970s when Doris was writing.

In those days many hands turned up to give a hand, there being many at a loose end in the evenings. There was plenty of cider made on the place in the cider mill near the house with a horse drawing round a stone crushing the apples to pulp, so with sand-wiches and cider many happy days got spent in that old mill after a day's haymaking round those old barrels.

Steam-driven threshing machines have existed for a hundred years and the smaller farms in Herefordshire hired the owner and the machine for their modest threshing requirements. Doris describes the arrival and work of this machine and its owner. Firstly this cumbersome huge machine had to be brought to the farm and to do so the Cookes collaborated with their relatives the Baylisses of Moorend Farm, Weston Beggard.

My brother generally had to take our two horses and go and fetch my cousin Charlie from the Moorend with their horses and go and fetch the thrashing machine, usually from Westhide, some 4 miles off, and it had to be between the hours of 5 and 6 a.m. After arrival he [Mr Townsend, the owner of the thresher] would fix the machine and then come in to breakfast. He was a huge man and seems to have a job to get about on his legs. Once the helpers had arrived he saw to it that no one was idle and everyone seemed to respect his word of command. He used to sit on a box behind the engine and stoke up (Jock [the Cooke's dog] was always with him). We had him there for a week once shelling clover seeds which sold in those days for 50 shillings per ton. Wheat straw is that price here in 1975. When he had fixed the next place to go for the thrashing these people came with their horses to fetch him. It nearly always ended with this steep pull-up from our rickyard in Percy having to fetch our horses or 'kittens' as Mr Townsend called them to get the tack up on the road, Jock looking very sad at the departure and indeed for several days.

Horses rather than tractors have characters. Doris describes Blackbird, the Cooke's first horse "she was good and produced many good foals", then Jolly, a wonderful worker whilst in foal but afterwards liable to kick and a pet horse called Robin who stayed with the family until she died aged nearly 30.

Doris Prosser does not dwell on the life of a farmer's wife and daughter, but to a modern reader the skilfulness of Herefordshire country women and their extraordinary hard work is so clearly revealed. Their rewards seem by modern standards to be meagre although fortunately it was general companionship and her happy marriage that mattered most to Doris. Not only did the women undertake all the domestic work – and this was before any kind of modern convenience – they also engaged in quite a lot of the farming activities. Doris's mother milked the cows, made the butter and plucked the chickens, preparing them for sale at her stall in Hereford. Before her marriage in 1937, Doris would have undertaken many of these chores. She obviously also tended the Ryeland sheep including lambing – the one activity which has hardly changed today. At key harvest times she evidently assisted other farmers in the neighbourhood.

Throughout her life Doris was also called upon to do heavy nursing. Her grandmother lived with the family at Old Court for 11 years, dying at 95. Doris considered her a remarkable person: "She had been a wonderful cook, very good tailoress and gardener, such a useful life" but in her later years she was highly incapacitated and "stayed mostly in her bedroom with her own things around her. But everything had to be taken upstairs, heating, meals and water. There was no bathroom there in those days, but I was young and managed it." Doris's father was lucky enough to remain vigorous for his age until he died at the age of 100. The men preferred the outdoor life and the farming women often undertook the paperwork and bills. Sadly Doris's mother, Ann, totally lost her sight for her last five years of life but Doris mentions that: "my mother still remained fully in touch with what went on, she would ask the date and then get Percy to pay the usual bills that have to be met at certain times".

In 1937 Doris married Arthur Prosser, a farmer's son and one of eight children, who worked at that time on a nearby farm. It was evidently a happy marriage, although childless, and she had the fondest memory of Prospect Cottage, Lugwardine where they lived from 1938 until after Arthur's death in 1976.

Old Court in the Second World War

In the Agricultural Census of June 1941 Old Court is listed as having 50 acres. Six and a half acres were under cereals, one acre under potatoes and another one and a half acres under turnips. The orchards, so vividly described by Doris and so productive, came to three acres. The remainder of land was pasture with a small amount of clover: this land included the 20 acres in Lugg Meadows. The census shows that the Cookes had succeeded in building up their herd of cattle. In 1941 there was a herd of 21 of which 10 were cows or heifers either in milk or in calf with a further six calves under a year old. There was no electricity. The flock of sheep comprised 21 ewes, a ram and 19 lambs. The breakdown of poultry reveals the business acumen of Doris and her mother. At this time in the Second World War it was difficult for farmers to keep poultry as they were allowed very few rations and often none at all. The Cookes had 121 poultry – 27 geese and 14 ducks, both no doubt very saleable for Christmas at this time of scarcity. There were two horses and although Doris remembers mares, both were geldings. Perhaps one of them was the much loved Robin.

Old Court after the Second World War

It is not clear from Doris Prosser's reminiscences when different labour-saving machinery came to the farm after the Second World War, but George Cooke was obviously keen on modern initiatives even in his extreme old age.

When George Cooke was still alive: "a man would come with a machine called a trusser which cut the hay into bales to be sold to a hay dealer, usually a Mr Jaine". This machine preceded the modern baler. Electricity came to Old Court in 1950 and was installed in both the farmhouse and in the dairy: "The chaff cutter and pulper were driven by it." Mrs Prosser speaks appreciatively of the combine harvester. She also speaks well of the potato harvester. "When we first came to Lugwardine we had planted the potatoes by hand from buckets in rows set out with the Bouter plough. Now one high machine came and did the job quickly and it was still more wonderful to see them harvested, lifted out of the soil in rows, sorted the size, conveyed on a banking platform, weighed, tied with wire and on the lorry sending to store." The potato planter and harvester probably only came to the farm nearer 1970.

The Cookes kept a dairy herd. The Milk Marketing Board advised the Cookes to sell milk rather than butter. The cows continued to be milked by hand even after the Second World War period. The milk was placed in churns outside the farm and collected each day. The milk that was not sold fresh or needed for the household was used to rear calves. By the late 1970s the Milk Marketing Board turned against milk churns and wanted Percy to go into bulk production. He did not want to do so – he was over 70 at the time – and consequently the herd was sold and the land of Old Court rented out to Mr Derek Powell of Amberley Court, Sutton. The flock of Ryeland sheep Doris Prosser had cared so much for and fostered so well also had to be sold at this time to a Mr Morgan of Kingstone. One advantage of the changing Lugwardine was the demand for building and Percy was able to sell to plots of land for development. This greatly assisted the paying off of the mortgage which still existed so many years later. Following the death of her husband in 1976, Doris moved back to Old Court to care for her younger unmarried brother, Percy, and ended up undertaking all the domestic chores thereby involved. The house had not previously really been modernised and she was glad when the bathroom and downstairs toilet were installed. Doris remembered that on her 80th birthday the vicar of Lugwardine: "asked me if I prefer the old days to the present and seemed surprised when I said I like the present days best. The day's wash is so much easier, ironing with electricity and so much quicker. But I have learnt that one thing [we] had, which the present lacks is 'contentment'".

In 1988 Old Court farmhouse and barn with a modest acreage including the remains of the old moat was sold at a most satisfactory price. Percy and Doris moved to a new house in Tupsley. Doris was grateful for the help she received in nursing Percy who was by then fairly disabled. She herself was similarly looked after in her old age. She much enjoyed an occasional drive back to Lugwardine to see the old farm but greatly appreciated the modern conveniences of Tupsley.

DORMINGTON PARISH

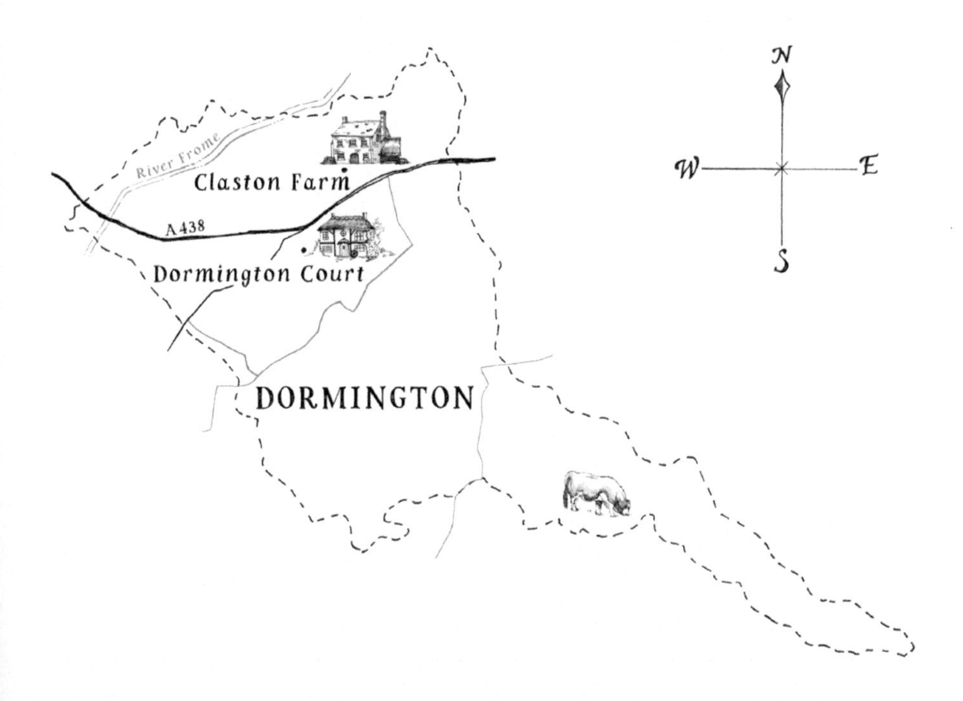

The small village of Dormington lies on either side of the main A 438 Hereford to Ledbury road some five and three-quarter miles from Hereford. The road between Dormington and Mordiford was constructed in the 1790s as was the present alignment of the Hereford to Ledbury road. The greater part of the parish lies on the rich Hereford sandstone and clay but Upper Dormington is on the lower reaches of the limestone Woolhope Dome, a totally different soil. Both soils in the past were valuable. The sandstone is rich, if heavy, agricultural land. The areas of limestone soil, though less valuable agriculturally, contained quarries when limestone was in high demand in the neighbourhood. It was also heavily wooded and coppice wood was a valuable source both for charcoal and for a wide variety of farm purposes.

The parish boundary was changed in 1886, reducing the size of the parish from 1,381 acres to the present 977 acres, of which 23 acres are water as the River Frome flows through this parish on its way to Mordiford where it joins the River Wye. The population has always been small. It varied a great deal doing the 19th century, possibly depending upon whether the limestone quarries were operational or not. The peak population was 189 in 1851. In contrast in 1881 the population was a mere 108. With the reduction in acreage the population fell to 93 by 1911 before increasing somewhat in the period between the two World Wars.

Dormington benefited at the turn of the 21st century from the construction of a new private estate, The Maltings. Consequently the population rose to 261 in 2011 but in contrast to the population up to the Second World War, few residents are now associated with farming.

Throughout the Middle Ages, and indeed before the Norman Conquest, the land of Dormington belonged to St Guthlac's Priory. The land tax records from the 1750s then show that the large farms of Claston Farm and Priors Court together with some smaller properties in Dormington already belonged to the Foley family at this time, forming part of the Stoke Edith estate. However a Mr Wallwyn Shepheard retained the Lordship of Dormington as well as Dormington Court and other substantial land in the parish until a descendant, confusingly also called Mr Wallwyn Shepheard, was made bankrupt in 1795 and Dormington Court, together with the lime quarries and the valuable woods the around Dormington were purchased by the Foley estate. In 1919/1920 the farmsteads and farmland in Dormington (but not the valuable woods) formed part of the Foley estate sale.

Six farms were recorded in the National Farm Survey of 1941–1943[5]. Three of these were by the standards of the time large farms which had all been owner-occupied since the Foley estate sale: Claston Farm with 172 acres and Dormington Court with 133 acres, both described below, and Priors Court with 214 acres. There were also three smaller farms: Prospect Farm with 75 acres, Cop Grove Farm with 65 acres and Wootton farm of 60 acres.

Of the six farms identified in the National Farm Survey only Claston Farm remains a farm in 2017. Most of the other farmland in Dormington is farmed by those living outside the parish.

Claston Farm

Claston Farm, house, barn and granary, 600 yards N.E. of the church. The House is of two storeys with attics; the walls are of rubble and the roofs are tiled. It was built in the 17th century on an L-shaped plan with the wings extending towards the N.E. and S.E. A modern wing makes the plan half H-shaped. Inside the building the timbering in the roofs is original.

Fig. D1 Claston Farm owned by the Thomas family with Edward and Verity Thomas.

> The Barn, S. of the house, is of the 17th century, timber-framed and of three bays. The Granary was built probably early in the 18th century, and is of two storeys; the walls are of rubble.[6]

For 140 years from 1864 to 2004 Claston was farmed by generations of the Davies family. Thomas Davies (1816–1895) took over the management of Claston Farm from the Stoke Edith estate in 1864 and the tenancy from 1866. His son William Henry Davies (1860–1943) farmed Claston Farm in addition to several farms in Weston Beggard. His grandson, Philip Davies (1893–1977), purchased Claston in 1919 when the acreage was 175 acres. Peter Davies, his great-grandson (1922–2017), who was born at Claston Farm and lived there until his retirement, described in detail the changing nature of farming during his lifetime in an excellent book entitled *A Herefordshire Tale*[7].

Until 1986 Claston was a typical East Herefordshire mixed farm with its hops, cattle, orchards and arable. From 1986, partly inspired by his son, Philip Davies (1955–1988), Peter Davies specialised in hops and cider orchards on the greatly enlarged acreage of Claston Court which by then had purchased the land of Dormington Court. At a time when others gave up on hops because of the problems of wilt, Peter Davies planted wilt-resistant varieties and pioneered the labour-intensive new variety of hedgerow hops. These are clearly visible from the south side of the A 438.

History of Claston Farm

The present farmhouse was probably constructed in the 1670s indicating Claston Farm's importance at this time. Remains have been found of earlier buildings, though sadly a 17th-century barn no longer exists. Records uncovered by Peter Davies show that a Thomas Newton acquired some Claston Farm land in 1656 and purchased more land in 1658[8]. A memorial inside Dormington church indicates there were no fewer than eight generations of Newtons, mainly called Thomas, in Dormington. The land tax records for Dormington date back to 1752 and show that, even at this early date, Claston Farm belonged to the Foley estate. In 1792 when the Dormington parish land tax records show tenants as well as landowners, another Thomas Newton was farming on an exceptionally large scale. He was paying £15 94s land tax for Priors Court, Dormington as well as £6 19s 7d for Claston Farm, which at this time was the smaller farm. The combined rent for these two farms was £660, a very large sum for this time.

By 1798 Thomas Newton had relinquished Claston, but still retained Priors Court. The land tax records for 1798 show William Atwood installed as the farmer at Claston and he was still there at the time of the census of 1841. He was then said to be 60, so he must have been very young when he took over the tenancy. His sister, Caroline, who had been governess to the Foley family, was living with him in 1841. The household at that time also consisted of four male servants and four female farm servants. When William

Fig. D2 The Attwood memorial in Dormington churchyard

Atwood died in the 1840s, the tenancy remained with Caroline, but the 1851 census shows Claston to be lived in by a bailiff, Thomas Hankins, aged 60, whilst Caroline was recorded in the census as a visitor to Stoke Edith House. Following Caroline's death in 1855, the *Hereford Times* of 8 January 1856 lists the sale of farm stock, including a herd of Hereford cattle and flocks of both Ryeland and Leicester sheep, as well as carthorses, colts and farm implements. The announcement of Thomas Hankins's death in 1858 states that he had worked for the late William Atwood, Esq. for 38 years, so presumably Claston was always run by a bailiff during the time of the Atwood tenancy.

Tenancy cut short by death

After this long period of stability, Claston then went through some periods of change. In 1856 John Taylor took over the tenancy. He was only 21 at the time, but seems to have been a vigorous farmer. In October 1856 the *Hereford Times* lists him as one of the judges for the Herefordshire Agricultural Society meeting. In January 1858 he was included as a subscriber to the new toll-free Corn Exchange in Broad Street, Hereford. He appears in the 1861 census as aged 26, unmarried, with a sister as housekeeper. Sadly he died young and the *Hereford Times* records the sale of the farm stock of the late John Taylor in February 1867. John Taylor seems to have given up farming before 1867 as records show that Thomas Davies was running Claston as a bailiff for the Foley estate from 1864 until 1866. Thomas Davies then took over the tenancy from 1866 – presumably because of John Taylor's ill health and then death – and so started the long association of Davies family with Claston.

The Davies family at Claston Farm: 1864–2004

Thomas Davies was a remarkably energetic and able farmer, associated in his youth with a number of Foley tenant farms. In 1859 he took over Moorend Farm, Weston Beggard and lived there until he moved to Claston in 1864. Later he had the tenancy of Pigeon House Farm, Weston Beggard and from 1876 he also had the tenancy of Hillend Farm, Weston Beggard. Consequently the 1881 census shows him as farming altogether 395 acres. In 1885 Thomas Davies took over the lease of Beans Butts, Woolhope and then purchased the freehold the following year, installing a tenant farmer until one of his sons, Walter Thomas Davies, took over the farm. Thomas Davies moved to Pigeon House Farm in the 1880s. The 1891 census shows that he had reduced the acreage he was farming, but only to a still substantial 295 acres. Unusually for Herefordshire at the time and giving an indication of the quality of Thomas Davies, the household at Pigeon House Farm in 1891 included a 25-year-old farm pupil.

After Thomas Davies moved to Pigeon House Farm, Claston was then farmed by one of Thomas's sons, Harry, who sadly was killed in 1891 when his horse bolted under a willow tree. For the next eight or so years Harry's widow, Isabella, continued the tenancy until she married again. William Henry Davies (1860–1943), another of Thomas's sons and the grandfather of Peter Davies, then moved from Hillend Farm, Weston Beggard to Claston.

William Henry Davies seems to have inherited, or learnt, the farming skills of his father and he was from the 1880s onwards a most successful hop farmer. At the peak of his hop growing he was selling no fewer than 1,000 pockets of hops. He was also a most successful breeder of Hereford pedigree cattle. This may have been the time of the Great Agricultural Depression, but the price for a prize-winning Hereford was many times higher than for the normal pedigree animal. William Davies's heifer, Miss Vera, won the supreme championship at the prestigious Royal Agricultural Society of England show and was subsequently exported to Argentina. Nor was this all. In 1906 he exported some 70 Hereford cattle, mostly valuable cows, again to Argentina.[9]

The difficult interwar years

Peter Davies's father Philip Davies had fought in the First World War and took over the farm on his return, purchasing it in 1920 in consequence of the large Foley estate sale. He married Mildred Thompson of The Hyde, Woolhope in 1922. Life was very difficult in this interwar period. Claston had to repay a heavy mortgage for the purchase of the farm. Conditions must have become especially hard in the early 1930s. Milk was one of the few ways of making money and some of the Hereford beef cattle must have been replaced by dairy cows. In *A Herefordshire Tale*, Peter includes a vivid description of the milk round his father instituted, which included dressed chickens and meat that had been slaughtered on the farm. He remembers his mother making butter whilst his job was to turn the churn. Philip must have been pleased that, as a registered hop grower, at least he had a hop quota. Hops normally made a profit following the establishment of the Hop Marketing Board in 1932.

Claston Farm in the Second World War

The National Farm Survey of 1941–1943 and the Annual Agricultural Census of June 1941 show Claston to be 172 acres. Around 70% of the land was good quality with 30%, presumably the Upper Dormington area, of fair quality. Unlike most farms it had been well maintained with the hedges and drainage in a good state of repair and only the ditches needing some attention. The farmhouse and the two farm cottages were in a good condition. There was no electricity. By June 1941 71 acres of the farm were down to crops. 26 acres were given over to hops but unlike most East Herefordshire farms there were only four acres of orchards. For the 1940 harvest seven and a half acres were ploughed up under CWAEC instructions for oats and 13½ acres for wheat. For the 1941 harvest and additional 20½ acres were ploughed up of which nine acres were wheat and 11½ were oats. Philip Davies had 87 sheep of whom 40 were ewes and two rams. Most of his 74 cattle were beef but there were 10 cows in milk. There were also three farm horses. In 1941 Claston had an old and not very effective tractor. In 1942, the farm was given permission to purchase one of the new Fordson tractors. During the Second World War, Philip Davies expanded the farm's hop production by increasing his quota.

Mechanisation and expansion 1945–1972

Farming in East Herefordshire at the end of the Second World War was dependent, as it had always been, on a significant number of skilled agricultural labourers. All the farms relied at least partly on farm horses and only the larger farms had even one tractor. Notable was the lack of electricity even though this had been installed in most other parts of the country.

The years that followed the Second World War saw a remarkable transformation to highly capital-intensive farming of a much larger acreage. In *A Herefordshire Tale*, Peter Davies describes in great detail the radical changes made at Claston in this period, many of which could also be observed on the other larger East Herefordshire farms at this time.

The first to be made redundant in that early post-war period at Claston and, indeed, throughout Herefordshire, were those lovely shire horses such as Prince, a horse described by Peter Davies, who were replaced with tractors. Electricity, which made such a fundamental difference to farming, was available at Claston from 1951. In December 1951 the farm bought a Weeks hop sprayer, the first to be power-driven, and in 1952, the new improved Ferguson tractor.

In addition to providing cider for the workers, a traditional requirement until the beginning of the Second World War, Claston sold cider apples to Bulmers. In 1952 Peter helped his father planted a new 'standard-type' orchard, the first orchard specialising in commercial cider fruit production on the farm.

The farm ceased to grow potatoes which had been required as part of the war effort and turned to purchasing year-old bullocks, keeping them for a year and reselling them to the big beef grazing producers in Leicestershire.

Taking advantage of the buoyant hop market and growing demand, Philip Davies first rented the hopyard at Eastwood Farm, Tarrington from 1946–1956. In a more permanent response in 1954 he then purchased a large hop yard at The Vauld, Marden where the traditional Fuggle variety of hops was grown until 1972, when that hop yard was converted into an orchard.

Hop production has always been capital intensive but was now even more so. Hop pickers, a feature of Herefordshire countryside for centuries, were becoming difficult to recruit and required higher remuneration. Throughout East Herefordshire manual hop picking started to be replaced by hop-picking machines. The first in the locality was at Dormington Court in 1953. Claston installed its first one in 1957, a Bruff machine made at Suckley. This was not the end of the expense. The machine needed to be housed, requiring a large new barn which cost £5,400, considerably more than a substantial house at the time.

The Davieses continued to increase their acreage, purchasing 50 acres of Sheepcote land from the Bartestree Longworth estate belonging to the Barnabys, an old established county family. Most of this acreage they planted up with hops. They started producing their own cuttings of hop plants, installing their first small greenhouse in 1962. From 1967 Claston was asked to take over management of the Allied Breweries hop farms – Dormington Court, Aldersend Farm in Tarrington, and Pomona Farm in Weston Beggard – a compliment to the Davieses clear competence and knowledge. They then started producing cuttings, not only for Claston but also for Dormington Court. Peter Davies was invited to become a member of The Association of Growers of New Hop Varieties and introduced Bullion, one such variety, to Claston.

Hop wilt, further expansion, tragedy and retirement 1973–2007

In the latter quarter of the 20th century hop farmers of East Herefordshire were faced with the deadly disease of Progressive Verticillium Wilt. This had been known in Kent for many years but was first identified at Claston in 1973, the very year that the United Kingdom joined the European Common Market. There were other challenges faced by hop farmers at this time, especially the increased competition from duty-free German hops and the abolition of the Hop Marketing Board in 1982, which had served farmers so well for over 50 years. However, it was Progressive Verticillium Wilt which was largely responsible for the decline of hop growing in East Herefordshire.[10] According to Peter Davies, Claston was the only farm in the West Midlands where Progressive Verticillium Wilt had been confirmed which still continued hop production. There were good reasons.

> *… we had just completed draining, treating the soil against eelworm, replanting with virus-free Early Bird, Northdown and Challenger, and renewing the wire-work where necessary on 125 acres, which was a very costly business …*[11]

It took eight years for Peter Davies to persuade the Ministry of Agriculture to reverse its policy of simply grubbing up the area around the infected plants and not permitting any replanting with Target, at that time the only known strain of hops resistant to Verticillium Wilt.

Until his death in 1977, Philip Davies oversaw the hop growing at Dormington Court and at the other Allied Breweries hop farms. Peter Davies then took over responsibility for these under their new name, Allied Hop Farms, and in 1983 he was instrumental in forming a producer group, Western Quality Hops Limited which, with its wider negotiating powers, was able to receive support under EC rules.

In 1984 Peter Davies bought 100 acres of Priors Court land in order to plant 50 of these up with wilt-resistant varieties of hops and the remaining 50 with cider apples. At the same time he sold the 50 acres which had been purchased from the Bartestree Longworth estate as it was further off. He was fortunate enough to receive a contract from Bulmers for the cider apples and planted a further 58 acres of Claston land with wilt-resistant hop varieties. He oversaw the purchase of another farm, Brierley Court, near Leominster for Allied Breweries as the brewery wished to expand its own production of hops in view of a perceived shortage. Dormington Court Hop Farms was renamed Brierley Court Hop Farms in 1986 and the company office moved to Brierley. Peter Davies was then able to buy Dormington Court and its 150 acres of land in 1986 when it was unexpectedly put up for sale by Allied Breweries together with the hop kilns and cottages for workers. Peter Davies was later able to sell the house, kilns and cottages for quite a reasonable price.

In contrast with Claston's 175 acres in 1919 and 172 acres in 1941, by 1986 Peter Davies was farming 600 acres. Claston was still a mixed farm as it had 350 acres of cereals as well as beef and sheep. The beef cattle were purchased as year-old Herefords crossed with the most popular dairy breeds, Friesian or Holstein bullocks. However, the Holstein cross did not produce a good quality animal and were becoming unpopular. Peter's son, also called Philip like his grandfather, was now fully involved in the farm business and he recommended that Claston should concentrate entirely on apples and hops. The closure of the abattoir in Hereford was also a consideration. The smaller abattoirs were being closed at the time and this meant that the cattle had to go long distances. The farm therefore sold both the cattle and sheep.

In addition to all his other activities Peter Davies entered a crop-sharing agreement with the Weston Beggard farm, Pomona Farm, and the Davieses continued with their imaginative farming, obtaining a contract for supplying daffodil bulbs and planting daffodils between the rows of young cider apple trees. In the next two years this was most appreciated by the local people. A daffodil walk arranged in 1988 was visited by around 1,000 people and raised significant and much needed sums for the little parish church of Dormington.

Tragically in 1988 Philip Davies, the talented only son of Peter Davies, who had suffered from periodic depression, was to take his own life with the terrible loss to his family and indeed to the farming community. With all their resourcefulness Peter and his wife, Pam, rose above this tragedy. Although Peter considered retiring, he decided to continue with Phillip's ideas. Most farmers in East Herefordshire had either given up hops or were about to give them up, disheartened by the disease and the abolition of the Hop Marketing Board; not so Peter and Pam.

In 1992 Peter Davies was the first British hop grower to introduce a totally new concept of 'hedgerow hops' and Claston was the only farm in Britain to produce a full crop in 1993. Indomitable, even when faced with difficult market conditions, Claston continued to experiment with different varieties of hedgerow hops throughout the 1990s and indeed into the early 2000s.

> *To pick 5 acres a day in the traditional system with 2 static picking machines, you needed 32 people, whilst with a mobile harvester that picks the same acreage a day you needed only 7 people.*[12]

The wire work needed to be only eight rather than 15 to 18 feet and the yield was also higher. However, in the late 1990s the market for hops collapsed. The price for crops fell from £35 per kilo in 1993 to £12 per kilo in 1999 and hops were difficult to sell altogether.

Claston Farm in the 21st century

In the early 2000s Peter Davies continued to experiment with different varieties of hedgerow hops including varieties with markets in the pharmaceutical industry and in animal feedstuffs. In 2004 at the age of 82 Peter Davies finally retired. The historic farm of Claston and farm buildings and land on the north side of the A 438 were sold to Derek Thomas of Perry Hill Farm, Clehonger. The land on the south side of the road, which had originally belonged to Dormington Court, was sold to Glyn and Richard Williams of Ross-on-Wye. Approaching on the main road hedgerow hops can still be seen. Hop production may well be at a much lower level than its heyday but as a result of the dedication of Peter Davies and a few others, a slow resurrection may well be underway.

Claston Farm, renovated to 21st-century standards, is lived in by Derek Thomas's son and wife. The farm now specialises mainly in the rearing of chickens.

Dormington Court

Fig. D3 Dormington Court with the late 17th-century house in the centre and the Tudor wing to the right

Dormington Court, 30 yards E. of the church, is of two storeys, partly timber-framed and partly of brick; the roofs are tiled. The house consists of a central block with side wings; the S.W. wing is of early 17th-century date, the N.E. wing of late 17th-century date, and the central block was built early in the 18th century. The S.W. wing has exposed timber-framing, but the rest of the house is of brick with a band-course between the storeys. The main block has a hipped roof with deeply projecting eaves; the N.E. wing has windows with solid frames. Inside the building, the middle block has an early 18th-century dog-legged staircase, with turned balusters, square newels and moulded strings repeated against the walls. The S.W. wing has some exposed ceiling-beams.[6]

Dormington Court ceased to be a farmhouse in 1986 when the house, hop kilns, cottages and farmland were purchased by Peter Davies of Claston Farm and the land largely put down to orchards. Dormington Court itself was first a country hotel and is now a most attractively maintained private house with lovely gardens. The kilns and cottages are also private houses. In 2004 the farmland was purchased by Glyn and Richard Williams of Ross-on-Wye on Peter Davies' retirement.

From at least the 18th century until the end of the 20th century Dormington Court was renowned for its hop production and was advertised as producing hops as early as 1795. In the famous Foley estate sale of 1919/1920 it was specifically described as a hop farm, the only one of the farms sold so described. Dormington Court was also famed for its racehorses through much of the first half of the 19th century under its then tenant, William Vevers.

History of Dormington Court

Memories of the 18th century

Land tax records are available for Dormington Court from 1752 when it was owned by Mr Wallwyn Shepheard, but the early tax records do not specify the tenant. This Mr Wallwyn Shepheard died in 1755. In 1791 Dormington Court was still owned by a Mr Wallwyn Shepheard, presumably the son or grandson of the original owner, and the tenant was Mr Robert Cotes. Unfortunately this Mr Wallwyn Shepheard was declared bankrupt in 1795 and Mr Robert Coates in 1796.

The bankruptcy advertisement for the sale of Dormington Court in 1795 specified that hops were grown. The land was described as containing: "One Hundred and Two Acres of very rich Meadow, Pasture, Orchard, Hop and Arable Land, within a ring fence." The ring fence indicates that, unlike other parts of Dormington, the land was already enclosed. The estate also included 102 acres of woodland, very valuable in the 18th century. With its good quality heavy land and woodland, Dormington Court was almost certainly also producing commercial quantities of wheat and timber. Dormington had the advantage compared with other East Herefordshire parishes of being close to the Wye and wheat and timber from Herefordshire were exported down the river to Chepstow. Cattle were also important. The subsequent bankruptcy notice for Mr Robert Cotes in the *Hereford Journal* of September 1796 describes him as "Grazier, Dealer and Chapman". Lime quarries and two lime kilns were also associated with Dormington Court. In happier times Robert Cotes was advertising lime for sale in 1791.

Famed for horse breeding 1798–1858

From 1795 Dormington Court was owned by the Foley estate of Stoke Edith. From 1798 until his death, the tenant was the distinguished and nationally known horse breeder and sportsman Mr William Vevers from a family previously associated with Yarkhill Court. He was an enthusiastic member of the local hunting fraternity. Whilst other well-known East Herefordshire farms of this period such as Stone House Farm and Thinghill Court, Withington were renowned for their early success in the breeding of Hereford cattle, at Dormington Court the success was in the breeding of horses – some flat racehorses, some shire horses and most of all steeplechasers. The steeplechasers seem to have been a cross between the flat racehorses and shire horses. They needed to be able to carry Mr Vevers himself who seems to have been a substantial weight. More often than not he was his own jockey and continued to be so right until 1848 when he was 66 years old.

An early success in flat racing was with Lady Byron, an unexpected winner of the Hundred Guinea sweepstakes at Newmarket in 1818. Lady Byron was later kept as a brood mare with several distinguished steeplechasers as her progeny. William Vevers greatest success was at Liverpool in 1841 when he won the predecessor to the Grand National on a horse called Charity.

The *Hereford Journal* regularly advertised the services of his stallions in covering the local mares. In 1813 it was Young Rattler, a steeplechaser, who performed this function. In 1827 it was the beautiful prize-winning grey carthorse Noble, almost 16 hands high, and in the 1830s it was Tom Brown, a steeplechaser, and Brown Stout, a prize-winning brown carthorse.

Following Mr William Vevers' death in 1858, Dormington Court was tenanted by his widow, Elizabeth, and their unmarried eldest son, Thomas Vevers. They do not appear to have continued the interest in breeding horses and Dormington Court reverted to being the normal mixed farm of the period. They certainly grew hops as Thomas Vevers advertised some excess cuttings in the *Hereford Journal.*

Yet another bankruptcy

Following Thomas Vevers' death in 1874, Dormington Court was let to Henry Scott Hall, whose parents farmed at Garford Farm, Yarkhill. From 1886 Henry Hall increased the acreage of hops at Dormington Court from 32 acres to a staggering 83 acres. Hops, though often profitable, were always expensive in capital and risky. In bad years the harvest could be negligible. An increase of this size required heavy capital investment. There was the inevitable investment in new wiring for the new hop yards, as well as the cost of labour, fertilisers for growing and harvesting, and the very significant cost of fuel for drying. Even more importantly, such a remarkable expansion required new hop kilns and other buildings for drying the hops. Few farmers would have dreamed of investing such huge sums. Henry Hall seems to have done so partly through using his wife's money and partly through borrowing. In 1903 he was declared bankrupt. At his bankruptcy hearing he stated that he relied on the hope "of good seasons and good prices".

Dormington Court was then let to Mr G. H. Bray who seems to have retained a high percentage of hops. In the great Foley sale catalogue of 1919, Dormington Court with its 141 acres was let for £351 to Mr G. H. Bray and was specifically described as a hop farm, containing not only the hop kilns but quarters for hop pickers.

Mr G. H. Bray purchased Dormington Court. He came from a family long distinguished for the breeding of Herford cattle at a number of farms in East Herefordshire and had himself started breeding cattle in 1908. Since Dormington Court was largely given up to hops he also purchased Priors Court, Dormington for his cattle. He was President of the Hereford Herd Book Society in 1931.

Dormington Court in the Second World War

At the time of the Second World War, Dormington Court was owned and farmed by Mr Beale, which seems to have been a misspelling for Mr G. H. Bray. The National Farm Survey of 1941–1943 showed that the farm comprised 133 acres. The fences, ditches and field drainage were all in a good state of repair as was the house, though the five cottages attached to the farm were designated as only 'fair'. There was private electricity for lighting only. No fewer than 75 acres were under hops with a further 10 acres in orchards. The capacity to plough up for cereals was limited as much of the land not under hops was liable to flood. However three acres had been ploughed up for oats for the 1940 harvest.

Hops were highly labour-intensive, consequently Dormington Court was employing 34 full-time workers and one casual worker. With such a high proportion under hops the farm kept very few livestock. There was a herd of 10 cattle. (This may have been a new venture as eight of these were heifers in calf with only one cow in milk and one bull.) There was a modest flock of 50 poultry and seven pigs but no sheep; the farm did have a tractor but made most use of horses. There were four farm horses together with one unbroken filly.

Throughout the Second World War Mr G. H. Bray served as Chairman of the War Agricultural Executive Committee. According to Heath-Agnew "much of the success of the war effort within the county could be attributed to his firmness and the fairness with which he interpreted the directives from Whitehall" [13].

Dormington Court after the Second World War

The history of Dormington Court from 1945–1986 certainly justifies its description as a major hop producer. Mr G. H. Bray retired in 1949. Soon after the Second World War there was a worldwide shortage of hops and Dormington Court, along with two other East Herefordshire farms (Aldersend Farm, Tarrington and Pomona Farm, Weston Beggard) were purchased by the brewery, Tetley's (later Tetley Walker and then Allied Breweries). Dormington Court was run by a bailiff until 1967 when the Davieses of Claston Farm were asked to take over the running of all three farms. This was a big undertaking as by that time between them they had 300 acres under hops. When Allied Breweries decided to sell Dormington Court with 150 acres of good land, much of it down to hops, in 1986, Peter Davies purchased it and the land formed part of the expanded Claston Farm throughout the remaining 20th century. Peter Davies subsequently sold off the hop kilns, such a feature of Dormington Court, and the farm cottages. With his typical concern for the local community, Peter Davies made sure that the cottages were offered first to those working at Dormington Court.

STOKE EDITH PARISH

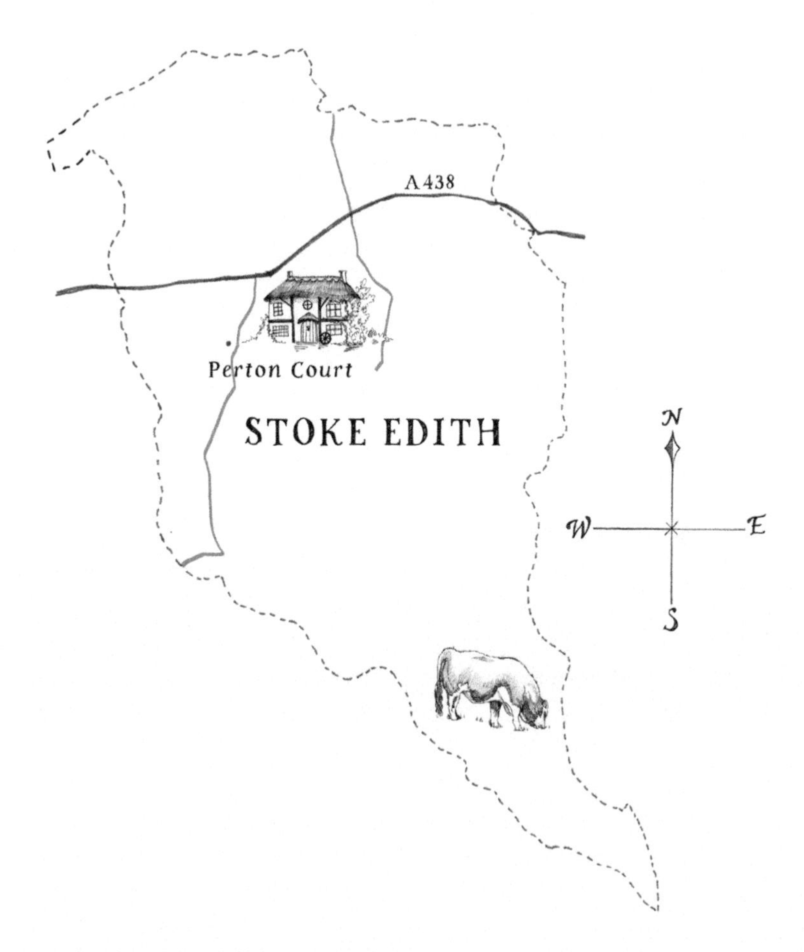

The parish of Stoke Edith lies around the A 438 Hereford to Ledbury road some six miles from Hereford. The extreme south part of the parish lies on the slopes of the Woolhope Dome with its ancient Silurian limestone soils and the remnants of limestone quarries, and is heavily wooded.

Stoke Edith is important as the residence of the Foley family, the principal landowners from the late 17th century onwards until early 1920 in five of the parishes considered here (Stoke Edith itself, Weston Beggard, Yarkhill, Dormington and Tarrington) and with some significant landholdings also in Woolhope. Stoke Edith

House, built in the late 17th century, was renowned for its superb Sir James Thornhill murals and ceilings. Sadly it was burnt down in 1927. The grounds were landscaped by Humphry Repton in 1792 and the gardens were renowned in the 19th century, though they are now largely decayed.

Following the Local Government Board orders of 1884 and 1885, outlying landholdings, possibly denoting medieval manors, which had been previously attached to Stoke Edith but actually located in other parishes, were redesignated in 1886 as being part of these other parishes. (Showle Court was moved to Yarkhill and Freetown to Ashperton.) Consequently the acreage at Stoke Edith parish dropped from 2,852 in 1851 with a population of 336 to 1,014 acres and a population of 171 in 1891. As much of the acreage was given up to the Stoke Edith parkland there were only a few farms, of which the largest was Perton Court. Until at least the Second World War many of the inhabitants of Stoke Edith were employed on the estate. Despite the great Foley sale of 1919/1920, the Foley family retains agricultural land and the former rectory of Stoke Edith, renamed Stoke Edith House, in addition to exceptionally well maintained woodlands which host an esteemed game shooting enterprise.

Stoke Edith at the time of the Norman Conquest, was possibly owned by Edith, the remarkable wife of Edward the Confessor. Despite being the sister of Harold she maintained her estates following the Norman Conquest and was reputed to be the richest woman in England at the time of the Domesday Book. William the Conqueror himself arranged her ceremonial funeral and interment beside her husband in Westminster Abbey in December 1075.

In the latter Middle Ages Stoke Edith was owned by the Walwyn family. In the 16th and 17th centuries Stoke Edith, together with the core of the Stoke Edith landholdings in the neighbouring parishes, was owned by the Lingen family. Sir Henry Lingen, a distinguished royalist in the Civil War with all that that implied in financial ruin, died in 1662 and his son and heir also died young. His financially constrained widow was compelled to sell the estate in 1670 to Sir Thomas Foley, a wealthy ironmaster who settled it on his son, Paul, later Speaker of the House of Commons. As indicated in the sections on Yarkhill, Dormington and Tarrington parishes, the Foley family purchased significant additional land in the 18th century from the Bodenham family of Rotherwas, and also from the creditors of Mr Shepheard Wallwyn of Dormington.

There were six entries in the National Farm Survey of 1941–1943 and seven entries in the annual Agricultural Census of June 1941.[14]

Perton Court

Fig. SE1 Perton Court in 2017

> ***House***, N. of the cross-roads at Perton, 800 yards W.S.W. of the church, is of L-shaped plan with the wings extending towards the E. and S.[15]

In the first three decades of the 20th century Perton Court was renowned for its prize-winning Hereford cattle which included the title Perton as a prefix. From around 1930 until sometime after the Second World War, the tenant farmer at Perton Court was Mr Owen Meredith. In the 1970s the Perton Court hopyards were farmed by the Foley estate and in the 1980s the house and farm buildings were sold as private residences.

History of Perton Court

Perton is a hamlet in the home parish for the Stoke Edith estate and it seems probable that Perton Court was part of the original Stoke Edith estate even in the 17th century. It is likely that the present Perton Court replaced the farmhouse which lies just at the entrance to the drive and is now called Perton Croft. Perton Croft was described as containing the remains of three mediaeval crutch-trusses in An Inventory of the Historical Monuments in Herefordshire.

Fig. SE2 Perton Croft probably original Perton Court farmhouse

Cheese production important in the early 19th century

Little is known about the farmers of Perton Court until the late 18th century when Jonathan Sirrell, the brother of Thomas Sirrell of Eastwood Farm, Tarrington was the tenant. Unusually for Herefordshire which is known as a beef county, dairying was an important activity at Perton Court at this time. Jonathan died in October 1832. The sale of his farm effects which was advertised in the *Hereford Journal* of 27 February 1833 included:

> *a quantity of very capital cheese, several glitches of prime home-cured bacon; an excellent assortment of dairy requisites, comprising three very capital milk leads, cheese presses, 2 churns, salting stone and frame, cheese-cowl, and curd-machine, cheese-vats, and numerous other articles.*

Cider was also important as the sale included five hogsheads of cider and two empty hogsheads.

John Badham 1833–1864: a farmer of the 'high farming' tradition

From 1833 until his death in 1864 John Badham was the farmer at Perton Court and his changing circumstances are revealed in the census records. In 1841 he and his wife, Sarah, had four young children, all boys. No fewer than four farmworkers were living in. In 1851 John Badham was recorded as farming 175 acres and employing four men. This seems quite a small number of farmworkers for the acreage but by this time Mr Badham's two elder sons were of an age to help – John was 19 and Thomas 15. There were now four younger sons varying in age from 10 to a few months, all of whom had been born at Stoke Edith. Only two of the farmworkers were living in. In 1861 John was assisted by two of his other sons, Richard aged 23 and Charles 17, and there were three farmworkers living in: William Cyril, a groom aged 23; John Adams, a carter of 21 and Andrew Pelham a carter's boy of 13.

Despite his age – he had been born around 1791 – John Badham was considered a progressive modern farmer and he received the first prize for the smaller farms at one of the Stoke Edith annual inspections. After his death Perton Court was farmed by his widow, Sarah, their son, Richard, and a bailiff. In 1871 Sarah was employing nine men and a boy. Sarah's niece was also living as part of the household.

By 1881 the Badham family had left. The census of that year shows the tenant to be Albert Watson. Unusually, he was not a local man having been born in Hampshire. The acreage attached to Perton Court had been greatly enlarged to 280 acres. His wife, Eliza, came from Yarkhill and it may be for this reason that they were given the tenancy by the Stoke Edith estate. They took over the tenancy at a difficult time for agriculture.

Henry James Dent a distinguished breeder of Hereford cattle

By 1901 the census shows that Henry James Dent aged 25 had already taken over the tenancy. Henry Dent was a most distinguished breeder of Hereford cattle as well as a hop grower. As early as 1907 he received first prize at the Royal Agricultural Society meeting of 1907 for the best Hereford bull born in 1905. He continued to win important prizes. In 1914 no fewer than two of his bulls won prestigious awards. His bull Perton Loyalist was both First and Senior Champion at the Hereford and Worcester Agricultural Society meeting of 1914.

His other bull Perton Grateful was both first in his class at the Hereford and Worcester Agricultural Society meeting and at the prestigious Royal Agricultural Society of England Show.

Like the other large tenanted farms belonging to the Foley estate, Perton Court was put up for sale by Paul Foley in December 1919. At this time it was 186 acres. Hops

Fig. SE3 Perton Loyalist[16]

were obviously important as there were no fewer than four hop kilns amongst the many farm buildings specified. The ownership as the result of the sale is not known but Henry Dent continued as a tenant farmer.

He remained a remarkably successful breeder and at the Cambridge Royal Agricultural Show in 1922 his young bull Perton Defence received second prize in the best yearling category. However this was the year when prices of pedigree cattle started to fall. At the 1929 Royal Agricultural Show his cow Lively 57 by Percentage was judged Reserve Female Champion. In the same year though, possibly a victim of the times, overcome perhaps by the deep depression in agriculture as well as his own personal difficulties (his wife Christiana had been a victim of the Spanish flu), Henry James Dent died of a self-inflicted gunshot wound. He did not live to see the triumph of his bull Pertonlute, a six-month-old calf at the time of his death, which later became both Junior Champion and Reserve Champion for both the Three Counties and Royal Agricultural Shows of 1930.

The tenancy of Perton Court was given up but not the Dent family's remarkable contribution to the breeding of Hereford cattle. Henry James Dent's younger son, Henry Cooke Dent, only 19 at the time of his father's death, spent some years in

Fig. SE4 Perton Grateful[16]

Australia at John Morrisey Ltd of Harbin Valley, well-known Australian breeders of Herefords. He later became a distinguished adviser on Hereford cattle as well as a breeder of the Perton line at Eastwood Farm, Tarrington and later in Tenbury Wells before returning with his Australian wife to Australia. Henry James' elder son, Oscar William Robert Dent, the father of John Dent of Withington Court, joined the major British company of ICI and was killed in the Normandy campaign in 1944. His son, and so a grandson of Henry James Dent, John Dent, together with his wife, Elizabeth, in their turn became successful breeders of both Hereford cattle and Ryeland sheep in the latter 20th century at Withington Court.

Mr Owen Meredith became the tenant farmer at Perton Court from 1930 until well after the Second World War.

Perton Court in the Second World War

In 1941 Perton Court with 219½ acres was farmed by Mr Owen Meredith. Cooke and Arkwright were land agents for the owner whose identity was not specified. There was no electricity supply. It was a hop farm and although Mr Meredith was considered a good dairy farmer, he had little experience of arable so was given a B grading. There were 64 cattle and 135 sheep of which 71 were lambs about to be sold. Mr Meredith was employing five men and six women and girls. They were 85 poultry but no pigs. There were six farm horses, two of which were as yet unbroken. The fences, ditches and drainage were all only in a fair condition, but the three cottages were in a good state. There were 14 acres of hops and 10 acres of orchards. For the 1940 wartime harvest Mr Meredith had planted five acres of peas and roots, and just over six and a half acres of oats. For the 1941 harvest he had planted just over nine and a half acres of oats. He had one 20-horsepower Fordson tractor and was paying £404 rent.

Perton Court after the Second World War

Perton Court continued to be farmed by Mr Owen Meredith for a number of years after the Second World War. From the last quarter of the 20th century the land has been farmed as part of the Foley estate.

TARRINGTON PARISH

Situated as it is some 10 miles from Hereford either side of the old Hereford to Ledbury 18th-century toll road, Tarrington has always been a significant parish. This is especially true as it is at the centre of the important Foley estate, the largest landowners in East Herefordshire until 1920, Stoke Edith House being a mere mile away. The parish contains a number of large houses including, in the 19th and early 20th centuries, the home of the land agent for the Foley estate and other important local people, such as the doctor. The parish also provided services to the surrounding area, consequently Tarrington was the home of a wheelwright, blacksmith and mason, as well as a baker, a general store and that important inn, called the New Inn in the 18th century, then renamed the Foley Arms and now called the Tarrington Arms. The parish boundaries have changed somewhat over time but throughout most of the time reviewed here the parish has remained around the same size: 2,224 acres from before 1841 until the changes of 1886 when it became 2,236, gaining a mere 12 acres. Boundaries since the Second World War have again moved slightly so that Freetown farmhouse described under Ashperton parish is now just in Tarrington parish.

The population according to the 1851 census was 534. It changed relatively little between 1841–1871 but declined to 500 in 1881 and reached a low of 456 in 1891 before recovering to 472 in 1911. There was a further fall in the period between the two World Wars, with a recorded population of 417 in 1931. A further fall in the latter part of the 20th century was reversed by 2001 and the 2011 population was 576. As elsewhere in East Herefordshire the 21st-century population of Tarrington is radically different from the population that lived here at least up to the Second World War. Up to that time most people would be working locally, principally in agriculture or agricultural services, and many would have left school at 14. Until the First World War the proportion of children would have been much higher. Now Tarrington attracts professionals often working elsewhere.

At the time of the Norman Conquest Tarrington was given to Ansfrid de Cormeilles. It then passed through the female line to John le Brun. The heirs to this part of the le Brun estate were the De la Barres. In the late 17th century ownership in the parish of Tarrington itself was mainly divided between the Lingen family of Stoke Edith and the Bodenham family of Rotherwas. Thomas Foley purchased all the Lingen property in 1670 but the Bodenham family remained Lords of the manor owning land until somewhat later. However by the mid-18th century the Foley estate was the principal landowner although the Hopton estate owned some land, including Little Tarrington Farm.[17]

The parish played an important role in the development of Hereford cattle. William Griffiths of the large farm of Aldersend was a distinguished breeder of Hereford cattle in the late 19th and early 20th century whose dispersal sale in 1920 raised a record £49,381. His stock and general support helped Percy Bradstock to build up the Bradstock herd at Garford Farm, Yarkhill and then at Freetown, Ashperton.[18] William Griffith's son, H. R. Griffiths continued his father's success with his own herd at Little Tarrington Farm in the interwar and immediate post-Second World War periods.

There were 18 holdings of five or more acres included in the 1941–1943 National Farm Survey[19], a number not very different from that recorded for the population census of 1851 which included acreage of the farms. The two farms over 200 acres were the 412-acre Aldersend Farm, by then mainly a hop farm and owned by Peter Walker and Co. Brewers, and the 263-acre Little Tarrington Farm, owned as well as farmed by Mr H. R. Griffiths. There were a further five farms of over 100 acres.

At the time of publication very few of these farms remain and those that continue, such as Aldersend and Little Tarrington Farm, are much larger. Described below are Eastwood Farm and Hazel Court, both of which ceased to be active farms around the turn of the 21st century.

Eastwood Farm

Fig. T1 Eastwood Farm and converted buildings, including a former hop kiln 2017

> ***Eastwood Farm***, house, about 1 m. E.S.E. of the church, has been lengthened at the N. end.[20]

The modest mention Eastwood Farm merits in *An Inventory of the Historical Monuments of Herefordshire* shows that at least part of the farm must date back to the 17th century as only 17th-century buildings were listed.

Eastwood Farm conceals its historic importance. The hop kiln and farm buildings of this farm, converted for high quality residential use at the turn of the 21st century, lie barely visible and close to the A 438 on an especially dangerous bend. Unusually throughout nearly all its history, whereas most farms belonged to large landowners, Eastwood Farm was at least partly a yeoman farm and was farmed by one farming family, the Godsalls, from the late 18th century until it ceased to be a farm at the end of the 20th century. Consequently it was associated with generation upon generation of this family. The only interregnum was between 1935–1943 when it was rented from Ernest Godsall, the then owner, by Mr H. C. Dent, a distinguished breeder of Hereford pedigree cattle. Like most other of the larger Herefordshire farms it was a hop farm from early times.

History of Eastwood Farm

Eastwood farm in the 18th and 19th centuries

The land tax records of 1792 show Eastwood Farm to be occupied by Elizabeth Godsall. The acreage was quite modest, probably well under hundred acres, as she was paying £3 in land tax. She was said to be the tenant of Lord Foley. By the time of the Tithe Map of 1841 though, Thomas Godsall (1779–1855) was listed as both occupier and owner of 144 acres of land at Eastwood Farm. Thomas was the son of William Godsall of Ashperton by his second wife. He was a hop grower and so subject to an extra tithe charge for six acres of hops. Orchards seem to have been important for Eastwood at this time with 26 acres described as orchards, of which 11 acres were classified as meadow orchard, 11 as arable orchard and four simply as young orchard. In 1851 Thomas was farming 155 acres with the aid of 10 men and three boys. His son, Thomas, was listed as farmer's son. As was common at this time, three of the labourers were living with the household: a wagoner, a cowman and a wagoner's boy.

Thomas died in December 1856. The *Hereford Journal*'s report on his funeral at Tarrington church stated that he was known for his kindness to family, friends and the poor as well as for his "strict integrity, industry and honesty". Significantly among the congregation were old servants who had been in Thomas Godsall's employ for up to 40 years and many of the poor.

Thomas Godsall was succeeded by his son, Thomas William Godsall (1827–1873). In the 1861 census Thomas William is recorded as farming 150 acres with the help of three men and two boys. The 1871 census lists Thomas William, his wife, Elizabeth, and their four small children: Thomas 12, Lizzie 10, Sophie six and Ernest four, and shows that he was farming only 90 acres with the aid of two living-in farmworkers: Frederick Nicolas, a cowman and the farmer's boy, James Thomas. In 1871 all agricultural land in England was listed and the records for Herefordshire show Thomas Godsall of Tarrington owning 99 acres and his brother, William, 46 acres. It may have been that Thomas's brother owned part of Eastwood Farm at this time and that Thomas was already ill. He died two years later in 1873.

Type of farming

In the absence of farm records, the type of farming at Eastwood has to be deduced. The Godsalls were competent farmers. In 1857 Thomas William Godsall received the prize for the best small farm at Lady Emily Foley's Annual Farm Inspection (see Chapter 3). Despite their capability, the Godsalls did not show quite the same interest in the new agricultural societies as some of their neighbours. They do not appear as prize winners for instance at the Ledbury Agricultural Show, which first took place in 1842. They did not breed pedigree Hereford cattle as was fashionable at the peak time of 'high farming'. Their cattle and sheep were bred commercially for their meat. The only evidence of the quality of their stock are references to the excellent carcass which Eastwood had provided for a Christmas Market in Hereford and the fact that in December 1863 Mr John Taylor of Tarrington's display of meat included "four excellent wether sheep fed by Mr Thomas Godsall".

Only more dramatic events referring to Eastwood appear in the *Hereford Journal* or *Hereford Times*. Two burglaries are mentioned. The first of these was in the 1840s and, if it shows anything, it indicates the extent of rural poverty. The dairy was broken into and a certain amount of food was stolen, including, rather amusingly, the pasty which had been specially prepared for Thomas Godsall. The perpetrators were clearly just hungry. A more commercial burglary took place in 1850, when some guns and valuables were taken. A reward was offered, but there are no records as to whether it was taken up. The most sensational event recorded was a major fire in 1863 which affected the barn. Fortunately, or rather providently, Thomas Godsall the younger was insured, but this only covered the buildings and not the contents which must have been expensive.

When Thomas William died in November 1873, his widow, Elizabeth, was left with the young children and the farm to cope with. The daughter of a butcher from the neighbouring parish of Ashperton but only a few hundred yards from Eastwood, Elizabeth (née Taylor) seems to have been a remarkably resourceful farmer in her own right. Despite the fact that these were difficult times for farming, Elizabeth was to continue as the owner and farmer at Eastwood until after 1901. In 1881 she was farming 96 acres. Her eldest son, Thomas, was at home and no doubt able to be of assistance. The youngest though, Ernest, was away at boarding school and this would need to have been paid for. There were three live-in farmworkers: Septimus Bevan aged 20 the wagoner, Francis Preece aged 12 the wagoner's boy and Edgar Preece aged eight described as a scholar. In the *Kelly's Directory* of 1891 Elizabeth was listed as a farmer and hop grower. Later in the 1890s Elizabeth took over Hazel Court land, which was probably around 40 acres at that time. Only around 1903, when her youngest son, Ernest, was aged around 35 and got married, did she finally retire to a house in Tarrington village.

Eastwood farm in the 20th century

Thomas and Elizabeth's youngest son, Ernest Godsall and his wife took over the farm in 1903. When Ernest retired in 1933 there was a farm sale of some cattle, sheep and three farm horses. Presumably the farm equipment and other farm animals had been disposed of privately. From 1935 Eastwood was rented by Mr H. C. Dent, the younger son of the late Mr H. J. Dent of Perton Court.

Mr H. C. Dent was a very different type of farmer from the Godsalls. Henry Dent brought with him some of the Perton line of pedigree Hereford cattle pioneered by his father and like his father became a successful breeder. His bull Perton Rear Admiral won first prize at the Agricultural Show in Liverpool in July 1939 in the class for bulls born before September 1937. Dramatically Perton Rear Admiral was then engaged in a bullfight with a less successful rival Grange Amilute (see Chapter 4). Henry, like his father, also bred Ryeland sheep and the Dent Perpetual Cup, a gift of H. C. Dent, is still awarded to the Breed Champion at the Three Counties Show.

Eastwood Farm in the Second World War

The National Farm Survey of 1941–1943 and Agricultural Census of June 1941 show Mr H. C. Dent as renting Eastwood with its 167 acres of heavy soil. There were 38 acres of orchards and 11 statute acres of hops. Unusually, there were four and a half acres under soft fruit. Of his herd of 45 pedigree cattle, 13 were bull calves being reared for service. He had a modest flock of 51 sheep of which only 14 were lambs. There were six breeding pigs, 10 piglets of five months or under and only 22 poultry. There were three cottages and the fences, ditches and drainage were only in a fair state of repair. There was no electricity. For the 1940 harvest five acres of grassland had been ploughed up for barley. The return records a response for the 1941 harvest when an additional six and one third acres of barley together with just under two acres of approved crops and a further four and a half acres of approved crops was stated to have been ploughed up for the 1941 harvest. Mr Dent, still only 30 at this time, seemed keen on tractors. He had no fewer than six, a record for the East Herefordshire farms described here: one 20-horsepower International, two Fordsons and three Austins. He had three farm horses. He was also renting Sheepcote land in Lugwardine and land from the Stoke Edith estate. He gave up farming Eastwood in 1943 and moved to Tenbury Wells. He married an Australian and eventually moved to Australia.

Eastwood Farm after the Second World War

Throughout the last half of the 20th century Eastwood was farmed by two more generations of the Godsall family: Horace Godsall (1908–1990) and Horace's son, Geoff. From 1946–1956 the Davies family of Claston Farm, Dormington rented a hop yard at Eastwood.

Hazel Court

Fig. T2 Hazel Court showing the barns and house 2017

> *Hazel Court*, house, about 2 m. N.E. of the church, has cross-wings at the N.W. and S.E. ends. The timber-framing is in large squares.[21]

A short distance further along the A 438 towards Ledbury at an especially hazardous corner is an ancient lane leading westwards to Durlow Common and then on to three farms, all associated with the word 'Hazel': Hazel Farm, Hazel Court and Upper Hazel Farm. They are the remnants of a very ancient medieval manor of the Hazel. For many hundreds of years the lane continued up to Woolhope and was only closed after the Second World War.

These three farms are in an anomalous position on the border of three parishes; Putley, Tarrington and Woolhope. Throughout most of the 19th century they seem normally to have been included in Woolhope. However, after the reorganisation of parish boundaries in 1886, Putley Township, previously part of Woolhope, was mostly moved to Putley, which caused some confusion. For instance in the 1891 census two farms called Upper Hazle and two farms called Lower Hazle were listed in Woolhope. In contrast, in the 1901 census, Hazel Court was specified as an area to be covered in Woolhope parish but none of the 'Hazel' farms were in actual fact listed. Guesswork is sometimes required. In 1932, *An Inventory of the Historical Monuments in Herefordshire* included Hazel Court in the parish of Woolhope but Hazel Court has been included in the parish of Tarrington in this book as its land is largely within this parish.

Hazel Court's position on the margins of three parishes makes its history difficult to document, but there is no doubt that it is the antithesis of Eastwood Farm. Whereas Eastwood had always been the home of yeoman farmers and apart from a modest interregnum was lived in by one family for some 200 years, Hazel Court was built as an early 17th century manor house and was the residence of a member of the powerful local family of Ravenhill in the 18th century. Increasingly in the 19th century it became a marginal tenant farm with many changes in occupancy before coming to its own again in the 20th century as the much loved home and farm of three generations of the Williams family.

History of Hazel Court

At the beginning of the 18th century, Hazel Court was owned by the Ravenhill family, who also owned other farms in Putley and Woolhope. There is an interesting early reference to Hazel Court in 1704 in the records of the Hereford Cathedral when a Ravenhill of Hazel Court gave permission for a field to be flooded periodically during winter months. This was a practice of the time intended to increase fertility for that all-important hay crop but was normally associated with the more significant local rivers.

When Thomas Ravenhill died without direct descendants in 1748, he left Hazel Court to his brother William, and the household goods and farm equipment to William's son, Thomas, and to Thomas's sisters, Martha and Mary. The land tax records for the later years of the 18th century show Mr Ravenhill of Hazel Court, owner and occupier, was paying £2 land tax. The acreage was therefore relatively modest.

Towards the end of the 18th century, through inheritance, Hazel Court came into the ownership of the Gwillims of The Brainge, Putley Township, who were related to the Ravenhills. From this time onwards, Hazel Court was transformed into a modest small tenanted farm.

Hazel Court did not seem to have provided a good livelihood. To the extent that Hazel Court can be identified, the tenants changed every 10 years. The Woolhope Tithe Map of 1841 specifies John Barnes as the tenant farming 78 acres. In the 1851 census a widow, Jane Shayter, is listed as farming 85 acres and employing two men. In the 1861 census Hazel Court was actually named. The tenant was Mr James Sissum farming 40 acres and Mr Baggum, a farmer, was also resident. In 1871 Edwin Baggum was listed as the farmer and the acreage was back up to 86. By this time John Riley of Putley Court had purchased the Brainge and its land, including Hazel Court. In 1881 Hazel Court was probably lived in by James Dean, listed as farm bailiff. The other two farms in the Hazel complex were lived in by farm labourers. In 1891 it was probably lived in by Samuel Tuck, a farm bailiff, although James Williams, a farmer, could have been the tenant as both were listed as living at farms called The Hazle. Hazel Court land was farmed by Mrs Elizabeth Godsall of Eastwood Farm. The landownership records of 1910 show that Hazel Court was owned by John Riley's son, Lawrence Riley, of Putley Court. The acreage was given as 50 and the gross annual value as £60.

In 1920 Hazel Court, together with other smaller farms owned by the Rileys of Putley Court was put up for sale, but it is not clear whether it was sold at this time. Sidney Archer Williams and his wife purchased Hazel Court on their marriage in 1930, taking up residence at the height of the agricultural recession. It says a great deal for the resourcefulness of this family that they were to stay there right the way through the 1930s and witness the better times for agriculture, both through the critical wartime period and the more supportive agricultural regime of the 1950s and early 1960s.

Hazel Court in the Second World War

The National Farm Survey of 1941–1943 shows Hazel Court to have 56 acres of which 49 were under permanent or temporary grass. The soil is described as light, 50% of naturally fair quality and 50% poor. The farm roads, ditches, fences and drainage were all in a good state of repair. There were no cottages. There was well water to the farmhouse, but only roof water to the farm buildings and no electricity. The Williamses had ploughed up four acres of grassland for oats for the 1940 harvest, but no additional land had been ploughed up for the 1941 harvest. The Williams had one six-horsepower petrol engine but no tractor. The annual rental value was estimated at £35. They had 15 cattle of which 10 were cows or heifers in milk or in calf. There was a flock of 53 sheep of which 20 were lambs and there were three piglets between two and five months old. There were 331 poultry, a fairly large number for this time. There were three farm horses of which one was an unbroken colt.

Hazel Court after the Second World War

Sidney Archer Williams and his wife and continued to farm Hazel Court until 1962 when they retired in favour of their son, Dennis, and his wife, Gwyneth, who had married in that year.

Fig. T3 Hazel Court looking towards Ashperton and Yarkhill [22]

It was a supremely peaceful and happy time. Hazel Court, with its wonderful scenery and tranquil position was a mixed farm of around 80 acres. Until the end of the 1970s, the Williams kept a modest milking herd but then switched to suckling beef cattle because of the problems with dairying. They also had a flock of sheep with an annual crop of lambs and produced wheat, swedes and potatoes for sale, as well as kale and oats for the livestock. With its light soil, Hazel Court produced exceptional quality swedes and potatoes, and the swedes were sometimes given as presents to the Williams's farming friends, the Bradstocks at Freetown.

Fig. T4 Hazel Court Friesen cows [22]

Sadly Dennis died young. Gwyneth and their son, Mark, continued to farm for another eight years. On their retirement in 1997 Hazel Court was sold and for a number of years became an equestrian establishment standing in its own 50 acres of land before being resold in 2011.

ASHPERTON PARISH

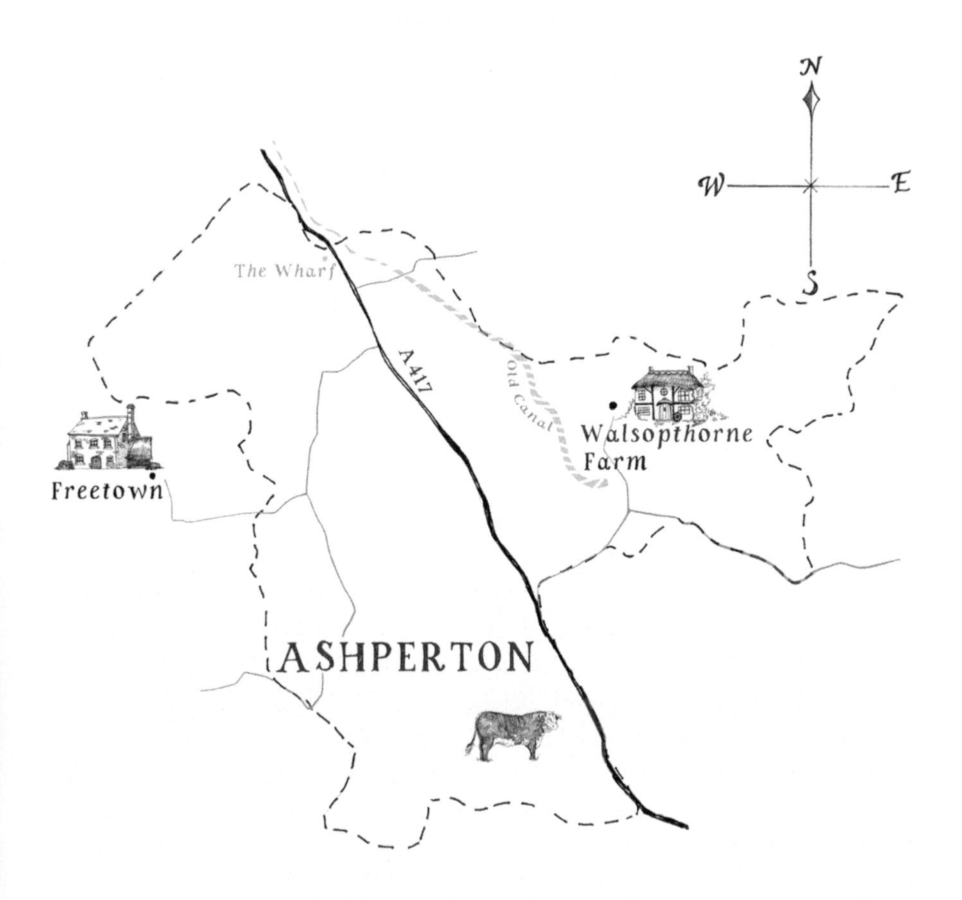

Even by the standards of Herefordshire the parish of Ashperton is unusually scattered. The parish boundaries have been changed somewhat over the years, but with little difference to the overall area. From the 1850s to 1886 the total area was 1,741 acres. In the radical nationwide change of 1886 Ashperton lost part of the Ashperton land from Monksbury Court to Yarkhill parish and Freetown was moved into Ashperton from its anomalous position in Stoke Edith parish some three miles away. As a result, the total area fell slightly to 1,692 acres and remains at this approximate level. However a change in boundaries in the latter half of the 20th century moved Freetown farmhouse into the parish of Tarrington.

The population in the census of 1841 was distorted by navvies working on the Ledbury–Hereford branch of the Gloucester to Hereford canal. The population in 1851 was 517 and remained approximately at this level until the 1870s. Between 1871 and 1881 the population fell from 492 to 409. In the last decades of the 19th century it fell again, although the exact fall cannot be assessed because of the boundary change. Under the new boundaries the population was 362 in 1891 and 344 in 1911. By 1931 it had fallen to 290. In 2011 the population was 211.

As elsewhere in East Herefordshire the modern population of the parish differs radically from its former population. Until the First World War the proportion of children under 14 was much higher throughout the country. Until after the Second World War the farms were dependent on local farmworkers and most households had some relationship with farming. Now relatively few households have any connection with farming and there is a high predominance of professional groups.

Land in Ashperton was distributed to a number of the followers of William the Conqueror with no fewer than four separate landholdings recorded in the Domesday Book. It is possible that it covered a wider area than the Ashperton parish of the 18th to 21st centuries – especially since Walsopthorne Manor was a separate parish in 1066.

An Inventory of the Historical Monuments in Herefordshire of 1932 identifies an unusually large number of buildings dating partially to the 17th century. In addition to the farms of Walsopthorne and Freetown described below, Moorend was given a special entry. The report also makes reference to 17th-century features in Lower Town Farm, Roakes, Tuston Farm, Wood End and Lower Poppinger.

The Hopton family of Canon Frome were the main landowners until 1886. Freetown, previously (and anamolously) recorded under Stoke Edith parish, was transferred under the national boundary changes of 1886 to Ashperton parish. Consequently, from this date until early 1920 the Foley family is also recorded as a significant landowner here.

There were 10 returns for the 1941–1943 National Farm Survey[23]. Only Freetown and Walsopthorne Farm were over 200 acres but there were four farms of over 100 acres: Lower Town Farm (115 acres), Moorend (119 acres), Pridewood (166 acres), Tuston Farm (105 acres). Hasnett Farm was 95 acres and there were three smallholdings Blacklands (20 acres), the Farm (18.5) acres and Wood End (11 acres). Only Freetown, Pridewood and the smallholding of Wood End were owner-occupied. The remainder were owned by the Canon Frome estate. All the seven larger farms grew hops but the acreage varied greatly. Pridewood had a surprising 78 acres under hops, Freetown 29, but none of the rest had more than 10 acres.

The annual Agricultural Census of 1941 was filled in by 20 holdings indicating that a maximum of further 10 holdings with under five acres were engaged in some limited farming activities.

Freetown

Fig. AS1 Freetown from the south [24]

Freetown, house, outbuilding and moat, 1¼ m. W.N.W. of the church. The House is of two storeys, with cellars and attics; the walls are timber-framed and partly of brick and the roofs are tiled. It was built early in the 17th century on an L-shaped plan, with the wings extending towards the N. and W. A rather later wing to the E. makes the present plan Z-shaped. Early in the 18th century the existing top storey was added. The S. front has been refaced but the timber-framing is exposed on the other sides. Inside the building are some exposed ceiling-beams and in the attics are four early 18th-century roof-trusses with braced collar-beams and various carpenters' marks.

The Outbuilding, S.E. of the house, has seven bays of timber-framing of the 17th century.

The Moat formerly surrounded the house but is now fragmentary. There are remains of an outer enclosure on the N.[25]

Freetown dates back to at least the 17th century and is probably on the site of a significant medieval manor. From at least 1700 until early 1920 it was owned by the Stoke Edith estate of the Foley family. Curiously, until the reorganisation of parishes in 1886, it was attached to Stoke Edith parish, itself a good three miles away, rather than to Ashperton. This anomaly could well be a further indication of an important distant past. For most of the 20th century the farm was attached to Ashperton parish, although it is now part of Tarrington parish.

Freetown is owned by Richard Bradstock and his wife, Margaret (née Davies), both of whom come from long-established East Hereford farming families. Freetown is world-famous for its pedigree Hereford cattle, identified by the prefix Free Town. Like other large farms owned by the Stoke Edith estate in the parishes of Dormington, Tarrington, Stoke Edith, Woolhope and Yarkhill, Freetown was sold in a major estate disposal in 1919/1920 and since that time has been owned by the Bradstock family.

History of Freetown

From at least the second half of the 18th century until 1846 Freetown was farmed by the Sirrell family. Samuel Sirrell died at Freetown in 1786 at the age of 48. He had married an Ann Elliott of Blakemere and the couple had had a large family of nine children. In his will Samuel Sirrell gave considerable responsibility to his wife, including the means of raising £100 for each of his children when they reached maturity, a more important role than one might expect for women of the period.

Samuel Sirrell was succeeded at Freetown by one of his sons, Thomas Sirrell, who remained there until his death in 1846. Little is known about the nature of the farming at Freetown at this time, but the old hop kiln may well date back as far as the 1830s and certainly hops were produced well before the Tithe Map of 1840 as indicated by the field names designating old hop yards. The land tax of £14 per year indicates that the farm was certainly a large one, probably of the order of 250 acres. The only reference to Thomas Sirrell in the newspapers of the period is when the *Hereford Times* of 25 November 1837 included an announcement of the death of "Thomas Hall who faithfully and ably performed the duties of wagoner during a period of 44 years effectually preserving from loss or injury the valuable property of his master".

Following Thomas Sirrell's death the tenancy of this important farm was taken over by Thomas Pitt, the brother of Stephen Pitt of Walsopthorne Farm (see below) and a member of an important farming family of the period. Thomas and Stephen's parents were longtime tenant farmers of White House Farm, Canon Frome, owned by the Hopton estate.

The Stoke Edith estate was very particular in selecting tenants of their valuable farms. Thomas would quite probably have been especially recommended by the Hoptons and he seems to have justified the confidence placed in him during this period of 'high farming'. The census records of 1851 show that Thomas Pitt was 34 and married to Mary Kate aged 35 with one son, John, aged three. Thomas was farming 248 acres with the aid of six men, two boys and three women. In addition to two female servants, two farm servants also lived in – Henry Garbutt, waggoner, and Henry Jones, cowman, both aged 21. In 1854 the prize for the best maintained large farm following the Annual Farm Inspection instituted by Lady Emily Foley (see Chapter 3) was awarded to Thomas Pitt. In 1855 he entertained the cavalcade of the Stoke Edith estate tenants who spent the whole of the final day of the three-day inspection visiting each estate farm and was warmly thanked, although there is no comment about the role of his wife in this entertainment.

By 1871 Thomas had retired to Bosbury and it was his son, John aged 23, who was listed as the tenant. John was already married to Elizabeth, also 23 and from Hartpury in Gloucestershire. In this and the next census, they were listed as employing approximately the same number of farmworkers as recorded in the 1861 census. The couple remained at Freetown for nearly 20 years but surprisingly in 1891 John was listed as retired and living in Hereford, although aged only 43. This was the time of the Great Agricultural Depression and it is possible that they could have been affected by it. However they seem to have adequate resources as he appears again in the census of 1901 living in the seaside town of Portishead, Somerset and died in 1931 at the ripe age of 83, Elizabeth having died a few years previously.

In contrast to the previous centuries Freetown was to see a rapid turnover of tenant farmers from the early 1890s, recalling of course the difficult farming of this time and also possibly reflecting the death of the kindly, if paternalistic, Lady Emily Foley on 1 January 1900. She was succeeded by her husband's nephew, Paul Foley, a very different character and one much more concerned with financial returns. In the 1901 census James Russell was the farmer, hop and fruit grower. The 1912 land valuation shows Jonathon Bishop as the tenant of Freetown, farming 263 acres from the Foley estate. The gross annual value of the farm was £224 and the rateable value £168.

Percy Bradstock, Richard Bradstock's grandfather, bought Freetown in the Stoke Edith estate sale of 1919/1920, moving from another Foley-owned farm, Garford Farm in Yarkhill, which was also sold at the same time. Freetown, with its approximate 350 acres, was a significantly larger farm than Garford Farm and had better access to water.

The famous Free Town pedigree herd of Herefords has a long history as Percy Bradstock brought his established pedigree herd with him. The pedigree line can be traced back to three other farms included in this book. When the young Percy Bradstock established the herd at Garford Farm in 1906 he took as the foundation for the line three cows from the herd of his relative, H. W. Taylor, who farmed at Showle Court. H. W. Taylor had inherited the herd from his father, William Taylor. His grandfather, also William Taylor, had purchased cattle from Mr Williams, the tenant of Thinghill Court in 1814.

No farm fully escaped the difficulties of the period between the First and Second World Wars. When Percy Bradstock took over Freetown his wife dearly hoped that they would not need to depend partly on hops with its heavy requirements of labour from the Midlands and South Wales during the hop-picking season and the dramas and work involved. For a while Freetown ceased to produce hops. However an outbreak of spontaneous abortion in the 1920s temporally affected the herd and Freetown had to return to hop production.

The Freetown stock from this time formed the basis for other important pedigree herds. For instance, the Honourable Mrs Deborah Rose's bull which was Reserve Champion for the Royal Agricultural Show at Newport in 1927 was Freetown Vincent. However, perhaps the most famous of all Freetown bulls of the 1930s was Free Town Admiral, three times Grand and the Senior Male Champion at the Royal Agricultural Society Shows of 1930, 1931 and 1932, and in 1933 Free Town Rear Admiral, by Free Town Admiral, was Grand and Junior Champion.

Fig. AS2 Free Town Admiral in the 1933 Hereford Herd Book

In 1938 Percy Bradstock was invited to be a judge at the Sydney Agricultural Show. His wife and son, Tom, accompanied him on this great excursion. It involved a seven-week journey there and back as well as the time in Australia. The invitation itself is indicative of the strong links that Freetown had with the Australian breeders. The whole visit had a lasting impression on Percy's son, Tom, aged around 18 at the time. It also shows the close contacts between the Herefordshire breeders of Hereford cattle. It was the Bradstock's neighbour Mr H. R. Griffiths of Little Tarrington Farm, himself a distinguished breeder, who looked after the valuable Free Town herd during their long absence.

Freetown in the Second World War

The National Farm Survey of 1941–1943 and the annual Agricultural Census of June 1941 show that out of the total 351 acres farmed by Percy Bradstock, some 42% was under permanent or temporary grass and a further 25 acres, 7% of the total, under clover in June 1941. Freetown had a much higher acreage of hops than most other hop farms at 29½ statute acres, just over 8% of the total. The acreage under orchards was also unusually high at 49½ acres or 14% of the total acreage of the farm. In order to satisfy the critical need to increase cereal production, Freetown had sown an additional 19 acres of approved crops for the 1940 and 1941 harvests. The ditches, drains and hedges were all in a good state and private electricity had been installed for both light and power. There were seven full-time male workers and a further four full-time women. In addition the farm drew on 10 part-time women. (This would have excluded hop pickers and those assisting with the apple harvest.) To house the agricultural workers, the farm had no fewer than six farm cottages. As a sign of the rather more difficult times, the farm, farm buildings and the farm cottages were only in a moderate rather than a good state of repair. There were 116 cattle, presumably all or nearly all pedigree Herefords. Unlike most other neighbouring farms Freetown did not have sheep and the two sows were probably for farm consumption. There were just under 100 poultry. Freetown did have one 17-horsepower tractor. Nevertheless it was the seven farm horses that played the major role in farm work.

During the Second World War all shows were cancelled. However at the Annual Spring Sale of Herefords in 1942 it was the Free Town bull, Free Town Aristocrat, which reached the highest price of £630.

Freetown after the Second World War

Freetown bred remarkable champions. In 1947 at the spring sale Freetown Ambassador was sold to Mrs Fraser of Westhide for an astonishing £2,205, and the bull went on to be Senior Champion at the Royal Agricultural Show at Lincoln of that year. The Grand Male Champion and Reserve Supreme Champion at the 1949 Royal Agricultural Show at Shrewsbury was Freetown Contrite.

Tom Bradstock, Percy's son, was the judge for Herefords at the Windsor Royal Show of 1954. In 1956 he was one of the two English representatives at the Second World Hereford Conference held in Buenos Aires. It was the export market that drove demand. In the 1950s and 1960s, when the Argentinians still demanded the highest grade Hereford pedigree bulls to improve their herds, some breathtaking prices were achieved.

After the entry of the United Kingdom into the Common Market in 1973, Europe became a significant purchaser. With the growth of artificial insemination, it was semen which was in highest demand, but the BSE crisis in the 1990s put an end for a considerable number of years to direct exports.

Although famous for its herd of pedigree Free Town Herefords, Freetown is a mixed farm growing wheat as a cash crop and producing cider apples. Until the dire years of the early 1990s, when the combination of bad prices and wilt pretty well destroyed the famous hop yards of East Herefordshire, Freetown was a major hop producer, but the old hop yards have now been replanted as cider orchards. Until the dreadful outbreak of foot-and-mouth in Herefordshire in 2001 the Bradstocks also kept a flock of sheep. In contrast with the number of people employed on the farm in the Second War this large and historically important farm now employs only two non-family workers.

Throughout the past century the Bradstocks have occupied important positions in the Hereford Cattle Society and Richard Bradstock is a former President as was his father, Tom, and grandfather, Percy, before him. The nature of demand for pedigree stock has changed radically since Percy Bradstock established his herd in 1906. The early 21st century has seen a considerable increase in demand for quality Hereford blood in British herds with supermarkets expanding their requirement for quality locally produced beef. There is a demand for pedigree Hereford cattle from both large farmers and also small hobby farmers. The pedigree herd of around 65 Hereford cattle continues to be a mainstay for Freetown and the feedstuffs for the Free Town herd are grown on the farm. Some of the most prestigious prizes open to Herefords are won by the Free Town herd. Their success continues with Richard's son, Tony, showing Free Town Decree who won the female and Grand Supreme Championship at the National Horned Hereford Show, Tenbury Wells in August 2017. Another Free Town heifer, Peace 29th, was second in class to Decree and Reserve Junior Female.

Fig. AS3 Free Town Decree 2017[26]

Walsopthorne Farm

Walsopthorne, house, barns and moat, ¾ m. N.E. of the church. The House is of two storeys with cellars and attics; the walls are timber-framed and the roofs are tiled. It was built c. 1600 on a half H-shaped plan, with the wings extending towards the S. The timber-framing is exposed except where the walls have been refaced in stone. The basement has stone walls and some original windows with stone mullions. On the N. front is an original window of eight lights with moulded frame, mullions and transom of oak. In the W. wall of the S.E. wing is an original doorway with a moulded frame, now blocked. Inside the building, several rooms have original moulded ceiling-beams and others have chamfered ceiling-beams; there are also some original doorways with stop-moulded frames. The roofs are of queen-post type."The Barns, N. of the house, adjoin one another and are of 17th-century timber-framing. The S. barn is of six bays.

The Moat, formerly surrounding the house, is fragmentary. There are traces of an outer enclosure to the N.E.[25]

Fig. AS4 Front of the early 17th-century farmhouse of Walshopthorne Farm

East Herefordshire is a treasury of remarkable farmhouses with long histories. Yet of all the historic farms discussed here surely Walsopthorne has perhaps the longest history and is one of the most outstanding, as reflected in the unusually extended comments on this remarkable survival in *An Inventory of the Historical Monuments in Herefordshire* in 1932.

Walsopthorne was already a parish in its own right in Anglo-Saxon times. Walsopthorne Farm is now farmed by Edward Davies and his son, Harvey, the grandson and great-grandson of Herbert Davies who moved to the farm from Beans Butts farm in Woolhope in 1920. The farm is around 250 acres, half the original manor and the same size as it has been since the late 17th century. A feature of the farm are the fine oak trees dating back at least 300 years and in a few cases, possibly to 500 years ago, when Walsopthorne was granted permission to develop a park. It still has cider orchards grown on contract for Bulmers and unusually, it has retained its hop yards. Rough shooting also provides a useful income. Until the beginning of the 21st century Walsopthorne retained its herd of Hereford cattle but Edward has reduced some activities as he approaches retirement.

History of Walsopthorne Farm

Its medieval past

Fragments remain of the ancient moat denoting the medieval manor. The Domesday Book includes Walsopthorne as an individual item under the rather charming name of WalesAlpedor meaning Waltheof's Appletree. In Anglo-Saxon times "Thorkell Wulmer's man held it; he could go where he would. 1 hide and 1 virgate which pay tax. In lordship 1 plough; 2 smallholders and 1 freeman with 1 plough; Meadow 2 acres Value before 1066 25s; now as much". After the Norman Conquest, the land was given to William, son of Baderon (the keeper of Monmouth Castle).

The Anglo-Norman family of Criketot were already holding the manor under the honour of Monmouth from before 1135 for a fifth of a knight's fee. It was for a time escheated to the Crown when the Criketots were involved in Simon de Montford's rebellion in 1263–1264 and then again in 1322 when they participated in Roger Mortimer's rebellion, but each time it was subsequently restored to them. The last record of the Criketot family is in 1360, the period of the Black Death. In the early 16th century it was owned by John Pychard of Suckley in Worcestershire. When he sold Walsopthorne in 1540 it comprised two messuages and 600 acres of land.

The 17th-century changes

From letters dated 12 May 1669 and 25 October 1669 written by Roger Farley to Hugh Philipps we know the history of Walsopthorne since this time. The manor had been owned by the Burghill family for some generations and was then sold to Richard Seycill at the beginning of the 17th century. Possibly it was the Seycills that built the current farmhouse. "Richard Seycill and William his sonne (my late father-in-law) enjoyed the same for neare 60 years without interruption of any." Roger Farley states that he had bought his portion of 234 acres plus the house and gardens about 12 years previously, paying £1,600 for it of which £300 represented a life interest to William Seycill and his wife, Susannah. William Seycill had died before the letter was written but Roger assures Hugh Philipps that Susannah, his widow, was not entitled to any further compensation.

It becomes apparent from Roger Farley's second letter that he was in the direst financial straits and was writing from a debtor's prison. He was indebted to the sum of £2,614 16s and was prepared to sell the property to Hugh Philipps for £1,219 3s, the very least his creditors would accept to permit his release:

> *Your proposition as Mr Vickers related in private from you betwixt him and me was: that if I would passe over all my tytles and interest I have in Walsopthorne to you then*

you would in the first place help me out of prison by paying off or compounding off all the actions upon me to all adventures whatsoever both concerning judgements & statutes & tytle during my life and moreover in the next place assure and make good unto me, £20 per annum during my life, send me beside to a place of your owne where I should be steward unto you and have £10 per annum for my paines and commend me besides to some chappell or place thereabouts to officiate, or at least commend me to some divines to that purpose.[27]

Rather poignantly Roger Farley requested that:

[...] if besides after the death of my mother Seycill you will make good £5 a year to Susan her daughter (who is darke and blind) during her life together with £10 a yeare already settled upon her by deed after her m(others) decease for I am bound in conscious and by promise to make so much good to h(er) upon the sale of Walsopthorne, she being my wifes sister whom she entirely loved an(d) who must of necessity have one to attend and looke to her as commun charity and humanity.[27]

Hugh Philipps certainly purchased Walsopthorne but it is not clear whether he granted these requests. Roger Farley died two years later.

Farley's description of the value of the property provides valuable insight both into the farming of the late 17th century and rents of different types of land. Cider was a valuable source of income. Some 57% of the total land was described as arable, with pasture taking up 28% and the meadowland, important for the production of hay, around 15 %. Orchards could be planted either on arable or pastureland, but the extent of arable does show the importance of wheat at this time. There is no reference to hops, so presumably Walsopthorne only started producing hops at a later date. In his desperate attempt to sell the property and secure his release Roger Farley specified the rent Mr Dowdeswell, his principal creditor, had obtained from renting Walsopthorne in the previous two years. The tenant "gave £90 for all except the coppice worth £10 per annum for diverse yeares together till these late cheape years come which was the only cause Mr Dowdeswell abated him £10 a yeare since". This rent excluded the house and garden, which was estimated to be worth £20 per year.

Hugh Philipps was resident in Lincoln's Inn Fields, London. The sources of funds to purchase Walsopthorne is obscure but there cannot but be some suspicion that Hugh's father may have been involved in illegal construction on meadows north of Lincoln's Inn Fields during the Civil War period which were known as 'Philipps piece'. The purchase certainly involved some considerable borrowing and was probably inspired by the desire of Hugh to rise in status to be a gentleman. He was later to purchase Putley Court to ensure the position of his son, Edmund Philipps.[28]

Owned by Putley Court until 1823

From 1668 until 1954 Walsopthorne was a tenanted farm. Until 1823 it belonged to the descendants of Hugh Philipps, first the Philipps family and then the Stocks of Putley Court. Land tax records of the late 18th and early 19th century show Walsopthorne to have been rented to a Mr Francis Holmes from at least 1794 to 1812. It was the most important farm in Ashperton, paying land tax of £11 12s 8d, the largest amount in the parish.

In 1823 William Stock arranged with the Hopton estate of Canon Frome to swap the farm of Walsopthorne for Hall Court, Kinnerton, Much Marcle. The total acreage at the time was 268 and the deeds list each field or part field. The proportion of arable to pasture is similar to the 17th century; mention is made of the coppice which is now said to be 22 acres. Coppice was a vital part of any farm when so many useful objects would be made of wood. There is no reference in the deeds to any hop yards, even at this date.

Then by Canon Frome estate until 1954

It was natural that the Canon Frome estate would wish to have a young man known by them to come from a good local farming family as a tenant for such a valuable holding. The land tax records of 1828 show that Mr Stephen Pitt, 23, a son of Mr Pitt of White House Farm, Canon Frome, was farming Walsopthorne. He married Ann Bishop, the daughter of a neighbouring farmer from Bishop's Frome in 1830 and they reared their family at Walsopthorne. The census of 1851 lists Elizabeth born in 1832, William born in 1845, and Harriet born in 1847. As was the habit of the time, in addition to one female servant, three farm labourers were living in: Thomas Perks aged 31 born in Bosbury, Frederick Evans aged 16 from Putley and Samuel Pierce aged 13 from Ashperton.

Is not known whether Stephen Pitt planted the hop yards but certainly hops were produced at Walsopthorne by 1828. The years 1829 and 1830 were bad years for hops and prices were very poor. In consequence around 550 farmers in Herefordshire petitioned the Treasury to be rebated the excise duty on the grounds that "the Crops of Hops [in the two years] were so deficient as scarcely to be sufficient for payment of Parish rates and Taxes leaving the Planters at the loss of the Greater Part of the Rent, Tithes, Labour and Interest of Capital". The signatories included Mr Stephen Pitt of Ashperton, one of only two farmers growing this crop in Ashperton.

Fig. AS5 The hop kiln at Walsopthorne Farm [29]

Mr Stephen Pitt was a modern mid-19th-century 'high farming' farmer who espoused the breeding of Hereford cattle. In the *Hereford Journal* of 8 October 1851 he was recorded as winning first prize for his two-year-old bull at the Ledbury Agricultural Society and won first prize for a pair of two-year-old steers at the same meeting. He also appeared in the Hereford Herd Book registering a pedigree bull.

The 1860s were a time of prosperity in farming and the Canon Frome estate rent books for the years 1860–1869 in the Herefordshire county archives show that this resulted in increased rental charges as these could be changed annually. Mr Stephen Pitt of Walsopthorne was farming 215 acres. In 1860–1862 he was paying £157 2s per half year (£314 4s per annum). In November 1862 the rent was increased to £183 half yearly (£366 per annum) and in 1867 it went up to £198 half yearly (£396 per annum). Over a ten-year period the rent for Walsopthorne rose by 26%.[30]

Between 1871 and 1881 Stephen and Ann Pitt moved to Over Court, Sutton and Walsopthorne was taken over by their son, William. William and his wife, Emma, do not appear to have had any children. Reflecting the more difficult times, the rent went down to £341 8s in the early 1880s and fell further to £293 in November 1887. In 1891 they, with Mary Holmes a female servant aged 20, John Nutt a farm servant of 17 and William Preece, a wagoner's boy of 15 were still living at 'Wessington' as Walsopthorne was termed at that time. Sometime between 1891 and 1901 William Pitt in his turn moved to Over Court, Sutton and the Pitt family's long association with Walsopthorne came to a close.

At the time of the 1901 census Walsopthorne, still termed 'Wessington', was lived in by Frederick Innes 49, his wife, Ann, their three children, a maid and a farmworker. They had previously been farming another of the Hopton estate farms, Redcastle in Canon Frome. Prior to this, as a young man of 29, Frederick is listed in the 1881 census as a farmer and wood merchant, living in a cottage in Canon Frome. Revealingly, and an indication perhaps of the hardships of the time, two agricultural labouring families were actually living in the barn and outbuildings in 1901: George and Jane Warren and their family of four children, and William and Harriet Davis and their family of five. Frederick Innis and his wife were still tenants in 1911. The household then included their son, Alfred, his wife and their two small children. The 1911 census asked each adult how many children had been born and how many were still alive. Two of Frederick and Ann's seven children had died, possibly an indication of the high infant mortality rates of this time. Frederick died in December 1917 and it is not known whether his widow and son continued to farm there until 1920. Frederick seems to have been successful at a difficult time: the probate accounts show that he left £7,532.

Fig. AS6 Old farm buildings, long unused: the Canon Frome estate rent book 1860–1890 shows that the barn roof was then thatched and needed periodic repair during this time[30]

From 1920 tenanted then owned by the Davies Family

Labour costs and activities 1925

In 1920 Herbert Davies moved from the much smaller farm of Beans Butts with its 40 acres owned by him to the much larger but tenanted farm of Walsopthorne.

A few of the Walsopthorne Farm account books remain for the 1920s and the account book for 1925 gives a fascinating glimpse of the year's activities and wage bills. The farm was employing up to seven workers, three of whom came from three generations of one family (J. Cheshire Senior, J. Cheshire and E. Cheshire). The workers seem to have been paid by the day with the rate of pay varying with the worker. E. Pocknell and J. Cheshire were paid 4s 6d per day, G. Brown and R. Badham 3s 4d and E. Cheshire, presumably a boy, only 1s 2d. The rate for J. Cheshire senior was not given. The wages bill for the year came to £277 19s 10d.

In January 40 man days were devoted to thrashing. In the week ending 6 February the total wage bill came to only £2 17s 2d. E. Pincher and J. Cheshire senior were absent for the week. E. Pocknell did one day's hedging, R. Badham was "cattling round pool" for two days and then absent, J. Cheshire was ploughing each day apart from Thursday, when he took the oats to the station together with his son, E. Cheshire. E. Cheshire's job throughout the week was driving. The wages for the week ending 13 February were almost as low at £3 6s 1d and covered taking the cattle to market on Tuesday. Up to the end of February the main activities were ploughing or "sundries" and the total wage bill varied between £3 to £4 apart from the week ending 27 February, when it rose to £4 10s 5d.

In the week ending 6 March nine man days were given up to pruning trees, three to hop work and two to ploughing up hops, two to putting wire around wheat, seven to sundries. The total wage bill rose to £6 13s 0d. Throughout the spring and summer season the bill was between £6 and £6 10s 6d for 21 of the weeks, and between £5 7s 6d and £5 19s 4d for nine of the weeks.

Hop growing is highly labour-intensive, and indeed this is confirmed by these accounts. No fewer then 65 man days were given up to hops in March, a further 93 in the four weeks ending 1 May, 56 days in the weeks to 29 May, 24 in the weeks to end 26 June. Activity then ceased until September. Then 72 man days were devoted to hops in the four weeks ending 25 September as the full-time workers undertook the many tasks required prior to harvesting and then supported the casually recruited hop pickers. The last activity in this period was to take the pickers to Ashperton station.

Other activities varied with the season, and eight man days were given up to ditching in May. On 2 June, two men took the pigs to Ledbury market. Haymaking started in the week ending 19 June and absorbed 25 man days in June and 63 man days in July.

Stacking oats took 13 man days in July, hoeing mangolds took 20 man days in July. In the week ending 14 August it was time for the cattle to go to market and three man days were given up to picking apples and three to "drawing" strawberries. In the week ending 20 August, five man days were given up to hauling wheat and five to hauling oats.

In October, the main activity was sundries, but ploughing also absorbed 19 man days in October and early November. In November it was time to pull and haul the mangolds – 25 man days were given up to this. In December, the main activity was again sundries but eight man days were given to hedge trimming, six to making cider, one to ploughing, two to harrowing and two to chaff cutting.

Walsopthorne in the Second World War

In the National Farm Survey of 1941–1943 H. D. Davies was listed as the tenant farmer of the Canon Frome estate farming 229 acres. He was given an A grading for competence. The ditches were in a good state of repair but the fences only rated a fair grading and drainage as 'poor' – a typical result of the strains of farming in the 1930s.

In response to the war effort 11 acres had been ploughed up for oats for the 1940 harvest and an additional 13½ for the 1941 harvest. Like most Herefordshire farms there was no electricity and the only well water supply was to the house. The fine old farmhouse was feeling its age, especially following so many hard years in agriculture. Unusually this was commented on in the National Farm Survey report – four rooms were in a good state of repair, three in a fair state and the rest in a poor state. The farm buildings too were only in a fair state, as was the cottage which was let on a service tenancy.

The Davieses were rearing beef cattle at this time. Of the herd of 50, there were 26 bullocks and heifers between one and two years old and 13 calves under one year. Unusually for East Herefordshire, pigs were a source of cash income (three sows, four gilts and one boar). Unlike many other farms there were no sheep. There were 20 acres under hops. Walsopthorne only had three horses – a modest number for a farm of this size – as the farm had an unusually powerful tractor, a 32-horsepower Fordson. The farm produced 12 tons of hay and eight of straw in 1941.

At the time of the National Farm Survey Mr Davies was paying rent of £283 15s, a rent of only 15s more than the rent payable in 1887, plus an additional £22 12s for the new barn.

Walsopthorne after the Second World War

The Davies family purchased Walsopthorne when the Canon Frome estate was put up for sale in 1961. At the time of the sale they were renting 208 acres and paying £670. The farm had had a quota for 22 acres of hops. The estate included in the sale an additional 14 acres of woodlands, old canal and banks, land which had not previously been rented out.

Throughout the latter part of the 20th century Walsopthorne continued to be a mixed farm with its herd of Hereford cattle, hops, orchards and some arable. Although Walsopthorne ceased to have cattle after the foot-and-mouth epidemic of 2001, it still has a cider orchard and, remarkably, it has never ceased to produce hops. Part of the keep of the orchards is now rented out annually and in 2017 the tenant's sheep could be seen grazing under the apple trees. For many years it has organised a rough shoot which includes the coppice. It remains a family farm owned by the Davies family and in 2016 William Davies was born, a great-great-grandson of Herbert Davies who moved to Walsopthorne Farm nearly a hundred years ago.

NOTES

[1] The National Archives, National Farm Survey of England and Wales 1941–1943: Lugwardine MAF 32/16/112.

[2] By kind permission of Ann Nellist.

[3] By kind permission of Ann Nellist.

[4] Prosser, Doris M. (August 1991). *Times of Change*. Doris Prosser.

[5] The National Archives, National Farm Survey of England and Wales 1941–1943: Dormington MAF 32/7/124.

[6] 'Dormington', in *An Inventory of the Historical Monuments in Herefordshire*, Volume 2, East (London, 1932), pp. 70–72.

[7] Davies, Peter. (2007). *A Herefordshire Tale: Claston, Hops and the Davies family*. Peter Davies.

[8] Davies, Peter. op. cit. p. 6.

[9] Heath-Agnew, E. (1983). *A History of Hereford Cattle and Their Breeders*. Duckworth. p. 120.

[10] See Chapter 3 for a more detailed discussion on the problems of hop production in the latter quarter of the 20th century.

[11] Davies, Peter. *op. cit.* p. 81.

[12] Davies, Peter. *op. cit.* p. 126.

[13] Heath-Agnew, E. (1983). *A History of Hereford Cattle and Their Breeders*. Duckworth. pp. 245–246.

[14] The National Archives, National Farm Survey of England and Wales 1941–1943: Stoke Edith MAF 32/23/121.

[15] 'Stoke Edith', in *An Inventory of the Historical Monuments in Herefordshire*, Volume 2, East (London, 1932) pp. 172–173.

[16] By kind permission of John Dent.

[17] Robinson, Rev., Charles J. (1872). *A History of the Mansions and Manors of Herefordshire.* Longman and Co. pp. 224–225.
[18] Heath-Agnew, E. *op. cit.* pp. 222–223.
[19] The National Archives, National Farm Survey of England and Wales 1941–1943: Tarrington MAF 32/24/166.
[20] 'Tarrington', in *An Inventory of the Historical Monuments in Herefordshire,* Volume 2, East (London, 1932), pp. 182–185.
[21] 'Woolhope', in *An Inventory of the Historical Monuments in Herefordshire,* Volume 2, East (London, 1932), pp. 220–223.
[22] By kind permission of Gwyneth Williams.
[23] The National Archives, National Farm Survey of England and Wales 1941–1943: Ashperton MAF 32/1/145.
[24] By kind permission of Margaret Bradstock.
[25] 'Ashperton', in *An Inventory of the Historical Monuments in Herefordshire,* Volume 2, East (London, 1932), pp. 2–4.
[26] By kind permission of Tony Bradstock.
[27] Herefordshire Archive Service (HAS) E 3/24; transcript kindly provided by David Lovelace.
[28] Currie, Jean Ila. (2009). *Three Centuries of a Herefordshire Village.* Owlstone Press.
[29] By kind permission of David Lovelace.
[30] Canon Frome estate rent book 1860–1890: Herefordshire Archive Service (HAS) BL 93.

JOURNEY 4: PIXLEY, AYLTON, LITTLE MARCLE AND WOOLHOPE PARISHES

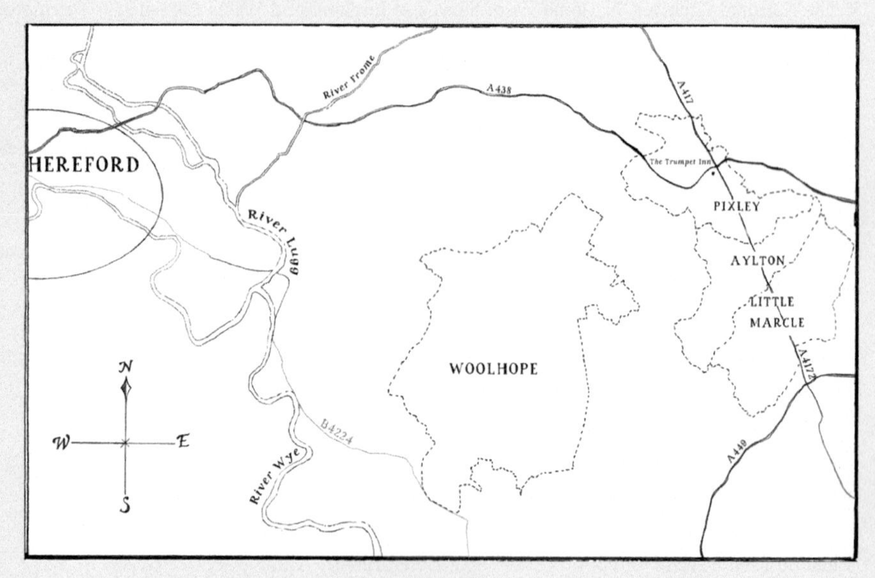

Journey 4 map and individual parish maps by Heather Colbert

The area between Pixley and Aylton and Woolhope comprises the parish of Putley which is covered in the first book in this series *Three Centuries of a Herefordshire Village.* The area to the south consists mainly of the parishes of Fownhope and Much Marcle which are not covered here.

PIXLEY PARISH

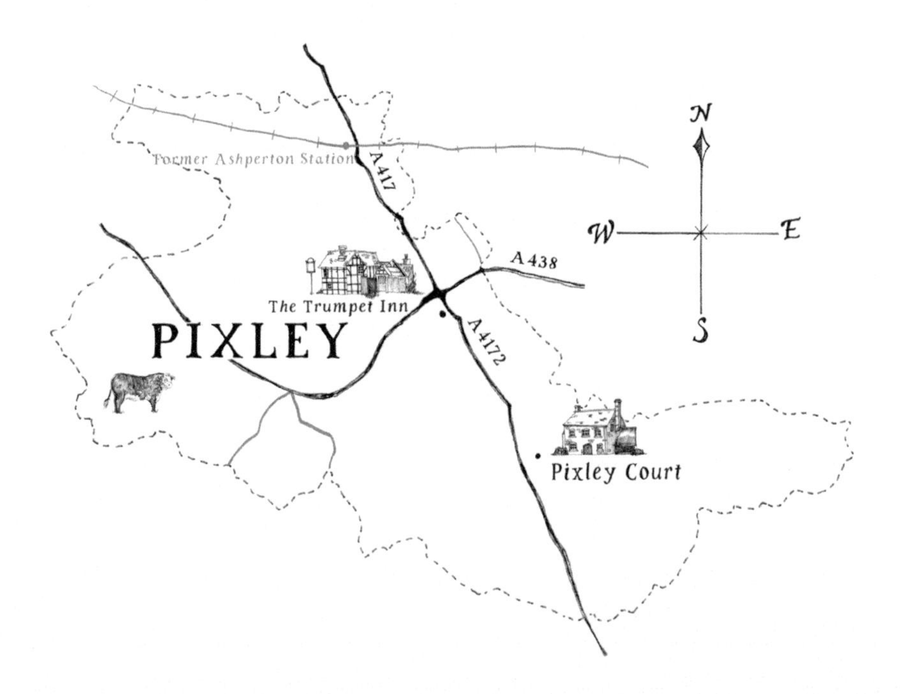

The parish of Pixley is one of the smallest of the parishes considered here. In 1851 the acreage was only 655. It was greatly enlarged in 1886 by including the township of Parkhold with its long established farms of Court-y park and Tipsgrove, but even so the total acreage is only 1,086 acres, which would be considered suitable for only one farm in the 21st century. The population has remained small. It was 113 in 1841 and 149 in 1891. Some council houses were built in the immediate post-Second World War and in the late 20th century Pool End farmhouse and farm buildings were turned into residential accommodation. Even so the population in 2011 was only 258.

In the 17th and early 18th centuries there were three separate landholdings. On the southern side of the main A 438 Hereford–Ledbury road at a sharp bend half a mile before the A 417 crossroads with the historic Trumpet coaching inn is Pool End Farm. In the 17th and early 18th century it belonged to branches of the Ravenhill family associated with Woolhope. On the northern side of the Trumpet Inn crossroads tucked away close to Munsley village hall can be seen the decaying entrance to Mainstone Court. The history of Mainstone Court, like Walsopthorne Farm, Ashperton and

Court Farm in Aylton, stretches back to very early medieval times and Mainstone Court was similarly required to contribute towards the cost of a knight. Until after the Second World War the moat surrounding the medieval dwelling was discernible. In the 17th and into the early 18th centuries Mainstone Court was occupied by the Jones family with landholdings both around Mainstone and in Putley. Unusually the Jones family supported the Commonwealth in the Civil War. Mainstone Court remains a fine country house but by the 19th century most of the surrounding land had been absorbed into the Canon Frome estate of the Hopton family.

The third landholding, which included Pixley Court and Knapp Farm, belonged to Little Malvern Priory until it was dissolved in 1534. As discussed under Pixley Court below, in the 17th and early 18th centuries it was associated with the Skinner family.

In the 1851 census there were three farms in Pixley parish (Pixley Court 200 acres, Knapp Farm 204 acres and Pool End Farm, acreage not given) and one smallholding (Birchend 15 acres). In 1851 the section of the township of Parkhold included in the parish of Pixley from 1886 contained two farms (Court-y-park 226 acres and Tipsgrove 55 acres). All these five farms were listed in the National Farm Survey of 1941–1943[1] although Pool End Farm had belonged to and had been farmed in conjunction with Pixley Court from 1929.

Most of the Knapp Farm land is now part of Haygrove fruit farm at Redbank in Ledbury parish. At approximately the same time as Pool End farmhouse and buildings were sold for residential purposes in the 1980s, Tipsgrove farmstead was pulled down and a replacement house is now a solar energy business with the land farmed separately. Court-y-park, which had been owned by generations of the old established East Herefordshire Pudge family, has been converted into the Alexander Park Resort, a golf, gym and spa leisure resort. The history of the successful Pixley Court 21st-century farm enterprise is discussed below.

Pixley Court

Pixley Court, house, outbuildings and moat, S.W. of the church. The House is of two storeys with attics; the walls are of brick with some timber-framing and the roofs are tiled. It is of T-shaped plan with the cross-wing at the S.E. end. The cross-wing dates from the 16th century but was re-cased in brick in the 18th century; the main block is of mid to late 17th-century date. Some late 17th-century windows remain on the S.W. front and some exposed timber-framing at the N.W. end. Inside the building, the cross-wing has heavy chamfered ceiling-beams and the main block has later beams.

Fig. P1 Painting by Robin Poole showing the east side of Pixley Court farmhouse together with the hop kilns and stables [2]

> The Stable, etc., adjoining the S.E. end of the house, is of brick and stone and probably of late 17th-century date.
>
> The Barn, N. of the house, is timber-framed and also of the 17th century.
>
> The Moat is fragmentary but surrounded the church and probably also the house.[3]

Pixley Court nestles beside the tiny early medieval Pixley Church, a church so isolated in the 16th century that it seems to have escaped the sharp eyes of the Royal Commissioners of Edward VI and to this day retains the medieval rood screen. The fact that the farmhouse is so close to the church indicates that the medieval manor house probably lies either on or at the very least close to the present dwelling.

Three generations of the Thompson family have now lived in Pixley Court and farmed here. The grandfather of the present owner, Edward Thompson, also an

Edward Thompson, bought Pixley Court with its then 350 acres together with another famous Pixley farm, Pool End Farm, from receivers in 1928. Unusually for Herefordshire at the time Edward Thompson senior did not come from a farming background. On the contrary he had been working in the City of London but made the change when advised by his doctor to move from London to a rural environment. Today Pixley Berries is famed both nationally and internationally for its quality fresh (as opposed to concentrated) pasteurised blackcurrant juice, as well as raspberry and other juices. Pixley Berries are a well-known product sold direct and through the major supermarkets. Even more important have been the sales of the juice to major companies as the 'Not From Concentrates' quality ingredient for drinks and other food products.

History of Pixley Court

At the time of the dissolution of the monasteries in the 1530s land on the Ledbury side of the A 417 and A 4172 in the parishes of Pixley and Aylton belonged to the Benedictine Little Malvern Priory. The ownership is still remembered in the name Priors Court, until the 1970s a farm in the small adjacent parish of Aylton. The Valor Ecclesiasticus of 1535 which lists the value of all monastic property provides very little additional information on this except for the fact that the valuation given was really very low.

Fig. P2 Remains of Little Malvern Priory Church

The ownership of Pixley Court for the two centuries after the dissolution of the monasteries is not clear. According to Robinson[4] the Skinner family lived at the nearby Knapp Farm, Pixley for nearly 200 years and sold it together with the manorial rights to the Cocks family of Eastnor in 1763. Possibly Pixley Court was also included in this sale as Pixley Court, along with Knapp Farm and Priors Court, Aylton, is shown as owned by the Eastnor estate in the earliest extant land tax records which date to the latter 18th century. All three properties remained part of the Eastnor estate right up until 1916.

Baylis family large farmers in the 18th century

Pixley Court was a rented estate farm, albeit one of the more important ones, for some 150 years. The Eastnor estate records for this period possibly exist but remain in private hands. However, some information on the 18th-century farmers of Pixley Court can be gleaned from a number of sources. Throughout much of the 18th century and indeed up to 1826 Pixley Court was the largest farm in Pixley and farmed by the Baylis family. It would seem to have been a prosperous time as the farmhouse was greatly enlarged in the 18th century. A George Baylis of Pixley died in 1777 with his will proved on 20 October of that year. In April 1806 the *Hereford Journal* announced the death at Madresfield, Worcestershire of Mrs Baylis, the widow of George Baylis of Pixley Court, at the exceptionally great age of 97. A George Baylis, presumably either a son or grandson, was residing at Pixley Court in the same year. The land tax records for both 1795 and 1808 show a George Baylis to be paying no less than £8 9s in land tax. This was almost double the land tax of Knapp Farm, which was farmed by William Drew in both these years, and considerably more than William Dowding was paying for Pool End Farm. When Pool End Farm was sold in the early 19th century it was stated to be 160 acres which suggests that Pixley Court was at least 200 acres in this early period. George Baylis died in 1818 with his will proved on 13 November. He was succeeded by his son, John.

The *Hereford Journal* advertised the sale of John Baylis's livestock in January 1826. He would seem to have been a progressive farmer who used carthorses rather than oxen. No fewer than 10 carthorses were included in the sale. He may have been breeding carthorses as five were three years old or less and one of his mares was in foal. He had a large flock of sheep: 56 ewes and 70 yearlings. His herd of 33 cattle included 17 cows and heifers. He was evidently rearing pigs on a commercial scale as 20 store pigs were also included in the sale.

It is not known when John Davies and his wife, Sarah, came to Pixley Court, but they were certainly there by 1840 when one of their sons, Edwin, married Miss Eliza Powell from Woolhope in the little 12th century Pixley Church. In the census records of 1841 the household comprised John Davies aged 60, his wife, Sarah 61 and their son, John 25. There were two female servants and four male farmworkers living in. It was clearly not a happy place.

In 1840 John Davies sold the entire (presumably spoiled) hop harvest from the 16 acres of hop fields at Pixley Court to John King, the publican at the nearby Trumpet Inn, for sixpence according to the *Hereford Journal*. In 1842 a messenger from Pixley Court arrived at Ledbury fire station requiring assistance. Fortunately the fire in the chimney was put out without too much damage. Then there was a series of disagreements with Pixley Court farmworkers taking up the time of the Ledbury Magistrates' Court. In July 1847 Mr Davies's son, William, was convicted of assaulting a farm boy, James Price, and fined five shillings with nine shillings costs. The very next week James Price was back before the magistrates, this time accused by Mr Davies of galloping a horse around a meadow when he had been instructed just to release it. The magistrates were not impressed and suggested it was a mere boyish misdemeanour, but felt obliged to deduct one shilling from James's wages plus costs (one wonders how long James Price remained at Pixley Court). Mr John Davies was back at the Magistrates' Court in April 1848 when George Baker, servant to Mr John Davies, was accused by him of spending the night away without leave. The magistrates chose to believe Mr Baker's version which was that he had returned at 9.45 p.m., but that Mr Davies had refused to allow him to come in. Mr Davies was required to pay the costs.

There were also two instances reported of theft of Pixley Court sheep. In one instance which occurred in October 1844 a ewe was stolen but the culprit was not found. In the second instance a ram was stolen and slaughtered sometime between 16–18 April 1845 by two farmworkers, George Gurney and George Thomas. The case for this serious crime was heard at the Ledbury Assizes. Gurney turned Queen's evidence for which he was said by Thomas to have been paid £10 by an organisation simply called 'the Association' (maybe a group of local farmers) and £50 in addition. As can be imagined there was a conflict of evidence as to who actually initiated the deed and slaughtered the ram. The *Hereford Times* of 5 July 1845 reported that:

> *The jury consulted a short time after which they returned the following verdict: – "We cannot find the prisoner guilty without the accomplice Gurney". They were again asked whether Thomas was guilty or not guilty, when the foreman said "Not guilty".*

This was a lucky, if surprising, escape. If convicted, Thomas would have been transported for at least seven years.

There was one piece of good news: the report that John Davies received second prize for the best two-year-old heifers at a Ledbury Agricultural Society Meeting. However this was about the only happy note from this period and Mr John Davies' tenancy of Pixley Court ended in tragedy. The *Hereford Times* of 16 June 1849 reported the inquest held into the death Mr John Davies on Saturday 9 June. On Friday 8 June he been found hanging from a yew tree. A farmworker gave evidence that John Davies had seemed confused for the last few months and this was similarly endorsed by the local Pixley Police Constable. The inquest verdict was suicide when his balance of mind was disturbed.

The very same 16 June 1849 edition of the *Hereford Times* which reported John Davies's death advertised the sale of Pixley farm stock and household goods. These, together with the legal cases mentioned above, suffice to give a picture of farming at Pixley Court at this time.

The crops were still in the field when John Davies died. Although the Corn Laws which protected wheat production had just been repealed, it would be another quarter of a century before wheat from North America and Australia swamped the British market and led to the collapse of prices. Pixley Court was a prosperous mixed farm with arable more important in this period than it would be again for nearly a hundred years. In June 1849 of some 200 acres no fewer than 88 acres were given over to arable (50 acres of wheat, 20 of beans, three of barley and 15 of oats). Although the high prices obtained for high quality cider and perry during the Napoleonic Wars had long since passed, these products remained a very important source of cash income. In June 1849 there were 5,000 gallons of prime and family cider and perry held at the farm. Surprisingly no hops were included in the sale, yet hops remained an important crop for Pixley Court in the latter part of the 19th century and at least 16 acres had been under hops in 1840.

Livestock was included in the sale, although other members of the Davies family may well have taken over at least some significant proportion of the animals. The flock at the time of the sheep-stealing case of 1845, including the lambs and the ill-fated ram, came to 89, but only 18 fat sheep were offered for sale in 1849. In the late 18th century dairying had been an important enterprise on the Gloucester/Herefordshire border and seven cows, three two-year-old heifers in calf and one with calf, and three one-year-old heifers from John Davies's dairy herd were included in the sale. 3 cwt of cheeses were also to be sold together with extensive dairying equipment including cheese presses, giving some indication of the significance of this commercial production. Pig production, naturally associated with dairying, was a very minor item.

The sales brochure refers to four store pigs and several sides of beautiful hams, which would have been mainly for household use or minor sale locally.

A large farm like Pixley Court had clearly been a purchaser of new farm equipment which came on the market in the early 19th century. The sales brochure states:

> *The implements which are of the best description include broad and narrow wheel wagon and carts, ploughs, harrows, drills, rollers, scuffers, threshing and winnowing machines, hurdles ...*

Despite this equipment, ploughing, as well as other farming activities on such a significant acreage of land, must have proved pretty challenging. The sale included four farm horses. Some carthorses may have been taken over by the family, but there are also suggestions that at least part of the ploughing may still have been done by oxen as the sales particulars make reference to "two bull stags (excellent workers)". The two donkeys included in the sale were presumably used for lighter work and transport. It was for his deficiency in harnessing one of these donkeys that James Price was assaulted by William Davies in 1847.

Pixley Court under Daniel Pope

Mr Daniel Pope was the farmer at Pixley Court from at least 1850 until his death in 1886. With his accession references to Pixley Court vanish from the local newspapers.

Daniel Pope came from a well-off and fairly numerous family in nearby Gloucestershire and his links remained in this area. His first wife, Caroline, whom he married in in 1847 when he was farming at Upleadon, came from Newent. His second wife also came from Gloucestershire and he had a remarkably large family of 13 children from his two marriages. However he was afflicted by early deaths which so often blighted life in the 19th century. His first wife, Caroline, died in childbirth together with the newborn baby, James, in 1855. He lost a young daughter, Mary, and at least one of his sons died before him.

Daniel Pope seems to have been a highly competent farmer and the acreage rented by the farm continued to grow. From 201 acres in 1851, the acreage had risen steadily to 300 acres by 1881. He accomplished this by taking over land from Knapp Farm and from Priors Court, Aylton.

A much more peaceful character than his predecessor, Daniel Pope took over the normal posts expected of a leading farmer of the period. He was for many years a guardian of the local Poor Law. The records of church expenditure in Pixley survive in the Herefordshire Archive and Records Centre and show that throughout much of the period he was a churchwarden. Expenditure on the church, which included outlays for wine and a very small amount for repairs, was very modest – normally under £5 – but as the largest farmer in the area, Daniel Pope was paying by far the greater part of this. The Tithe Map and notes of 1841 had listed hop yards at Pixley Court, Knapp Farm and Pool End Farm and certainly hops were an important crop at this time. From 1871 when the trade directories specifically identified hop growers, they all show Daniel Pope to be a hop grower.

Rented then owned by the Davies family 1886–1928

From 1886 until 1928 Pixley Court was rented and then owned by the Davies family. John Charles Davies (1856–1932) was a son of Thomas Davies of Moorend Farm, Weston Beggard and Claston Farm, Dormington. He had married in 1882 Ann Pearce Pope, whose father, Edward, was a younger brother of Daniel Pope. It was natural that John Charles should wish to take over the tenancy of Pixley Court. He and his wife eventually had 15 children and he fulfilled his wish which was to set up each of his sons with a farm. At the time of the 1891 census John Charles and his wife were living in Flights Farm in Ledbury parish and moved to Hill Court in the same parish around 1901. Pixley Court was lived in by a bailiff, Emmanuel Grimmett, at the time of the censuses of 1891 and 1901.

At the time of the 1911 census Pixley Court was lived in by Thomas Edward Davies, John Charles and Ann Davies' eldest son. The land valuation of 1910 gave the acreage as 269 acres of which there were 25 acres of orchards. According to the particulars of the Eastnor estate sales of 1916 the acreage was 282 of which around three acres were in the adjoining parish of Aylton. Thomas Edward Davies was entrepreneurial. Part of the acreage at Pixley Court was given over to soft fruit and he established a commercial-style jam factory at Pixley Court itself. In the difficult times of the early 1920s it experienced financial problems and was put up for sale in 1923, five years before the sale of Pixley Court and land to Edward Thompson. Thomas Edward Davies seems to have had a complex marital life with at least eight children by three wives. After leaving Pixley Court, Thomas emigrated to South Africa.

Pixley Court in the Second World War

At the time of the National Farm Survey of 1941–1943 and annual Agricultural Census of June 1941 Pixley Court was owned and run by Edward Thompson and his son, Denys. They also owned Pool End Farm and the two were run as a joint enterprise of 429 acres, creating an exceptionally large farm by the standards of the time. It was also well capitalised. Public electricity was not available in this part of Herefordshire until well after the Second World War. However the Thompsons had installed private electricity for both power as well as lighting. The farm also had tractors.

Before the war the farm income must have been generated almost exclusively from hops, orchards and livestock. No fewer than 79 acres were under orchards in June 1941 whilst the farm had a statutory 34 acres of hops. The fattening of store cattle was also an important enterprise with 54 store heifers of one to two years old and 37 bullocks under a year. The farm had a flock of 116 sheep, including the 72 lambs that were to be sold that very day. There were no pigs but a small commercial flock of 212 poultry.

Pixley Court had responded well to the war effort by ploughing up 10½ acres for wheat for the 1940 harvest and an additional 33½ acres for wheat for the 1941 harvest. Consequently in June 1941 55½ acres were under wheat, with a further 14 under oats and 10 under potatoes, all vitally important strategic crops. Unusually for Herefordshire nine acres was given over to vegetables. Altogether 25% of the total acreage of the farm was by this time under arable.

There were 13 full-time male workers and four part-time women. Of the 12 farm cottages, 10 were allocated to Pixley Court farmworkers. There were four working horses and two as yet unbroken.

Shortly after the survey and the census forms were completed, Pixley Court was struck by tragedy. Edward Thompson contracted anthrax. Penicillin was in its early stages. Supplies were short and access restricted. Nevertheless it could be made available for civilian use, but in this case it was not released to save the life of a Herefordshire farmer responsible for a large scale and progressive farm. The current owner was born to Denys and his wife shortly after Edward Thompson's death and called Edward in memory of his grandfather. It was thought that the anthrax had been contained in meat bonemeal imported from Argentina.

Pixley Court after the Second World War

Early post-war

From the end of the Second World War until the mid-1980s Pixley Court, like the other bigger farms described in this book, remained what it had previously been, a mixed farm with a significant hop acreage. Denys Thompson, like his father, Edward, before him, was a director of the Hop Marketing Board, and Denys's son, Edward, also later became a director. The government support schemes of the time encouraged a higher proportion of arable than had been the case in the 1930s; hops produced under quotas from the Hop Marketing Board were normally especially valuable and the farm also had cider orchards dating from about 1952 and beef cattle. Silage and grass drying came and went in the 1950s and 60s.

Changes after 1973

Joining the then Common Market in 1973 brought changes. The introduction of the Common Agricultural Policy initially further improved the returns from arable. In contrast Herefordshire apples faced increased competition from other EC suppliers and the return from hops, previously a most important generator of income, started to sharply decrease. Denys Thompson had the honour of being made a Chevalier (Knight) of the Order of the Hops for his contribution to the development of hops in 1981 but increased competition, combined with the abolition of the Hop Marketing Board in 1982 which was deemed contrary to EC Competition Policy resulted in Pixley Court moving away from being a mixed farm in the mid-1980s.

Fig. P3 Document marking Denys Thompson's appointment as a Chevalier (Knight) of the Order of the Hop in 1981 [5]

Blackcurrants were already being grown on contract for one of the major soft drink companies at this time and it was decided to specialise in soft fruit. Mechanisation had been replacing labour even in the 1960s and 70s, but it is far from easy to mechanise the harvesting of soft fruit. Edward Thompson, Denys's son, read engineering at Cambridge. Working together with a skilled local draughtsman, a specialised raspberry harvester was converted so that it harvested blackcurrants. The design was then successfully commercialised. The farm now employs some 15 full-time workers and around 50 in the main harvest season.

Nature is a hard taskmaster. Pixley Court grows a wide variety of blackcurrants. Seasons alter. It is hard to guess the impact of climate change. To ensure flexibility and diversity Edward Thompson selected good quality plants from Poland and elsewhere. These are well established but it took seven years to accomplish this. The farm grows Pixley Black, Pixley Noir, Pixley Velvet, and Pixley Silk, and the varieties are selected on the basis of flavour, aroma and agronomic properties.

It is the juicing plant which is the most capital-intensive and complex part of the enterprise. Again resourcefulness and adaption have been the order of the day. A machine originally designed for grapes was specially adapted to remove the stalks and prunings from blackcurrants. Temperature control needs to be varied and the sugar content monitored. Pixley Berries is a 21st-century quality processing plant transported to the Herefordshire countryside.

Such a remarkable enterprise requires highly skilled and motivated staff and modern laboratory equipment. The Pixley Berries website6 provides a brief summary of the background and talents of seven personnel who ensure the working of this remarkable and highly successful enterprise right from the agronomy of the plants themselves to the processing and then marketing of the juices. Pixley Berries is believed to be the only fully integrated venture of its type.

Although of lesser importance than Pixley Berries, Edward Thompson has also ventured into the new dwarf hops which have been planted on land originally associated with Pool End Farm. The Thompson family has always had close links with the Hawkins family of Thinghill Court, Withington and the hops on both farms are grown in close association with Hawkbrand Hops, a hops marketing co-operative. Pixley Court also retains some of the cider orcharding dating from circa 1952.

AYLTON PARISH

The little parish of Aylton is some five miles from Ledbury, located either side of the A 4172 Leominster to Gloucester road two miles south-east of the Trumpet Inn crossroads. It adjoins Pixley parish to the north-east, Little Marcle to the south and Putley to the west. Most of the parish with its 830-odd acres lies to the west of the A 4172 with the houses tucked away from the main road. Only a quarter of the acreage, historically associated with the farm of Priors Court, is situated on the east side, but again this farm is hidden from sight.

Between 1700 and 2001 the parish of Aylton remained small and the population tiny. In 1851 for instance, with slightly different boundaries, the population was 93 and the acreage 812. The change of parish boundaries, instituted nationwide in 1886 made little difference: the acreage was increased to 838 but the population was 92. In 2011 the size of the parish stayed the same but the population jumped to 144 as a result of the transformation of Aylton Court, the largest farm and its associated farm buildings, into a variety of residential dwellings.

Historic importance should not be judged by present size. Research by the late Dr Higgins of Birmingham University in connection with the restoration of the Tithe Barn at Court Farm discussed below has shown Aylton to have been a far more important place in Anglo-Saxon times. Interestingly the name derives from Aethelgifu, a female name. Dr Higgins considered the adjacent sites of both the manor house (Court Farm) and Aylton parish church to pre-date even the parochial and diocesan organisation of the English Church. There is in existence a riveting account of a Shire meeting held at Aylton during the reign of King Canute in the early eleventh century to settle a lawsuit whereby a woman named Enneawnes disinherited her son Edwin in favour of a kinswoman, Leofflaed.

Aylton was erroneously included in Much Marcle in the Domesday Book but is separately distinguished in the Herefordshire Domesday Book (HDB) under the name of Ailmeton. In the margin of the HDB the name De Broye is added denoting the Anglo-Norman family as the subtenants of the manor.

The De Broye family gave the land to the east of the present A 4172 to the Priory of Little Malvern – hence the name of the farm, Priors Court. This farm (161 acres in 1851), like Pixley Court, eventually found its way to the Eastnor estate in the 18th century, as did Ast Wood which is also in Aylton and was the location of the famous poaching case described in Chapter 8.

However, and unusually for East Herefordshire parishes, Aylton land west of the A 4172 – three-quarters of the total parish and the original manor of the De Broye family – was never owned by any of the larger estates between the 18th and the 20th centuries. Consequently for most of the period under discussion Aylton remained in the hands of small freeholders or modest small landowners. The Tithe Map of 1838 lists no fewer than 12 owners of land but this included four cottages of under five acres. All the eight holdings of five or more acres had different owners.

Indeed the returns show remarkably small changes in size and number of farms in Aylton, as revealed by comparing the census of 1851 with the 1941–1943 National Farm Survey6. In the 1851 census eight holdings were headed by farmers. In 1941–1943 there were nine holdings of five or more acres but this included the Glebe land which was now owned and farmed by a resident farmer. The names of the other farms had not changed and the acreage was not substantially different between these two periods. Court Farm and Aylton Court are discussed below. Of the remaining six farms Priors Court had 160 acres in 1851 and 165 in 1941, White House Farm 150 acres in 1851 and 135 in 1941, Jacobs Leys 45 acres in 1851 and 49 in 1941, Yew Tree Cottage 20 acres in 1851 and 38½ in 1941, Newbridge Cottage 10 acres in 1851 and 16½ acres in 1941, Old Castle 10 acres in 1851 and 10 acres in 1941.

The four larger farms all grew hops in 1941. The eight farms continued until well after the Second World War. The first to go was Priors Court with the farmhouse and buildings converted to residential use in the 1970s. In the early 1990s Newbridge Cottage was converted into a farm park with a play barn, farm animals and tractor rides and received a TripAdvisor Certificate of Excellence in 2015. White House Farm was converted into a residence with attractive self-catering cottage accommodation in the old farm buildings from around 2000 and it too receives accolades from TripAdvisor. The very last of the old established Aylton farms to vanish was Yew Tree Cottage, a viable agricultural holding traceable for well over 200 years. At the time of its sale in September 2017 it comprised 25 acres.

Aylton Court

Aylton Court, outbuildings, ½ m. S.S.W. of the church. The Outbuildings, N.E. of the house, consist of stables and two barns all of early 17th-century date and timber-framed. The stable with the loft over has queen-post roof-trusses. The barn, N.E. of the stable, is of five bays, and the second barn, to the S.E., is of six bays.[7]

For over 200 years Aylton Court was the largest farm in Aylton. It ceased to be a farm only in 1989 and had been owned by the Davies family for some eighty years. The house and farm buildings have been converted to residential use and the land is part of the much expanded acreage of Lillands, Little Marcle.

Aylton Court was always a mixed farm and until the 1980s it was a major hop farm. Whilst other large farms were known for their Hereford cattle, Aylton Court was from 1936 until 1963 famed for its prize-winning herd of Friesian cattle.

History of Aylton Court

The first reference to Aylton Court is in January 1783 when the newly completed mansion house, which must have replaced a substantial earlier building, was advertised to rent together with 190 acres. It was in the possession of Mr Thomas Hammond. It

Fig. AY1 Aylton Court in 2017

was described as enclosed in a ring fence, included a hop ground and: "It was capable of producing a great quantity of cider of the best sorts of fruit."

The next reference to Aylton Court was in 1795 when it was advertised for sale with 142 statutory acres. It contained quality orchards, possessed a hop yard and included valuable oak and ash timber suitable for hop poles. It was rented to a Mr Bishop for £110 a year. The Court Farm records discussed below show that Court Farm was also leased to John Bishop of Aylton Court in 1788. John Bishop was then farming on a large scale. This was the time of the Napoleonic Wars and the vendor considered that a rental of £160 or over £1 per acre would be possible. However, Aylton Court does not appear to have been sold at that time as the land tax records of 1812 still list Thomas Hammond as the owner. The land tax was £17 8s, by far the largest in the parish (in comparison the land tax for Court Farm was only £6) and the tenant was Anne Brooke.

In 1829 the land tax records show that Mr William Miles was the owner and Thomas White the farmer. Mr White left the farm in 1837 selling his pure-bred Hereford cattle, prime flock of sheep, carthorses and colts, plus many farming tools and feed stocks. He was therefore a modern farmer of this time interested in the breeding of Hereford cattle for meat, ploughing with horses not oxen and purchasing modern farming equipment. The fact that he was selling colts might suggest that he was also breeding carthorses.

The 1841 census lists Jane Shale described as farmer's wife at Aylton Court. In fact Jane was a widow and her husband, James Shale, had died in 1837. In 1844 their daughter, Eliza, married Thomas Davies (1816–1895) who later farmed Claston Farm, Dormington and Moorend Farm, Weston Beggard. Jane Shale was therefore an ancestress of the very large Davies dynasty described in Chapter 7. They were associated in addition to Claston and Moorend with three other farms described in Part III (Beans Butts in Woolhope, Walsopthorne Farm in Ashperton and Pixley Court). Margaret Bradstock (née Davies) of Freetown, Ashperton is also a descendant. In 1851 Aylton Court was farmed by Mrs Avis Perry and comprised 261 acres employing seven labourers. She gave up the lease in 1853 and John Foulger became the tenant. It was in 1855 that a great tragedy occurred when Henry, John Foulger's 12-year-old son, accidently shot dead his 15-year-old sister. Understandably in September 1858 John Foulger gave up his lease. He was replaced by John Badham aged 29, the son of John Badham, the farmer at Perton Court, Stoke Edith. In 1861 John Badham junior was farming 250 acres employing 15 men and a boy. Evidently women workers were additional to this because living in the household was Catherine Harris, described as a milkmaid. So Aylton Court was probably producing commercial cheese. Also living in were four farmworkers, including John Birrell a carter's boy. John Badham was only to stay at Aylton Court a short time before being replaced in 1863 by Samuel Cowles. In 1871 the census records show that Samuel was farming 264 acres, employing two men, four boys and three women. Samuel appears again in the 1881 census, but by 1891 he had left to be replaced by Robert Lomas. Robert and his wife, Phoebe, came from Lancashire. This was a hard time for farming and Robert Lomas had left by 1897 to be replaced by Arthur Aaron Yapp, who retired only after the first World War.

Whilst other farms were breeding Hereford cattle Arthur Yapp developed a dairy herd. Newspaper advertisements from before the First World War and again in November 1915 advertised for experienced a cowman to work at Aylton Court.

At an unknown time in the 19th century the ownership had moved from Mr Miles to the industrial-based Blades family of Lancashire which may explain the Lancashire tenant of 1891. The Blades were to remain as owners until around 1910 as the land registration of that year crosses out "executors of C. Blades", replacing it with Mr J. Davies of Hill House, Ledbury. From the time of Arthur Yapp's retirement, Aylton Court was to be occupied by the Davies family. As described in Chapter 7, John Charles Davies, a son of Thomas and Eliza Davies of Claston Farm and a grandson of Jane Shale, had an exceptionally large family of 15 children and was determined that each of his sons would have a farm. Following his purchase of Aylton Court, it was farmed by his son, Frederick Pope Davies. Arthur Yapp's interest in dairying was continued by the Davies family and Frederick Pope Davies established a pedigree Friesian herd in 1936.

Aylton Court in the Second World War

In the 1941–1943 National Farm Survey Aylton Court was a farm of 259 acres owned by Mr F. Davies. The ditches, fences, drainage and the four farm cottages – all let on service tenancies – were all only in fair condition. It was naturally heavy land of fair quality. 20 acres of grassland had been ploughed up for wheat for the 1940 harvest. No additional grassland had been ploughed up for the 1941 harvest.

Of the total acreage, 152 acres were still under grass. There were five carthorses and a total of 14 farmworkers – 11 full-time (eight men and three women) and three part-time women. The principal arable crop was beans with 20½ acres, followed by oats with 15 acres. There were three acres of potatoes. Unusually there were no sheep. There was a significant dairy herd with 35 of the 45 cattle either cows or heifers. There was only one sow kept for breeding, with three pigs over five months and 13 piglets. The farm kept 100 poultry. Both hops and cider apples were important with 17 acres under hops and 27 acres of orchards, including unusually, three acres of the orchards with soft fruit under the trees. The farm had one 20-horsepower Fordson tractor. There was private electricity for lighting but not for power.

In November 1941 the farm was advertising for an experienced cowman. One of the attractions was that milking had been mechanised at Aylton Court. It would have been one of the very few milking machines in Herefordshire at this time and because of the lack of electricity, it had to be run on a generator.

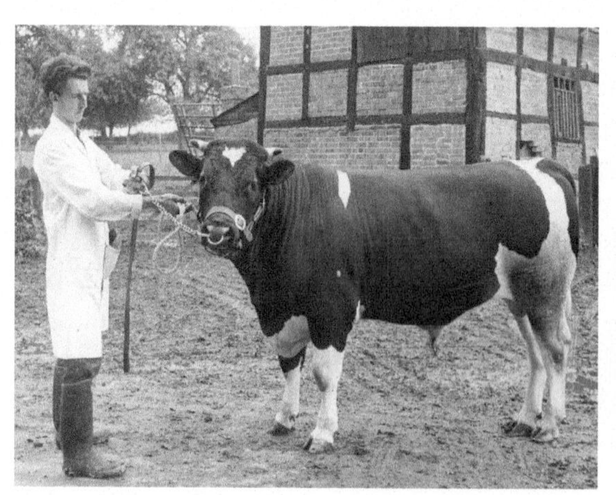

Fig. AY2 (above left) Aylton Court pedigree Friesian bull, probably Aylton Beechmast[8]
Fig. AY3 (above right) Two generations of the Davies family in 1955 (left: Peter Davies; middle: Raymond Davies, Peter's younger brother; right: Frederick Pope Davies)[8]

Fig. AY4 Converted historic farm buildings at Aylton Court in 2017

Aylton Court after the Second World War

In 1950 Mr F. P. Davies purchased and moved to Mainstone Court, Pixley and his son, christened Walter Pope Davies but always known as Peter and his wife, Phyllis (née Jakeman), took over the farm. Phyllis had not come from a farming background. She was a Londoner but had always liked country life and so had volunteered for the Women's Land Army, working at Pixley Court. Phyllis had met her future husband at the local Ashperton station whilst both were supervising the dispatch of produce. The young couple had married in 1944 and had initially farmed Pound Farm in nearby Gloucestershire. Peter and Phyllis reared a family of four, Frederick, Penelope, Diggory and Susannah at Aylton Court and until 1963 the farm continued with the large herd of Friesian cattle in addition to the hops, arable and orchards.

In 1963 the financial arrangements were changed and the family company was wound up. From this time onwards Peter and Phyllis were officially tenants. They could not afford to purchase the large herd of pedigree Friesian cattle and to the relief of the family who had disliked social engagements having to be worked around the essential daily milking routine, the pedigree Friesians were sold to be replaced with sheep and beef cattle. The farm continued to grow hops until the 1980s and over the course of time the beef cattle were changed to pedigree Herefords. When Peter Davies died in 1986, Aylton Court was then farmed by his son, Frederick, until 1989. 250 acres of the land were then sold to the adjacent farm of Lillands, Little Marcle. Susannah, Frederick's sister, bought a small amount of the land and built a new farmhouse in order to set up a chicken farm. The large Georgian house and the ancient farm buildings were converted into residential accommodation.

Court Farm

Fig. AY5 Court Farm: the original farmhouse with its 18th-century brick extension

Court Farm, house and barn, 30 yards S. of the church. The House is of two storeys partly timber-framed and partly of brick; the roofs are tiled. It was built early in the 17th century, but the brick N.W. wing and the E. extension of the original wing are 18th-century additions. The timber-framing is exposed on the N. side and on part of the S. side of the original block. One window on the N. side has original moulded frame and mullions and diamond-shaped oak stanchions. Inside the building are some original framed partitions and exposed ceiling-beams and joists to the ground-floor rooms. There is one original door of moulded battens, and between the staircases is a balustrade with 17th-century turned balusters.

The Barn, N.W. of the house, is timber-framed, and of six bays with crutch-trusses of mediæval date; the whole frame leans heavily towards the S.[7]

Like a number of other farmhouses, at the turn of the 21st-century Court Farm was finally separated from most of the land it had cultivated over several centuries. Sometimes this is a sad business with newcomers not necessarily involved in the community, which instead feels diminished as it loses yet another farmer with local roots.

Here the reverse is true. The current owners of Court Farm with its remaining 20 acres, Ian and Rebecca Jones, aided by funding from Natural England's Higher Level Stewardship scheme, enthusiastically embarked on a complete restoration of the semi-derelict but exceptionally rare manorial cruck barn attached to the farm. The major renovation and research work involved has provided information which is of the greatest historical importance.[9] The barn, now restored to its original condition of 1503 is a major attraction enhancing local events. The Big Apple promoting local artisanal cider, perry and apple juices includes ploughman's lunches in the barn and other celebrations also take place there.

The research work and documents involved have also provided much better information on the house than was available at the time of the 1932 publication *An Inventory of the Historical Monuments in Herefordshire*, revealing that Court Farm actually incorporates part of the early medieval manor.

Fig. AY6 Court Farm from the moat

History of Court Farm

The De Broye Anglo Norman family

The Hereford Doomsday Book, which lists the De Broye family as subtenants of the manor of Aylton in its margin, dates back to the reign of Henry II at the end of the 12th century and the family appear in different medieval documents until the early 15th century. In 1242 William De Broye held three hides (around 360 acres). Especially relevant for royal finances were the Inquisitions Post Mortem when the crown was entitled to take possession of the estate until the rightful heir reached the age of 21. In 1311 Nigel, son of William De Broye of Ayliston escaped this financial disaster. A number of worthies swore that Nigel was indeed 22:

> *William de Scabenore, knight aged 44 or more, says the said Nigel is 21 or more for he was born at Lamboghan on the morrow of S Laurence and baptized and this he knows because Robert his first born son was born on the said day and baptized in the said church (the same) Day and year.*

There is similar confirmation of the age of Nigel's son and heir Robert in 1341 when he was shown to be aged 27. In 1351 Robert De Broye was the patron of Aylton church when Robert Maryot was inducted as its priest. He was still patron when Robert Maryot resigned in favour of Walter De Broye in 1352. By 1396 when John Rankine was inducted as priest, Christina De Broye was the patron of the church. The De Broye family then seem to have faded out. In 1411 John Warde, possibly the husband of Isabella De Broye, was listed as patron and in 1414 Philip Warde, possibly their son, fulfilled the same role.

Owned by the Walwyn family in the 15th and 16th centuries

The estate must have then moved into the hands of Thomas Walwyn of Hellens, Much Marcle. In one of the earliest wills in the English language, the estate is recorded as being passed to his eldest son, Richard Walwyn, in 1415. The estate was leased to Leonard Walwyn in 1501 and it was probably during his tenure that the manorial barn was built in 1503.

Dendrology has shown that the original barn was constructed using timbers felled in the winter of 1502/1503. In 2008 the late Dr Higgins described the cruck barn to the visiting Woolhope Archaeology Research section. He explained that the threshing floor would have been in the central bay with the doors kept open to facilitate winnowing. The sections to the north and south of the bay are slightly higher because of the debris from centuries of this activity. Hay would probably have been kept in ricks outside on the west side of the barn and fed to cattle folded beneath the barn on the east side. An additional bay was built on the north side probably some 50 years after its original construction. Another later addition was an 18th-century lean-to on the south side, possibly intended as a byre to house the valuable oxen team. The storage capacity of the Court Farm barn for peas, beans and oats would have increased the number and quality of the animals overwintered.

Fig. AY7 The renovated manorial barn at Court Farm

The estate was sold to Roger de Walleden in 1532 in order to satisfy the debts of Thomas Walwyn II. At this time it comprised 24 dwellings and 414 acres of land, including 100 acres of wood and 12 acres of heath. Later in the 16th century it was owned by the Warnecombe family, sometime Mayors of Hereford.

Documents show that permission was given to build a crosswing to the house in the late 16th century. The crosswing still exists, therefore the beams behind it must predate it, indicating that the part of the house behind the crosswing is older and probably incorporates part of the medieval manor house.

In 1567, a 99-year tenancy was first given by James Warnecombe to "William ap Gwillim, his wife Ellen and daughter Alice ... the farm place of the Manor of Aylton, all the lands, meadows leasowes and pastures ...". Around 1570 James Warnecombe died leaving, amongst other property, the manor of Aylton to his sister Maude, the wife of John Harley of Brampton Bryan.[10]

Alice later married William Hankins, yeoman, and a lease of 1597 conveyed to William Hankins and his wife, Alice, all the land specified in the lease of 1567 for

Fig. AY8 Court Farm, showing the pre-1596 section of the house

£100 for the life of Alice and 80 years thereafter. William Hankins was to pay 53s 4d to Thomas Harley and his heirs annually after the death of Alice.[11] From at least 1597 generations of the Hankins family were at first tenants and then owners of Court Farm. Descendants on the maternal side would continue to be owners until 1921 when it was sold to the sitting tenant, Mr Bull. By 1647 a William Hankins was buying and selling land with the Hammonds in Aylton and had already purchased "the farm place at Aylton" from the Harley family, although the Harleys retained the advowson of Aylton church until 1900.

The ownership of Court Farm can then be traced through a series of marriage agreements. In each of these settlements, arrangements were made for the older generation to receive an annual payment and to be allowed to live in part of Court Farm. In 1661 through the marriage settlement with Jane Myle of Woolhope the estate passed to John, a son of a William and Elizabeth Hankins. In 1689 John Hankins died. In 1699, Jane Hankins, widow conveyed the property to William Hankins on his marriage to Anne Greenway. In 1732 John Hankins, cousin and heir to William

Hankins, arranged for the £250 he received on his marriage with Eleanor Birchley to be used to repay a mortgage on Court Farm. When John's brother, Thomas Hankins, died in 1745, his will stated that all his property was to be left to John, although he left in addition £200 each to John's daughters, Betty and Jane. In 1765 Eleanor, the widow of John, arranged the marriage settlement of her son, confusingly also called John, with Elizabeth Brace.

This marriage seems to have been unsuccessful judged by the fact that scratched on one of the windows in the parlour is a poem by Pope lampooning wives. Possibly because of this, when John died quite young at 39 most of his money and estate was left to his sister, Betty, and his mother, Eleanor, who continued to own and live at Court Farm. John's will also made reference to his sister, Jane, the wife of John Brocklehurst, a mercer of Ledbury, and in the early 19th century Court Farm was inherited by Jane's daughter, Eleanor, who married a Colonel James Skey of Upton-upon-Severn.

Cider apples and hops grown from at least the later 18th century

The marriage settlement of 1765 between John Hankins and Elizabeth Brace lists 11 different fields with their names. The total acreage comes to 115, which suggests that these are Herefordshire acres rather than standard acres. (In Little Marcle a list of the same period gives an acreage both in Herefordshire and standard acres.) Although only two fields were listed as orchards, six of the other fields have a certain amount under orchard. Including these, there were around 22 acres under orchard. There was one acre of hops.

The importance of cider apples and hops continued into the early 19th century as indicated by a map of 1831[12] which shows both hop kilns and the cider mill house.

Tenanted farm until 1920

From 1788 onwards, Court Farm was tenanted and the first tenant agreement[13] was with a John Byshop. The lease of 21 years was at an annual payment of £90 and stated: "Eleanor Hankins, widow, should have for life one of the best bedrooms and free use of the old parlour and kitchen for herself and visitants and wood for firing". Eleanor was also receiving an annuity of £30.

When John Bishop's tenancy expired, the farm was supposedly let to William Cowley for 10 years from 1809 but he appears to have died soon after the agreement was made as his widow, Ann Cowley, is shown as the tenant in the land tax records of 1812 with James Skey as the owner. Although this was a difficult time for farming, the succession of tenants that then followed is most unusual and suggests that there was some considerable disagreement between tenants and the absentee landlord. In 1824 Court Farm was let to a Mr Hall, in 1825–1829 to Thomas Powell, in 1831–1833 to George Green and in 1833–1835 to Thomas Jeffes.[14]

There was then slightly more continuity in the next two decades. In 1835 Court Farm was let to James Shale. Regrettably he died soon after, so from 1837 it was his widow who took over. She was paying an annual rent of £145 for the 107 acres, chargeable quarterly. In the 1841 census she was recorded as living at Court Farm with her three daughters, Eliza 19, Elizabeth 18 and Jane 11, and one son James aged 15. There were four servants living in, one woman, two men aged 36 and 18, and one boy aged 13.

In 1845 John Mason took over the tenancy effective from February 1846. The rent had increased yet again to £185 per annum. He was to stay until 1855. He was quite elderly, aged 67 in the census records of 1851. His wife, Mary, was much younger, at 54. The household also contained a resident female servant and two live-in farmworkers, John Thomas aged 30 a wagoner and Thomas Fields aged 14 a farmer's boy. Mary sadly died in 1852 and when John Mason retired in 1855 the *Hereford Times* of 20 October 1855 advertised the stock to be sold on 2 November 1855.

Despite Mr Mason's age, the sales particulars are suggestive of a successful early Victorian farm incorporating modern ideas. Mr Mason had a substantial flock of sheep with no fewer than 52 ewes, considerably more than was recorded for Court Farm in the annual Agricultural Census of June 1941. A major consumer demand for meat at the time was for mutton rather than lamb or beef, consequently there were 23 fat wethers (castrated male sheep) as well as 48 lambs. There were only 11 cattle but these were said to be "Well bred White-faced HEREFORD CATTLE" so these were of the new fashionable beef breed. The advertisement points out that "The just celebrity Mr Mason's herd has attained at agricultural meetings, will be sufficient to recommend the cattle." The "fine Cart HORSES and MARES, excellent Cart COLTS" seem a major feature. There were 10 of them. Of these, five were working carthorses including a mare in foal. However five were colts so Mr Mason could well have been breeding carthorses. Gone was any reference to oxen.

Court Farm was the normal mixed farm with considerable arable: "Three well-ended wheat ricks, two mows of wheat, one mow of barley, and one rick of beans". Mr Mason was producing cider for sale, as well as for home consumption: "12 pipes, 200, 300, and 400 gallons each; 20 excellent hogsheads". However the description of "the apples and pears in heaps and not gathered" suggests that Mr Mason could recently have been in poor health.

Particularly noticeable compared with previous periods was the extent of farm machinery and equipment for sale which was described in detail. It included in addition to two wagons:

three broad-wheeled carts, one pair of drags, pair of breast harrows, pair of light harrows, and one pair of light iron ditto; one hammock plough, … new feet dray, an excellent heavy roll nearly new, four suits of long gears, three suits of short ditto, chaff box, … winnowing machine …

The list continued.

For at least 20 years Court Farm was then farmed by the Williams family. Jonathan Williams came from Oxenhall some 10 miles away in Gloucestershire and may well have known Captain James Skey, the owner. The lease, which was on an annual basis, shows that the rent had gone up yet again to £220 per annum. However Captain Skey agreed to pay the land tax, property tax and tithe charge, as well as provide sufficient wood for the gates and stiles. In 1861 Jonathan Williams aged 55 was living at Court Farm with his wife, Mary Ann aged 45, and was farming 100 acres with the aid of one man and three boys. It would seem that dairying (probably cheese and butter) was a feature as the household included a niece, Mary Anne Weobley aged 17, described as a dairy maid. There were three farmworkers living in, Charles Price aged 36 a carter, Thomas Weaver aged 16 a cowman and a farmer's boy aged 13. In 1871 Jonathan Williams was still the farmer, farming 110 acres, employing two men and two boys; the niece had married in 1870. In 1881 Jonathan Williams's widow, Mary Ann, was described as the farmer, assisted by a bailiff, Elijah Powell.

Following Captain Skey's death in 1864 Court Farm was inherited by his sister, Mrs Russell of Edgbaston, and then passed on first to her son, Dr Russell of Hampshire, and following his death to her grandson, Thomas Herbert Russell. They were absentee landowners, and it would appear that the farm became fairly run-down. The Inland Revenue Succession Duty of 10 May 1877 described the farm as:

the Homestead consisting of a Farm House in bad repair, Cider Mill and Implement Shed, Hop Kiln, Cider House and Granary over Stable, Cot, two barns, Bulls Cot, Open Shed, Cart Stable with Loft over and Rick Shed, Piggery and Fowl House with Fold Yard and all the buildings with the exception of Hop Kiln, Implement Shed and Open Shed are covered with thatch and are in a dilapidated condition.[15]

In 1891 Henry Shaw aged 28 was the farmer, assisted by his brother, Sydney. In 1901 Sydney Shaw now aged 30 was the farmer, living with his sister, Kate aged 28, assisted by one female servant and a boy of 11 described as a carter. However in 1911 a new name occurs, John Ball aged 37, described as a farmer and cider merchant. He had been born at Jacobs Leys, a farm a mile away and had been farming Court Farm since 1905. He was famed for his cider.

Court Farm in the Second World War

At the time of the National Farm Survey 1941–1943 the farm of 107 acres was owned and farmed by Mr Ball who was given an A grading. The survey noted that the condition of the buildings was poor, as was the condition of the ditches, and that the fences and drainage were only in fair condition. The soil was medium quality and medium heaviness. There were no cottages. Mr Ball had planted 13 acres of oats for the 1940 harvest and just over eight and a half acres of approved crops for the 1941 harvest. 62 of the 107 acres were down to grass but these seem to have included 27 acres of orchards. There were six acres of hops and, unusually, six acres of vegetables. The main arable crop was wheat with 21 acres in 1941. Three and a quarter acres were down to potatoes, a key crop at the time. There were 27 cattle of which 12 were calves under a year old. There was a small flock of 60 sheep, including 20 lambs. There were only 60 poultry. There were no tractors. The farm employed two full-time male workers and two part-time women who were employed for the hop harvest.

Court Farm after the Second World War

On the death of John Ball in 1955 Court Farm was owned first by Mr Roberts, a fruit farmer from Putley. In the early post-Second World War period hops were an important and normally profitable crop with additional hop kilns built in the 1950s. From 1965 Mr Ben Tremayn was the owner. Throughout this period Court Farm continued to be a mixed farm until Mr Tremayn sold most of the land in the years before his retirement in 2000, leaving only 20 acres at the time of the final sale to Ian and Rebecca Jones in 2000. The farmhouse, Tithe Barn and farm buildings are now restored to a state worthy of such a historic site.

LITTLE MARCLE PARISH

Little Marcle is a small parish with an area that has changed little over the centuries. In 1851 the total parish was only 1,218 acres. In the 1886 revisions it gained a small acreage which included the farmstead and part of the land of Flights Farm which had previously been in Ledbury parish. Even so, the total acreage only rose to 1,249 and has remained around this level. Throughout the 19th and early 20th century the population barely changed. The census recorded the population at 152 in both 1841 and 1891. It reached its peak of 162 in 1921 and then fell throughout the 20th century to a mere 103 in 1991. Partly in consequence of the conversion into housing of the old farm buildings at Brook Farm the population rose again and reached 152 in 2011.

The Domesday Book records two manors in Little Marcle. The larger of the two was comprised of five hides. It was originally held by the Saxon Turchill but was then given to the important Norman De Lacy family. By the early 13th century it was held by the De Somers family. In the 17th century this formed the basis of the Little Marcle estate owned by the Catholic family of the Bodenhams of Rotherwas and comprised farms in Little Marcle and also in the parishes of Aylton and Pixley. In 1670 this was purchased by Thomas Hanbury and subsequently purchased in 1750 by Lord Somers from the then owner Velters Cornewall of Moccas Court who had acquired it following his marriage to the Hanbury co-heiress, Catherine. Of the six farms discussed below, Brook Farm, Laddin Farm, Lillands and Little Marcle Court all formed the Little Marcle parish part of this estate. It is also possible that Baregains Farm formed part of this estate.

The smaller Domesday manor had been held by the Saxon Britac but was included in lands granted to Turstin Fitz Rolf. For a time the De Somers family became the overlords for this manor. Subtenants of the De Somers family were the Tyrell family whose name remained at least until recently in the smallholding Tyrell's Frith. In 1407 14 acres of woodland in 'Tirrells' Frith were bequeathed to St Katherine's Hospital, Ledbury in 1407 by Marjorie Wynde. The smallholding belonged to St Katherine's Hospital and then to its successors as land owners, the Church Commissioners, until after the Second World War. The land farmed by Lower House Farm in the 18th century was originally part of this smaller Domesday manor. Lower House Farm was owned by a succession of small landowners in the late 18th and early 19th centuries and was purchased by the then farmer sometime before 1910.

As was general throughout East Herefordshire there was a remarkable continuity in the number of farms right from the time of the population census in 1841 until well into the latter part of the 20th century. This can be seen by comparing the 1851 census which lists the farmers and acreage with the returns to the National Farm Survey in 1941–1943[16]. In 1851 nine different farm holdings were listed. In 1941–1943 the same nine holdings were recorded (the six farms discussed below and three smallholdings: Tyrell's Frith 25 acres, Putsons 20 acres and Lady Meadow nine acres). In addition Flights Farm, included under Ledbury in 1851, appears in the National Farm Survey in 1941–1943. By 2017 three of the farmhouses discussed below, Brooks Farm, Little Marcle Court and Lower House Farm were no longer associated with their long-standing land holdings.

Baregains Farm

Fig. LM1 Baregains Farm: the early 18th-century farmstead and buildings were replaced after the Second World War

Barns, 150 yards N. of Baregains and 2¾ m. N.N.W. of Ledbury church. Both have exposed timber-framing and the N. barn incorporates some late 16th or early 17th-century moulded timbers.[17]

Marion and Desmond Samuel moved to Baregains Farm following their marriage in 1972. At this time the farm was 142 acres. To respond to the increasing needs of mechanisation, the Samuels purchased first an additional 17 acres and some years later a further 40.

Around half the farm is arable (wheat, barley and rapeseed). The Samuels also keep a herd of 30 sucker cows and a bull, and graze sheep belonging to the upland farmers from around the Builth Wells area during the winter period.

The other farmhouses described contain at least a vestige which dates back to the beginning of the 18th century or more likely to the 17th century. In contrast, both the farmhouse and the buildings of Baregains Farm were constructed shortly after the Second World War after the complete demolition of the much older farmhouse and buildings, including some historic barns listed in *An Inventory of the Historical Monuments in Herefordshire* in 1932.

History of Baregains Farm

The apparent modernity of the present buildings belies the antiquity and importance of the farm.

The land tax records of the late 18th century show Baregains to be owned at this time by the Bishop of Hereford. Baregrains formed the major part of the exchange described in Chapter 1 whereby the Bishop of Hereford received land in Little Marcle parish in exchange for the manor of Eastnor.

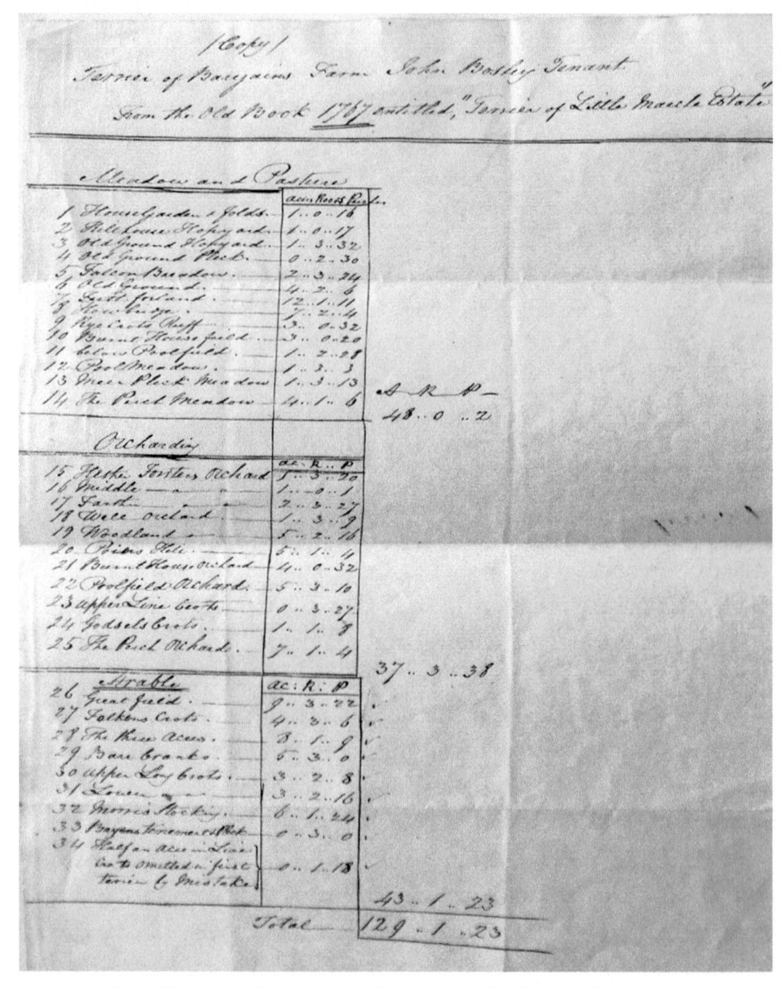

(Copy)

Terrier of Baregains Farm John Bosley Tenant

From the Old Book 1767 entitled, "Terrier of Little Marcle Estate"

Meadow and Pasture

	acres Roods Perches	A R P
1 House garden & folds	1..0..16	
2 [illegible] Hopyard	1..0..17	
3 Old Ground Hopyard	1..3..32	
4 Old Ground Pleck	0..2..30	
5 Falcon Meadow	2..3..24	
6 Old Ground	4..2..6	
7 [illegible]	12..1..11	
8 [illegible]	7..2..4	
9 Rye Croft [illegible]	3..0..32	
10 Burnt House field	3..0..20	
11 below Poolfield	1..2..28	
12 Pool Meadow	1..3..3	
13 [illegible] Pleck Meadow	1..3..13	
14 The Porch Meadow	4..1..6	48..0..2

Orcharding

	ac. R. P	
15 Hither Forters Orchard	5..3..20	
16 Middle	1..0..1	
17 Farther	2..3..27	
18 Well orchard	1..3..9	
19 Woodland	5..2..16	
20 [illegible] Hill	5..1..4	
21 Burnt House Orchard	4..0..32	
22 Poolfield Orchard	5..3..10	
23 upper Lime Crofts	0..3..27	
24 Godsels Crofts	1..1..8	
25 The Porch Orchard	7..1..4	37..3..38

Arable

	ac: R: P	
26 Great field	9..3..22	
27 Folkens Crofts	4..3..6	
28 The three acres	3..1..9	
29 Bare [illegible]	5..3..0	
30 upper Long crofts	3..2..8	
31 Lower	3..2..16	
32 Morris's [illegible]	6..1..24	
33 [illegible]	0..3..0	
34 Half an acre in Lime Crofts omitted in first terrier by mistake	0..1..18	
		43..1..23
Total		129..1..23

Fig. LM2 Copy of a terrier of 1767 showing land use at Baregains18

Amongst the documents of the Church Commissioners in the Herefordshire Archive and Records Centre relating to this exchange is a copy of a 'terrier' (a description of a manor which follows a topographical arrangement) for Baregains Farm in 1767 shown below which provides a remarkable picture of 18th-century farming. This gives the acreage of Baregains and its division between meadow and pasture, orcharding and arable. Significantly, just over one acre is identified as "an old ground hop yard" showing that Baregains had been producing a small amount of hops for quite some time. Cider was presumably very important as no fewer then 37 acres of the 129 acres listed were given up to orchards. The tenant was a John Bosley.

In keeping with the times, the Bosley family were associated with Baregains for at least a hundred years. The population census of 1841 shows the tenant to be another John Bosley, who was living there with Elizabeth, his wife, and their two sons, James and William. No fewer than four farm servants lived in. The Tithe Map assessment of 1840 shows John Bosley to be farming 163 acres including just over four acres of hops for which he was paying an extra tithe of £1.3s 6d. In 1851 the tenant was Benjamin Bosley aged 50, unmarried, living with his sister, Mary, and nephew, Edward Bosley, described as a farm labourer. By 1861 Edward Bosley had taken over the tenancy and was farming 100 acres. He was still farming there in 1871 but the acreage had dropped to 80.

By 1881 the long association of the Bosley family with Baregains was at an end. The tenant now was William Stephens aged 41 whose mother, Mary Stephens, was farming the historic Little Marcle smallholding called Tyrell's Frith. William had previously been farming another Little Marcle smallholding, Putsons, with only 28 acres. William Stephens seems to have been an energetic farmer. The land valuation of 1910 shows the Church Commissioners as owning Baregains and the land farmed by William Stephens to have increased to 234 acres. It was not the best quality land, consequently the estimated rent was only £93 15s.

William Stephens and his wife, Mary Anne, were recorded at Baregains in the census of 1911. Two of his younger sons were still in the family home. They were very much a working family. Albert aged 20 was described as a wagoner and his brother, Ralph, aged 18 as a shepherd. By this year one of his other sons, also called William, was farming Tyrell's Frith. Albert volunteered at the beginning of the First World War, joining the King's Shropshire Light Infantry. Sadly in June 1915 his parents received a letter from the sister in charge of the 3rd Casualty Clearing Station at Bailleul informing them of his death.[19]

Baregains Farm in the Second World War

The National Farm Survey of 1941–1943 and the annual Agricultural Census of June 1941 draw a dismal picture of Baregains at this period. It was farmed by the owner, Mr J. Tristram, and comprised around 111 acres. He had farmed there for 22 years. The farmhouse and buildings were in bad state. The hedges and ditches were also in a bad state and drainage and the cottage only designated as 'fair'. There was no electricity. Mr Tristram was given a C rating on the grounds of old age and personal failing, indicative of his extreme difficulties and total inability to farm effectively in these most difficult of times. He had planted five acres of wheat for the 1940 harvest and a further seven acres for the 1941 harvest. The CWAEC minutes show that the wheat crop had failed and that the land had been replanted with oats. The main activity of the farm was dairying, with a dairy herd of 22 plus a bull. The farm was put up for sale in April 1942 but was tenanted by a Mr M. Dawe in June 1942. Mr Dawe seems to have previously farmed three acres of Baregains' land for eight years paying an annual rent of £9.

Baregains Farm after the Second World War

After the Second World War Baregains was farmed by Mr Reginald Williams. It was a mixed farm of 130 acres with both arable and a herd of pedigree Hereford cattle. Mr Williams also purchased the historic Ast Wood now owned by the Olivers of Lower House Farm and others. Baregains Farm was purchased from Mr Williams in 1968 by the Samuel family of Orlham Farm, Leddington, Ledbury and is now farmed by Desmond and Marion Samuel.

Brook Farm

Brook Farm and Little Marcle Court were always the largest and most important farms of Little Marcle.

The land of Brook Farm is now owned and farmed by Mr David Watkins in conjunction with another of his farms in Holme Lacy. The fine largely 18th-century farmhouse and many of the buildings have consequently been converted into attractive residential accommodation.

History of Brook Farm

Brook Farm was tenanted by one family for at least two generations in the 18th century. In 1728 John Drew of Little Marcle died. In his will he provided £150 each to his two daughters to be invested in securities with the interest paid to them half yearly. He also

Fig. LM3 Side view of Brook Farm, showing the 18th-century farmhouse, 19th-century additions, hop kilns and other farm buildings

provided for his granddaughter so he must have been an elderly man. In 1741 another John Drew of Brook Farm died, probably his son, and his inventory provides a glimpse into farming in the early 18th century. As was common in this period, ploughing at Brook Farm must have been done almost exclusively by oxen. John left five oxen, seven cows, a bull and five calves valued at £75. He also left horses, sheep, pigs and tack valued at £42 10s. A considerable acreage must have been given up to arable as wheat, barley and other grain of all sorts were valued at £78 10s. The hay was valued at only £14. John Drew was a provident man; he had £275 let out at interest and in total the estate was valued at £566 7s.

In 1750 Brook Farm along with the other farms which comprised the Little Marcle estate was purchased by the Cocks family of Eastnor. Around one third of the Brook Farm land seems to have formed part of the exchange described in Chapter 1 whereby the Bishop of Hereford exchanged his ownership of the Eastnor manor for land in Little Marcle in 1785. In 1789 William Drew was paying £19 15s in land tax, £6 5s to the Bishop of Hereford and £13 10s to Lord Somers so the Brook Farm acreage was very substantial at this time. He died shortly afterwards and in 1795 it was his widow, Lydia, who paid the land tax.

In contrast, in the early 19th century there were a number of tenants. In 1801 the tenant would seem to have been a William Bishop. In 1808 the tenant was a Thomas Gwilliam.

In the aftermath of the Napoleonic Wars there was a calamity at Brook Farm. On 27 November 1816 the *Hereford Journal* announced the sale of a bankrupt, William Thomas, at Brook Farm. The sale particulars indicate a very different type of farming from that practised by John Drew over 70 years earlier. Gone were the oxen. In their place were horses: "seven very useful cart mares and geldings, four three-year-old cart colts, two yearling ditto". Dairying was of some significance as there were four dairy cows, one three-year-old bull and a number of pigs: "One sow with eight pigs, one ditto with five pigs, one ditto with three ditto, six store pigs and one fat pig". For the first time there was a reference to hops: for sale were 1,400 hop poles. As in the time of John Drew, arable was clearly important but a wider variety of crops were included in the sale with not only a rick each of oats, barley and beans but also a quantity of unthrashed peas, vetches, barley and oats in the barns.

Most striking of all was the extent of the farm equipment included in the sale. Wagons had only come in during the 18th century and were used to take goods to market. They were very expensive but for sale were no fewer than "three narrow wheel wagons, one broad wheeled ditto, two broad wheeled carts, one narrow wheeled ditto, one dray". There is no reference to the old 14-foot oxen-drawn plough, which had been replaced by a variety of 'modern' ploughs: "Two Double-furloughed ploughs, three Hammock ditto, three light ditto, three drill ditto and two pairs of harrows, five suites of long and two of Pfillers gearing".

In place of the bankrupt William Thomas the land tax records from 1816 show that John Dallimore was the tenant. He was to remain at Brook Farm until his death around 1850. In 1836 his son was involved in a sensational court case accused with two others of poaching in Ast Wood, part of the Eastnor estate, which was a serious indictable offence (see Chapter 8), and there are also records of some animosity between John Dallimore and his farmworkers.

After John Dallimore's death the census of 1851 shows Samuel Birchley, born in Eastnor, as the tenant. However this tenancy did not last long.

Brook Farm under John Sparkman

Brook Farm was tenanted by John Sparkman from around 1854 until his death in 1873. Born in 1824, he was descended from a family associated with Bosbury and Ledbury, but he also had close connections with North America. John Sparkman was a 'high farming' agriculturalist of mid-Victorian England. He was a very successful breeder of the new Hereford cattle and a member of the prestigious Royal Agricultural Society of England. He appeared as a judge at the local agricultural societies, including the Ledbury Agricultural Society. In the early 1860s he also became the tenant of Little Marcle Court, farming much of its 266 acres of land. He was a churchwarden and as such instrumental in ensuring that a new church should be built at Little Marcle in 1870, overcoming the indifference of Earl Somers, the owner of the Eastnor estate, to the dilapidated 17th-century church which had replaced the original parish church. It is clear that John Sparkman was not impressed by his landlord.

The Powell family history[20] gives an indication of John Sparkman: "John was a townsman's idea of a typical farmer – tall, stout, blue-eyed and with a bluff manner – very popular in the parish. Ann was dark, small and very direct bearing. They were a devoted couple." The memoirs make it clear that John Sparkman, his wife, Ann, and their five children, three girls and two boys, lived and dressed well. They owned "the Stedman clock which registered the minutes, hours and days, [which] is played by the means of a musical box type cylinder" and there is a delightful description of the three daughters sitting with their parents and brothers in the two pews reserved for the family in church on Sundays: "The three little girls were dressed in their best frocks, white striped silk, with trimmings piped in black velvet down the front and round the skirts, and white ratcheting round the neck and sleeves." Sadly the happy family life of the Sparkmans drew to an end. First Ann died in 1869. In 1871 Alice, the eldest daughter of John and Ann, married John Powell of Hall Court, Much Marcle. John Sparkman presented them with two of his pedigree heifers as a wedding present. The descendants of these heifers still form part of David Powell's herd at Awnells, Much Marcle.

Also in 1871 John, to the chagrin of his family, married Emily Hobbs, the governess he had employed after his wife's death. In 1873 John himself died, followed shortly afterwards by his second wife. The two boys attempted to continue farming Brook Farm but then gave up the struggle and emigrated to America. By this time John and Ann Sparkman's eldest daughter, Alice, was married, and her two younger sisters and her baby half-brother, Grant, came to live with her and her husband, John Powell, in Much Marcle.

From 1876 until at least 1905 *Kelly's Directories* show that Brook Farm was tenanted by John Lloyd. He too was a successful farmer and continued to farm much of the acreage of Little Marcle Court in addition to the land attached to Brook Farm until the late 1890s. In 1905 he was unusually described as a cider grower as well as a hop grower. By 1911 Robert Fitzpatrick had taken over the tenancy. At the time of the sale by the Eastnor estate of their farms in Little Marcle, Aylton and Pixley parishes in 1916 he was farming 199 acres at Brook Farm and paying a rent of £207 2s. Brook Farm was then bought by Mr John Harrison.

Brook Farm in the Second World War

The National Farm Survey of 1941–1943 and the annual Agricultural Census of June 1941 list Mr J. Harrison as the owner and farmer of Brook Farm. With its 305 acres, Brook Farm was the largest farm in Little Marcle. Mr Harrison was given an A grading. Like many other farms, Brook Farm reflected the strains of farming in the interwar period. The fences were in a poor condition and the ditches and drainage only designated as fair. There were four cottages on the farm, all in a good state of repair, and six elsewhere. Only two were let out on service tenancies. The farm relied on well water. Mr Harrison had installed electricity but only for private lighting. The soil was medium rather than heavy. Mr Harrison had already responded to the need to increase arable: 12 acres had been ploughed up for oats for the 1940 harvest, and 22 acres for wheat and eight and a half of oats for the 1941 harvest. He had two oil/diesel engines of four- and six-horsepower and one Fordson tractor.

Despite ploughing up land for the war effort, Brook Farm remained largely pastoral with two-thirds of the acreage under permanent grass for mowing or grazing. The 13 acres under hops were low for a farm of this size and also unusually, there were only five acres of orchards. There was a herd of 94 cattle, mainly one- to two-year-old beef heifers. For the time there was an exceptionally large flock of 370 sheep of which 190 were lambs. The 219 poultry were also rather a large number for the period showing that this was a commercial venture. The farm had five farm horses as well as one riding horse and one store sow with her 11 piglets. Surprisingly Mr Harrison employed only two full-time male workers and one part-time female worker, fewer farmworkers than any other farm of even approximately this size in the area. Perhaps there was close cooperation with his son at nearby Laddin Farm.

Brook Farm after the Second World War

After his father's death, it was Mr Harrison's son who farmed Brook Farm having moved there from Laddin Farm in 1951. This Mr Harrison was a bachelor. Although he appears in the National Farm Survey and was generally known as Mr J. Harrison, his Christian name was Thomas. He had the reputation of being a good but conservative farmer. Brook Farm continued to be a mixed farm, including a herd of Hereford pedigree cattle. He was well thought of by the local Young Farmers' Club and was always ready to provide them with the Brook Farm barn for their events. Brook Farm was also the venue for two of the annual ploughing matches of the Trumpet Agricultural Society. Following Mr Harrison's death in 2002 this important farm was sold to Mr David Watkins.

Laddin Farm

Fig. LM4 Laddin Farm around 1980[21]

Laddin Farm, house and outbuildings, 700 yards S. of (2). The House was built late in the 17th or early in the 18th century. It contains some early 17th-century panelling from Little Marcle Court and has a wide open fireplace with seats.[17]

In 2007 Laddin Farm was purchased by William Chase. It continues as an arable farm and forms part of his enterprise, Chase Distilleries, producing the raw materials for his specialised gin and vodka.

History of Laddin Farm

It is possible that parts of Laddin Farm date back to the 16th century. In the Transactions of the Woolhope Naturalists' Field Club of 1965 Mr Tonkin recorded that Laddin

Farm has a "17C hop room with upper cruck trusses. This building was apparently dismantled soon after being built and rebuilt in its present position." [22] Laddin Farm must have been a very early producer of hops.

There are references to Laddin Farm which date back to the 17th century. A branch of the Powell family had owned Preston Court In the first half of the 17th century. As Royalists they were dispossessed in the Commonwealth period. According to family records written up in the 1970s the Powells had difficulty in proving their title to farms in Much Marcle which had been in the possession of the family for generations. In a desperate state financially, Richard Powell was for a time employed as a simple labourer at Laddin Farm. The Powells were a large extended family. The daughter of another branch of the Powell family, Anne, married Sir Thomas Hanbury, the new owner of the Little Marcle estate and it was probably through her request that the tenancy of Laddin Farm was granted in the late 17th century to Richard's son, Thomas. (Richard retired as tenant to a property called the Mill previously in possession of the Powells.) It is possible that Thomas Powell married a Penelope Smith as in his will of 1709 Thomas Smith of Huntleys Farm, Much Marcle left a ring to "my sweet sister Penelope of the Laddin".

Throughout most of the 18th century Laddin Farm, or the Laddin as it is usually known, was farmed by members of the Powell family. John, a younger cousin of Thomas, was granted the tenancy on condition that Thomas could remain there until he died. John was later to move to Woolhope and the tenancy then went to his brother, Henry. Sadly John died young and his four children, Thomas (born 1744), John (born 1751), Peter (born 1754) and Henry (born 1756) were looked after by their uncle, Henry, and his wife at the Laddin.[23]

When Henry Powell retired around 1770 the tenancy was taken over by Joseph Dobbs, who was said to have been Henry's son-in-law. In 1789 it was Joseph Dobbs who was paying the significant sum of £4 4s land tax for the Laddin showing that it was a substantial farm. His son, Samuel (1774–1837), married Elizabeth Powell (1777–1856) in 1795 so there remained a connection on the maternal line with the Powell family.

The Dobbs family were to farm the Laddin until the last decade of the 19th century. In 1851 Elizabeth Dobbs aged 78 was described as the farmer and her son, Thomas (1815–1873), as the farmer's son. Thomas married Hannah Protheroe in 1858. In 1861 he was farming 160 acres. In 1871 he was farming 200 acres with the aid of three men and two boys. Following Thomas's death in 1873 the Laddin was farmed by his widow, Hannah, and her family until her death in 1892. The tenancy was then taken over by a John Cowell who was still the tenant in 1916 when the Laddin, like the other farms of the Eastnor estate, was put up for sale. The rent at this time was £165 for 186 acres.

In 1916 the Laddin together with Lillands and Little Marcle Court was purchased by Captain W. P. Jeffcock. It was probably at this time that the wooden panelling from Little Marcle Court was moved to the Laddin. Unfortunately the new owner experienced financial difficulties and the Laddin, Lillands and Little Marcle Court were sold again in 1921. It was then purchased by James Harrison who had previously purchased Brook Farm, Little Marcle. By 1937 his son, Thomas Harrison, was farming the Laddin.

Laddin Farm during the Second World War

The National Farm Survey of 1941 shows that the Laddin was farmed by James Harrison. (He described himself as James although his real Christian name was Thomas.4 It was owned by his father, James Harrison, of Brook Farm, Little Marcle. Mr Harrison was given an A grading. The farmhouse and buildings were in a good state of repair but hedges, drainage and ditches were only fair. The agricultural and pastoral land was in a good state and sufficient fertilisers were being used. There was no electricity. The farm comprised 187 acres of which 88 acres, rather under half, were down to permanent grass. There were 30 acres of orchards and only eight and a half acres of hops. There were 141 sheep of which 76 were lambs about to be sold. There were 42 cattle of which 25 were over two years old. The farm had no pigs or poultry. There were five working farm horses and a further four unbroken horses. The Laddin employed three full-time men and two part-time women.

Laddin Farm after the Second World War

In 1951 Thomas Harrison moved to Brook Farm following the death of his father, James Harrison, and the Laddin was sold to the well-known local farming family of Blandford. Godfrey Blandford and his wife, Pat, reared their large family of six children – Celia, James, Anthony, Tim, Julia and Lynne – at this fine old farmhouse. By the time they purchased it and despite the comments of the National Farm Survey 20 years before, the old farmhouse was in need of extensive repair. Godfrey sold the hop quota in the 1950s and in its place planted potatoes. The farm continued as a mixed farm, with cattle together with some pigs and poultry in addition to potatoes and other arable crops. For a while in the 1950s the farm also grew rhubarb for which at that time there was a good demand. To respond to the need for intensive production an additional 70 acres was purchased from Preston Court. The farm was then around 360 acres.

In the last quarter of the 20th century Tim and Anthony Blandford joined their father in the farming enterprise. To make this viable in 1983 Tim and his wife, Ann, purchased Underhill Farm, Putley together with its 100 acres. The two farms were run as a joint enterprise. Apart from 40 acres planted with cider apples sold under contract to Bulmers, the farms were entirely arable. Godfrey died in 2007 and shortly afterwards Tim and Anthony sold the Laddin as well as the land attached to Underhill Farm.

The Laddin was purchased by William Chase who had previously developed Tyrrells Crisps.

Lillands

Fig. LM5 The old orchard at Lillands with the farmhouse in the background

A significant farm for many centuries, Lillands is now owned and farmed by Michael and Lesley Skittery and James and Jane Skittery. Michael and James are the fourth generation of the Skittery family to farm here. It is a cider and arable farm with James mainly concentrating on the cider and Michael on the arable. Their elder brother, Graham, advises on landscape gardening.

Lillands has been farmed by the Skittery family for over 125 years. William Ward Skittery, the great-grandfather of the present owners, was the tenant farmer in the

1890s and then bought the farm in 1921. Records show that from the late 1860s to the late 1970s the acreage of the farm has hardly changed, varying from between 210 and 220 acres. However, with the much changed agricultural conditions of the last quarter of the 20th century, substantial additional acreage has been added, including historic acreage from the adjacent Aylton Court, and the present farm is around 650 acres.

History of Lillands

The land belonging to Lillands formed part of the Little Marcle Court estate. In contrast with the other farms in Little Marcle there is little direct information on Lillands until the census of 1841. However by a process of elimination it is possible to make an informed guess as to the name of the farmer and the approximate acreage attached to Lillands. From 1786 until at least 1808 the land tax records suggest that that John Hammond was farming Lillands. He was paying £5 in land tax so Lillands almost certainly was not much more than a hundred acres. He was related to the Hammond family of Aylton Court. The land tax records show that in 1817 and 1819 the tenancy was held by a Thomas Gwilliam. The tax was still £5.

The Tithe Map of 1838 shows Lillands to be 142 acres and tenanted by William Nutt. He was a hop grower paying an extra five shillings per acres acre for three acres of hops. According to the census of 1841 the household comprised William Nutt, his wife, Abigail, their son, Richard aged 26, and three living in farm servants, Samuel Tyler and Henry Lees both aged 14, and Charles Thomas aged 20. William and Abigail were local people as both had been baptised in nearby Checkley. The 1851 census shows that William was farming 135 acres. The household consisted of his wife, Abigail aged 60, and four live-in farm servants, Elizabeth Hill aged 17, George Maile aged 23, John Hughes aged 24 and Joseph Lewis aged 18. There was no record of Richard their son. William died in 1855 and his widow Abigail seems to have given up the tenancy soon afterwards.

By 1861 the Ledbury-based auctioneer, John Hartland, had taken over the tenancy of Lillands with 134 acres. However he had other important responsibilities as an auctioneer and land agent, and by 1864 William Mathias Skittery aged 24 was organising Lillands in addition to Flights Farm, his stepfather, James Ward's farm, which was situated just over a mile away but at that time was in Ledbury parish. This first recorded involvement of the Skittery family with Lillands seems only to have lasted a few years as the 1871 census shows Charles South aged 40 and his family at Lillands. By 1871 additional acreage had been attached to the farm as Charles South was farming 210 acres, making Lillands a large farm by the standards of the time.

He was employing seven men and three boys. The South family continued to farm at Lillands until 1886 when Charles South died. One of his sons continued to farm in the parish of Eastnor.

The arrival of the Skittery family

It was a son of William Mathias Skittery, still confusedly called William Skittery, who took over the tenancy of Lillands in the 1890s. William Ward Skittery (1868–1937) was born at Flights Farm and married in 1896 Mabel Annie Hartland, the niece of John Hartland the auctioneer and the daughter of William Hartland of Preston Court in the parish of Preston. He was therefore exceptionally well connected locally.

In 1910 all properties in England and Wales were valued for rateable purposes which gives us a window into the farm at this time. The records show that Lillands (sometimes known at this time as Lyons Hall) was in good condition with 207 acres of farmland and a little over two acres given up to the farmhouse and buildings. The estimated rent payable was £148 18s and the gross value £5,276. The acreage under orchards was low at 12 acres but these had a significant annual value of £120. All the other crops grown on the land were valued at only at £250. There were four farm cottages and four footpaths crossed the farm.

When Lillands was put up for sale by the Eastnor estate in 1916 it comprised 211 acres of land and the rent payable was £186, payable at Candlemas. There were 26 separate fields, including three pasture fields laid down by the tenant, William Ward Skittery. Slightly over two acres of pastureland were in the parish of Much Marcle, otherwise all the land was in Little Marcle and it included just over two acres called Patches Coppice – coppice land was of appreciable benefit to farmers as wood was used for so many purposes. As indicated in the sales details shown below, Lillands had all the facilities needed for a substantial mixed East Herefordshire hop farm of the period with its cider mill and cider house, facilities for hop pickers and two square hop kilns, as well as the buildings required for cattle, pigs and poultry, and those all important farm horses.

Lillands, like Little Marcle Court and Laddin Farm, was purchased in 1916 by a Captain W. P. Jeffcock, together with Laddin Farm and Little Marcle Court, but all three farms were put up for sale again in 1921 and Lillands was bought by the tenant William Ward Skittery.

The period between the First and Second World Wars was a hard time for all farmers. In addition to low prices from the mid-1920s, Little Marcle had to endure the worry and restrictions imposed by the 1924 foot-and-mouth epidemic. It seems

The **Farm Buildings,** which are almost entirely of brick with tile or slate roofs, comprise a range of coal-house, cider mill house with mill, and hop pickers' room over; a lean-to shed, the brick-built fire stacks of which were fixed by the tenant; a newly-built range comprising cider house with cement floor, poultry house, 2 pigscots and 2 good loose boxes; open cattle shed with manger and fold yard adjoining; a second shed with corrugated iron roof is the tenant's; cart stable for 6 and loft over, open cattle shed with manger, range of cattle stalls with covered yard adjoining and piggery at one end, meal house and granary, poultry house, a newly built range comprising two square hop kilns, bagging room, nag stable for two and trap-house; barn with brick floor and lean-to shed and bull house adjoining, wagon house etc. (The Dutch barn is the tenant's, as are also the sheds in Nos. 147 and 191 and the creosote tank in No. 135.)

Fig. LM6 Lillands' extensive farm buildings as listed in the Eastnor estate sale of 1916

that W. M. Skittery, known by his second name of Martin, took over the running of the farm from his father in 1926 and financial problems possibly reached their nadir in 1930 when he took his sample of hops to Worcester and received no offers at all. The entire hop harvest was ripped up and provided bedding for the cattle and horses.

The establishment of the Hop Marketing Board in 1932 considerably improved the position of farms like Lillands which were allocated a hop quota. Nevertheless, it must have been a difficult time, which was compounded in September 1938 when Little Marcle and the adjoining parishes were affected by a further foot-and-mouth epidemic in 1937–1938.

Lillands in the Second World War

The National Farm Survey of 1941–1943 and the annual Agricultural Census of June 1941 record W. M. Skittery as the owner and farmer, and the farm size as 226 acres. W. M. Skittery was given the highest grade of A for his competence at farming and had occupied the farm for 16 years. Unlike many farmers of this period the fences and ditches were in a good state of repair. Public electricity was not available at this time in Little Marcle but W. M. Skittery had installed private electricity for light but not for power. The water supply to the farmhouse and buildings was by well. Unlike many other larger farms in the area, he had not as yet ploughed up land for arable for the war effort. By the standards of the time the farm was well equipped. The farm had two oil or diesel engines of eight- and two-horsepower and one 22-horsepower Fordson tractor. There were four full-time male workers and five part-time female workers. Lillands was principally a pasture farm with 148 acres, around two-thirds of the total acreage, under permanent grass. There was a herd of 70 cattle, mainly beef, plus a bull.

There was a flock of 153 sheep including the 80 lambs, and 230 poultry. There were 15 statutory acres of hops and seven and a half acres were under orchards. There were six farm horses but no leisure horses.

Fig. LM7 Old farm stables at Lillands

Lillands after the Second World War

The early post-Second World War period was a prosperous time for agriculture with deficiency payments and other subsidies removing a great many of the anxieties suffered in the pre-war period. During this time Lillands remained a mixed farm of livestock and arable although, encouraged by these payments as well as benefitting from improved farm machinery, the proportion of land given over to arable was appreciably increased. Lillands was fortunate in having its hop quota as hops were usually an exceptionally profitable enterprise at this time. Consequently David Skittery increased the hop acreage from 20 to 50 acres in 1966.

However Lillands, like other farms in Herefordshire, endured the restrictions imposed by the foot-and-mouth epidemics of the 1950s and 1967–1968. This was particularly grave at the beginning of 1968 when neighbouring farms, including Lower House Farm, Little Marcle, were infected.

The late 20th century purchase of more acreage

As usual with Hereford farms the generations worked together on the farm with David Skittery working together with his father, Martin, who died in 1986. Especially in the last quarter of the 20th century with labour increasingly difficult to obtain, much higher wages, and farm machinery more complex and accordingly expensive, a higher acreage was required in order to obtain a reasonable return. In 1972 David Skittery bought a small farm of 45 acres, Merrivale Farm, Tarrington. By 1975 David Skittery had already planted an orchard of the new bush variety of cider apples. In 1979 he purchased The Sladd Fruit Farm, Putley which was a producer of dessert rather than cider apples. The farm however continued to have cattle until the 1990s. Despite the problems of hop wilt, through his rigid control of hygiene David Skittery unusually was able to continue hop production right until his retirement in 2003. In 1989 the family had the remarkable opportunity of purchasing 250 acres of the adjacent land to Lillands from the historic farm of Aylton Court and were able to add some additional land from Aylton parish in the 1990s.

Lillands is now a farm of 660 acres jointly farmed by David Skittery's two sons and their wives: Michael and Lesley Skittery who live in the old farmhouse, and James and Jane Skittery live at the modern house of Brierley. Hops are no longer grown and much of the land given over to hops until 2003 was replanted with cider fruit. As well as being an arable farm with the necessary rotations but concentrating mainly on wheat and rapeseed, Lillands has 160 acres of orchards. In 2017 their cider apples won the prestigious Heineken Golden Apple Award, exactly 20 years after David Skittery won the same award in 1997.

Fig. LM8 Harvesting apples at Lillands

In addition to their arable production James and Jane rear some ewe sheep for breeding with 25 acres of the farm devoted to grass for this purpose. They also produce the now locally well-known single variety apple juices simply called 'Jus', growing many of these different varieties of apples at Lillands, as well as sourcing less common varieties grown locally in Herefordshire. Jus has won many competitions and awards.

Fig. LM9 Bottling a batch of Jus

Little Marcle Court

Little Marcle Court, N.W. of the old church, is of two storeys with attics and cellars; the walls are of timber-framing, stone and brick, and the roofs are tiled. The original timber-framed building dates from early in the 17th century, or perhaps earlier, but has been so much altered and added to at subsequent dates that it is difficult to determine the original plan. Part of the E. end has an original moulded plinth of stone. The elevations have been largely re-faced with 18th-century and later brick and the projection at the W. end is faced with stone. Inside the building, several rooms have chamfered ceiling-beams and there is some exposed timber-framing. The S.W. room has a wall-post with a shaped head and a wall-post on the first floor has a carved bracket at the top. The staircase-hall is lined with original panelling and the fireplace has an overmantel of two enriched arcaded bays with a fluted frieze.[17]

Fig. LM10 Little Marcle Court seen from the front of the house [23]

Little Marcle Court, on or near the site of the original medieval manor and to this day retaining the remnants of medieval fishponds, was a fine manor house in the 17th and first half of the 18th century before becoming a tenanted farm from 1750 until 1916 with the house becoming increasingly neglected.

Owned and farmed by the Barretts, a Herefordshire farming family from 1930 until 1995, Little Marcle Court was then sold and the house and farm buildings separated from the farm's 200 acres of land. This wonderful house was extensively and authentically restored by Irene Skelton and her late husband. It is now a fine secluded private house with attractive gardens. Its very extensive farm buildings are separated from the house and restored as beautiful holiday accommodation.

History of Little Marcle Court

The land associated with Little Marcle Court passed into the hands of the Bodenham family at the beginning of the 16th century. The main seat of the family then moved to Rotherwas in 1570. In 1651 a Parliamentary Commission speaks of an Act for the sale of several lands and estates forfeited to the Commonwealth for treason. According to this a Thomas Rotherwas was living in the old Marcle Court, but a new mansion house, the residence of Robert Holford Gentleman, called New Court, is also mentioned. Was this the present Little Marcle Court and, if so, was Thomas Rotherwas perhaps living in the old medieval house? Amongst the assets of Little Marcle Court at the time of the Act were said to be: "The quitrents due to the Lord [from] freeholders of the sd manor payable at Michaelmas yearly-4s" and "Court Baron finds and Amoriants Waifs, Estraries, whim fishing fouling and other perquisites commumibury annis worth 5s".[25]

Despite the charge of treason, the Bodenhams retained Little Marcle Court, but then sold it later in the 17th century to Thomas Hanbury who on his death in 1708, passed the estate to his son, William. In 1737 William Hanbury died leaving four daughters as coheirs. It was purchased in 1750 by Earl Somers from Velters Cornewall of Moccas Court who had inherited the Little Marcle estate which also included the farms of Lillands and the Laddin through his wife Catherine, one of William Hanbury's four daughters. From this time Little Marcle Court formed part of the Eastnor estate.

As an estate possession Little Marcle Court remained a substantial farmhouse until the mid-19th century. The late 18th century land tax records give the tenant as a Thomas Morley who was paying the significant sum of £13 2s in 1792, so the farm would probably have been close to 200 acres. By 1808 the tenant was Thomas Holland and the Holland family remained at Little Marcle Court until the 1860s. According to the 1841 census Little Marcle Court was occupied by Thomas Holland's son, also Thomas, aged 25, unmarried and living with his sister, Caroline. By 1851 the son appears to have died and his father, Thomas Holland aged 70, was farming 270 acres, living with Caroline, his daughter. Despite his age Thomas Holland played an active role as a modern farmer, exhibiting at the annual Ledbury Agricultural Society Meeting and winning first prize for his bull in 1847. After his death Little Marcle Court was farmed first by a Thomas Jenkins. In the census records of 1861 he was farming 266 acres. Shortly afterwards, much of this land was then taken over by John Sparkman, who was already farming at Brook Farm.

According to the Powell family records the Little Marcle Court farmhouse: "had for some time been left empty and had become very dilapidated. Therefore John Sparkman and his wife decided to live in the unpretentious but comfortable house at Brook Farm". The Rev. Robinson was to endorse the Sparkman's attitude when he wrote somewhat disparagingly that "Little Marcle is now a farmhouse without any special features to mark".[26]

By 1871 Little Marcle Court had therefore ceased to be lived in by the tenant farmer and Little Marcle Court land was farmed by John Sparkman in conjunction with Brook Farm. The combined farm was a remarkably big venture with 460 acres employing 15 labourers and three boys, but sadly as indicated above under Brook Farm, John Sparkman died in 1873.

For the rest of the century Little Marcle Court was occupied by farm labourers. In 1871 no fewer than three families were included in the census records: Richard Adams and his wife, John Farley and his wife, and George Watkins and his wife and five children. In 1891 there were two separate families: John Farley and his wife and eight children, and Joseph Davies and his wife and three children as well as a labourer of 64 called Henry Warren. (A brief history of the extensive farm labouring Farley family of Little Marcle is given in Chapter 8.) In 1901 Little Marcle Court was farmed and occupied by William Turner. He was still there in 1910 when the land valuation of that year gave the acreage as 185.

In 1916 the Eastnor estate sold its farms in Little Marcle and Pixley. Little Marcle Court was offered for sale together with 191 acres of land and its outbuildings. It comprised "a picturesque OLD FASHIONED FARMHOUSE of considerable interest approached by a carriage drive". The tenant was Mr T. C. White who paid £180 15s rent. It was purchased by Captain W.P. Jeffcock together with Laddin Farm and Lillands. In 1921 Captain Jeffcock sold all three farms. The purchaser of Little Marcle Court was a Mr Gordon Williams. In 1922 he was recorded as a farmer and hop grower living at Little Marcle Court.

Little Marcle Court then seems to have fallen on especially hard times as it was auctioned again by mortgagees in 1929, this time with only 177 acres. According to the *Hereford Times* the bidding started at £4,000 and the property was withdrawn when it failed to reach more than £4,650. It was eventually bought by the Barrett family in 1930.

Little Marcle Court in the Second World War

At the time of the National Farm Survey of 1941–1943 and the annual Agricultural Census of June 1941 there was no electricity at Little Marcle Court and it was dependent upon well water for both house and buildings. The soil was described as medium. Mr Barrett was given an A grade as a farmer. However, as was the case for many other farms at this time, the hedges, ditches and drainage were described as in only a fair rather than in a good condition. There was no electricity. There were two farm cottages. There were seven farm horses, of which three were unbroken.

Little Marcle Court was still largely a pasture farm. Out of the total of 179 acres, 101 were down to grass, either permanent or temporary. There were 15 statutory acres of hops and a relatively modest 10 acres of orchard. The farm had both cattle and sheep.

There were 91 cattle kept mainly for beef – 45 heifers or bullocks between one and two years old and 33 calves. Out of a flock of 104 no fewer than 63 were lambs still with the ewes. The farm kept 270 poultry of which 40 were ducks and 20 geese, both with good commercial value. There were just six piglets of between two to three months old.

Little Marcle Court after the Second World War

Generations of the Barrett family continued to farm Little Marcle Court until 1995. The land was then sold separately and the house, garden and farm buildings were purchased by Irene Skelton and her husband. The house was in a very poor state but through remarkable endeavours has been devotedly restored to a glory not fully seen for 300 years yet incorporating the best comforts of 21st-century living.

Lower House Farm

Fig. LM11 Lower House Farm with an old cow house in the distance

There has been a farmhouse at Lower House Farm since at least the 17th century and almost certainly well before this time. Lower House only ceased to be a farm in 1970 when the major part of the land was sold off with the house, farm buildings and remaining 13 acres sold later in the 1970s to the present owners, Robin and Penny Oliver.

History of Lower House Farm

Lower House farm in the 18th century

Much of the earlier history of East Hereford farms is shrouded in obscurity as the farming families were not generally keen on the written word. The first written references to Lower House Farm are in the later 18th century. The land tax for 1792 lists Thomas Truman Esq. as owning Lower House and Richard Jones as the tenant. He was paying £3 1s 8d, which suggests a holding of perhaps 60 to 70 acres. In 1796 Richard Jones was "leaving off business" and the *Gloucester Journal* of 7 March advertised the farm sale. Richard Jones had been farming on a considerable scale with cattle, sheep and pigs, equipped with 'modern' wagons, carts, ploughs and harrows. Significantly, he was producing hops. There is mention of cart mares and geldings but none of oxen. Oxen were of the greatest use on heavy soil, but Lower House land is medium rather than heavy.

Lower House farm in the 19th century

In 1801 George Woodyatt both owned and occupied the farm. In 1818 he was still the owner but James Chadney was the tenant. The land tax was £3 1s 2d. At the time of the Tithe Map in 1838 George Woodyatt was still the owner and Thomas Bosley the tenant. The farm was 68 acres spread over no fewer than 14 fields. Of the total acreage around 29 acres were listed as arable and the remainder as grass.

Very occasionally though farms and farmers reach the public gaze, normally for some legal reason. This occurred with Lower House.

In early 1836 when Thomas Bosley was already farming at Lower House at the age of only 19, he and two others described as farmer's sons (John Dallimore, son of John Dallimore of Brook Farm and John Peddington), were accused of poaching in Ast Wood which was the preserve of the Eastnor estate – a transportable offence. This remarkable trial is described in detail in Chapter 8.

It is perhaps quite surprising that Thomas Bosley remained as the tenant of Lower House. In the census records of 1841 he had a young wife called Mary. He was still at Lower House in 1851 but he now had a different wife, Matilda (née Hall), whom he had married in 1848. He was farming 70 acres with the aid of two live-in farmworkers. The Bosleys then moved to Bentleys Farm, Bosbury in the 1850s, living there until Thomas died at a good age in the 1880s.

In 1861 George Dobbs aged 57 with Sarah, his wife aged 53, and two unmarried daughters were at Lower House. He was farming 104 acres with the aid of two live-in labourers and a boy. In 1871 George Truman, a widower of 67 from Dymock in

Gloucestershire and Hannah, his daughter, were there. He was farming 90 acres with two live-in men, William Daniels 60 and William Walker 18, and one boy. In 1881, 1891 and 1901 Charles Rudge, a bachelor, was the farmer at Lower House living alone with one housekeeper. Between 1838 when Thomas Woodyatt owned Lower House and its 68 acres, and 1910 when the land valuation shows Mr E. Colley as owning and farming 100 acres at Lower House, the ownership of Lower House is unclear. From the census of 1911 it would seem that it was Matthew Edward Colley who was the farmer. He and his wife, Sarah Jane, had seven living children. His son, Edward, was 17 at this time. It would seem that it was a dairy farm as his eldest daughter aged 18, like his wife called Sarah Jane, was described as a dairy maid. Matthew Edward died in 1923 after which the farm was owned by his son, Edward Colley.

Lower House Farm in the Second World War

The National Farm Survey of 1941–1943 records that in February 1942 this farm of 66 acres and was owned and farmed by Mr E. Colley. He was given an A grading and, unusually for this time, his ditches, fences and field drainage were all in a good state. There was no electricity. He had ploughed up three and a half acres of both wheat and oats for the 1941 harvest. He had owned 44 acres for 10 years and 22 acres for two years. (It may have been that other members of the family, possibly his mother, owned Lower House after Matthew Edward Colley's death.) There were 41 acres under grass of which 20 were for mowing and 10 acres of orchards. The rest was down to arable. There was the one acre of potatoes which was the minimum that the CWAEC normally required of farmers but the major crops were cereals. Dairying was important. Of the 21 cattle, 14 were cows and heifers in milk, a further five in calf, and the remaining two were calves. There was a flock of 56 sheep: 30 lambs, a ram and 25 ewes. There were 67 poultry and two carthorses. No labour was employed and there was no motor power on the holding.

Lower House Farm after the Second World War

After Mr E. Colley's retirement in the 1950s Lower House with its modest 60 acres was farmed by Mr and Mrs Walker and Mrs Walker's mother, Mrs Brewer, who specialised in the dairy. Even in the relatively prosperous period of the 1960s farming can be a hazardous business. Sadly Lower House had experienced brucellosis and then in 1967 contacted foot-and-mouth disease. The modest herd of dairy cattle, treasured by the family, had to be put down and buried in the adjacent field. This must have been heartrending. All the cows, their characteristics known, had their own names above the appropriate stalls and these remained in the then abandoned cowshed for many years. The Walkers and Mrs Brewer gave up farming two years later.

In the 1970s, after the majority of the land belonging to Lower House had been sold off separately, Robin and Penny Oliver bought the farmhouse, farm buildings and remaining 13 acres.

The Olivers retained an existing small cider and perry orchard, replanting 170 new apple trees and adding a few young perry pear trees to replace fallen veterans. The resulting certified organic fruit is sent to Westons Cider of Much Marcle. In the early 1990s they purchased 42 acres comprising most of the remainder of Ast Wood in the adjoining Aylton parish, then threatened with becoming a golf course. The southern part of this historic ancient woodland had been felled for agriculture in the 1960s, but the Olivers and other owners continue to maintain the rest of Ast Wood in a traditional manner.

WOOLHOPE PARISH

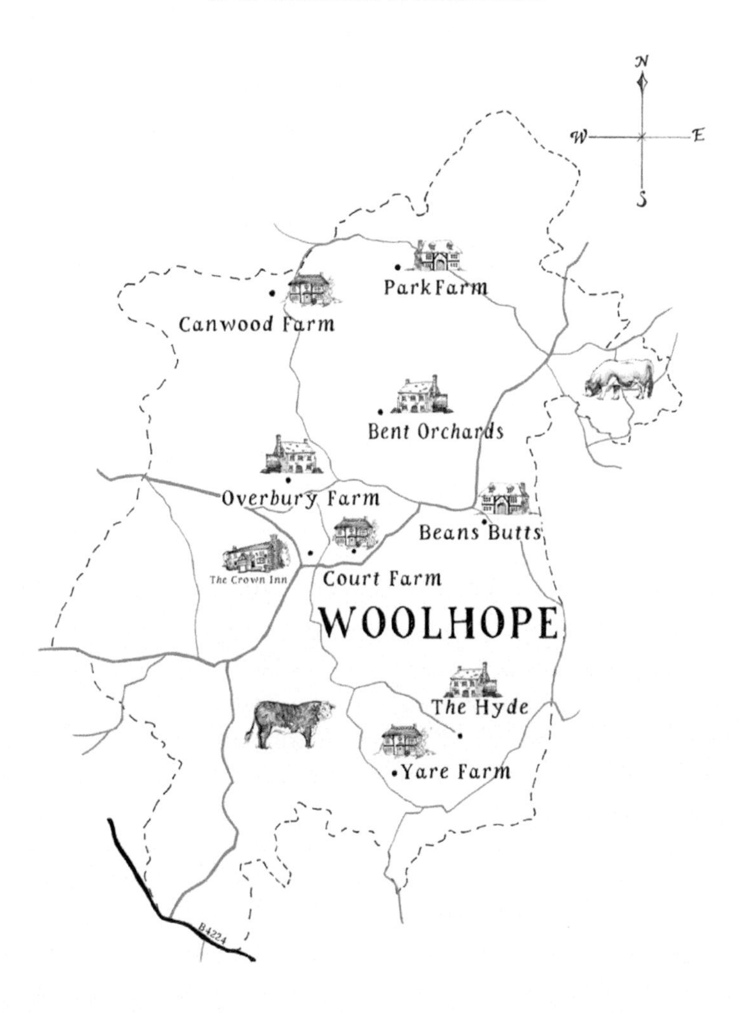

Woolhope parish is not only the largest of the parishes considered here but the most interesting both geologically and historically. The Woolhope Dome, much of which lies within the parish, is like a saucer. The sharp ridge which soars above much of East Herefordshire is of ancient Silurian limestone and is heavily wooded – a most valuable endowment throughout much of the period discussed here. The lower centre of the parish, closer to the church is, like much of East Herefordshire, comprised of heavy Devonian sandstone overlaid with recent ice age moraine and so difficult to work.

The manor of Woolhope was bequeathed to the Dean and Chapter of Hereford Cathedral before the Norman Conquest by Lady Godiva and her sister Wulviva. In the Middle Ages the Dean and chapter also acquired the ancient manor of Overbury. Consequently the freehold of much of Woolhope stayed with the Dean and Chapter until at least the latter part of the 19th century and sometimes into the 20th century. Information on the farms, some of it dating back to medieval times, is still retained in the Cathedral archives. The Cathedral leased out the land on 'copyhold' terms. The copyholder paid a capital sum for a lease either for certain number of years or on a specified number of 'lives', usually the farmer, his wife, and their heir. In addition there was a much smaller annual rent. Woodland, especially coppice, was very valuable particularly when charcoal rather than coal was the principal fuel before the coming of the railways, and the Cathedral often retained such land.

The parish boundaries have changed over time but Woolhope has always been the largest of the East Hereford parishes discussed in this book in terms of area. In the 1830s the acreage was 3,970. The boundaries were then changed to increase the area to 4,653. There was a further adjustment in 1886, but even so, the acreage only fell to 4,414 and has remained at this level ever since. Although beautiful, with so much of the land marginal, Woolhope suffered a larger fall of population in the late 19th and early 20th century than any of the other East Herefordshire parishes. The population in 1821 was thought to be 825. It reached its peak of 902 in the census of 1851. It then fell consistently at each census: the population was 769 in 1871, 647 in 1891, 584 in 1911 and 536 in 1921. This fall reflects the difficulty of farming and the hardships consequently suffered by farmworkers, sometimes dependent on seasonal work on marginal Woolhope farms.

The population in 2011 was 486. As in other parts of East Herefordshire, and indeed in rural Herefordshire as a whole, the local community from the late 20th century is very different from its predecessors. Until the 1970s the population was mainly concerned with local agriculture. Now with all the modern facilities available and beautiful surroundings, Woolhope attracts the prosperous middle-aged. Those in employment often work some distance away although now some now work from home. Despite these changes, Woolhope has an active local community with its gardening club, Women's Institute, parish lunches and the August Bank Holiday fête. There are still, moreover, strong links with agriculture further strengthened by the monthly Farmers' Market.

Traditionally Woolhope was always an area of small farmers. There were no fewer than 98 separate owners, principally copyhold, recorded in the 1843 tithe apportionment. Mostly these had title to a cottage garden or at most perhaps one or two acres. The 1851 census, which covered a slightly larger area than the current Woolhope, recorded 28 households headed by farmers or similar. Of these 12 were farming under 25 acres. There were seven households farming 50 to 99 acres, eight between 100–199 acres and only one farm larger than this, Green Hill Farm of 280 acres. The Hereford Cathedral Archive records show that a number of farms are on sites dating back to medieval times. The individual farms continued to exist until well after the Second World War and to a greater extent than in the other parishes described, some remain.

The National Farm Survey of 1941–1943[27] recorded a remarkable 35 holdings of more than five acres. (The annual Agricultural Census of June 1941 which covered those of more than two and a half acres recorded 48 holdings.) Many of the 35 were smallholdings. Only Hyde Farm with its 358 acres was more than 200 acres. There were 12 farms of 100–200 acres: Bent Orchards 120 acres, Canwood Farm 153 acres, Court Farm 110 acres, Croose Farm 188 acres, Lower Buckenhill 103 acres, Park Farm 153 acres, Underhill Farm 161 acres, Upper Hazel Farm 132 acres, Sapness Farm 106 acres, Welcheston Court 116 acres, Wessington 114 acres, The Yarr (Yare Farm) 102 acres. There were six farms of 50–99 acres, a further five between 25–49 acres and 11 of under 25 acres.

The parish was surveyed by a Mr Foxwell in March 1943. He was deeply concerned at the quality of farming here. No fewer than 17 farms were given either a B or even a C, a much higher proportion of lower ratings than in any of the other East Hereford parishes. Mr Foxwell may well have adopted a rather more rigorous approach but the survey results are also indicative of the particularly challenging farming conditions faced by Woolhope with its limestone and clay soils at the difficult time of the 1930s. Public electricity was not available in Woolhope parish and no farm had invested in private electricity.

Many of the smaller holdings are now private residences albeit often with a few acres for leisure pursuits. However as shown in the discussion of individual farms below, Woolhope still contains a higher number of working farmers then the other East Herefordshire parishes described in this book.

Beans Butts

Beans Butts continued as a farm until the 1970s when the smallholding, as well as the much larger Green Hill Farm was bought by the Rogers brothers from a local farming family. In around 2000 their sister purchased the old Bean Butts farmhouse. The old farm buildings have been converted into self-catering holiday lets.

Fig. WO1 Beans Butts farmhouse

History of Beans Butts

The smallholding of Beans Butts with its 20 acres is mentioned as early as 1618 when the main copyhold was leased to a family in Worcester: William Winston, Margery, his wife and their son, William. It is not known whether it was subleased to a local family.

It was in 1731 that the first mention is made of the Hooper family, successive generations of whom were to occupy Bean Butts until 1885. Following a local tradition, the eldest son of each family was called James and then his eldest son was called Richard in the next generation. It was Richard Hooper who was granted the lease of Beans Butts for 21 years in 1731. In 1751 the lease was taken over by James Hooper. A succession of leases follows, all to succeeding generations of the Hooper family.

There are two extant maps from around 1808. Both show Beans Butts to be just over 20 acres. The first map indicates the importance of orchards and also of woodland, so essential for charcoal in the days before coal. The second map of around 1808 provides a different breakdown of the fields and names them. Significantly, it includes a field called Little Busland of approximately one and a half acres on which hops were grown.

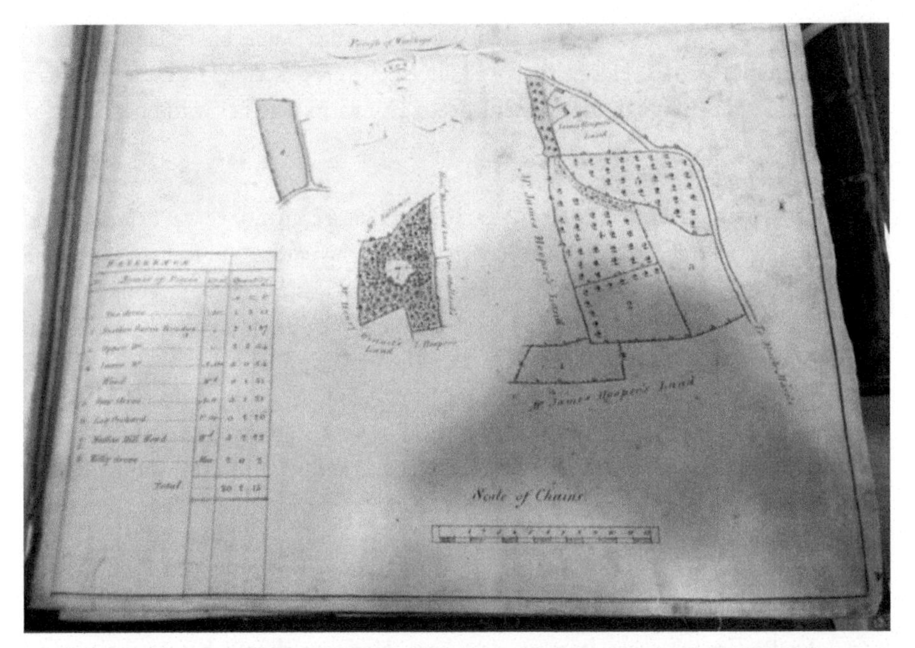

Fig. WO2 Map of Bean Butts of around 1808 showing the coppice and orchards [28]

At the time of the Tithe Map of 1838 Bean Butts had a higher acreage, just over 36, divided into 13 fields. Of this total 19 acres were under either arable or grass orchard. Although James Hooper was the copyhold owner, the farm was occupied and farmed by Anne Hooper. James Hooper, though, continued to occupy the additional nine acres of woodland also attached to the holding. In the census of 1841 Anne Hooper aged 40 is the farmer. The household also comprised her two sons, Reuben aged 20 and Richard 15, and two living-in farmworkers, Henry Edwards aged 12 and Hannah Jones aged 18.

In the 1851 census it was Richard Hooper aged 30 who was farming 50 acres and employing two boys, John and Joseph Hill aged 14 and 10, both living in. The household also comprised his uncle, James aged 64, described as a farm labourer and a nephew also called James aged 4. A cousin, Sarah Badham aged 18, was the housekeeper. This Richard Hooper was to remain at Bean Butts for at least 30 years. He never married and the household in 1861 comprised Elizabeth Earle aged 50 the housekeeper, two visitors and one living-in agricultural labourer. In 1871 the census shows that the household had shrunk to three: Richard Hooper, still farming 50 acres, a housekeeper and a living-in farmworker. The census of 1881 shows Richard and his housekeeper, still Elizabeth Earle, as the only two occupants of Bean Butts.

In 1885 the copyhold lease was surrendered to Thomas Davies but by James Hooper, not by Richard. Richard Hooper was still alive in 1891, described in the census as a retired farmer and living in the adjacent Green Hill Farm together with one lodger.

Beans Butts under the Davies family

Mr Davies was granted his lease for 21 years but in 1886 a conveyance was drawn up and he purchased the freehold. Thomas Davies was a highly successful farmer associated with a number of farms in Weston Beggard and with Claston Farm, Dormington. As was common at this period he had a large family and the purchase seems to have been made for one of his sons, Walter Thomas, who was farming at Lower Town Farm, Ashperton. Initially Beans Butts was farmed by a tenant, William Holder. However by 1901 Walter Thomas was farming there with his family, including Herbert, his 17-year-old son. It was Herbert Davies who succeeded his father by 1910. At this time he was farming 36 acres. In addition the nine acres of valuable coppice woodland described in the Tithe Map still belonged to the farm. The family remained at Beans Butts until Herbert moved to Walsopthorne Farm, Ashperton in 1920.

The *Kelly's Directories* for the interwar period show Bean Butts to have been owned by a John Rogers who was farming elsewhere. However shortly before the Second World War it was purchased by William Prosser.

Beans Butts in the Second World War

In 1941 William Oliver Prosser was the owner and farmer of Beans Butts. He was farming 47 acres. Just under 10 acres was arable, four and a half acres were orchard and the rest was down to permanent or temporary grass. There is no further reference to a wood. He had a small herd of 13 cattle and calves but the flock of 61 sheep seemed more important with 37 ewes and 24 lambs. Like most of the other farms in the area at this time, Beans Butts reared poultry – there were 120 chickens over six months old and 43 ducks. Mr Prosser had no pigs. There was no tractor but to assist with the farm there was one gelding horse. Mr Prosser was given an A grading. Unusually all the fences, ditches, drainage and farm buildings were in a good state of repair.

Beans Butts after the Second World War

Mr Prosser continued to farm after the Second World War. As indicated above, in the early 1970s the old farmhouse and the land was sold to the Rogers brothers and since around 2000 the 17th-century farmhouse has been owned by their sister and the farm buildings turned into much appreciated holiday apartments.

Bent Orchards

Fig. WO3 Bent Orchards farmhouse[29]

> ***Brent Orchards***, house and outbuilding, ¾ m. N.E. of the church. The House is a long rectangular range. The Outbuilding, N.E. of the house, comprises a cattle-shed, barn, cider and oast-houses.[30]

Bent Orchards (not Brent as erroneously given in *An Inventory of the Historical Monuments in Herefordshire*) was purchased in 1926 by Tom and Mabel Cryer. Sadly Tom died in March 1938 leaving a widow and two daughters, Mollie and Betty, to run the farm at this most difficult of times. It was then farmed by three generations of the family before the farmhouse and most of the land was sold in late 2016.

History of Bent Orchards

Throughout the 18th century, and indeed right until 1851, Bent Orchards was owned by the Winniatt family. Memorials to the family can be seen in Woolhope Church.

In an early surviving land tax record of 1752 Mr Richard Winniatt was paying £1.13s for Bent Orchards. It must therefore have been a fairly small farm at this time. In the land tax records for 1793 Mr Winniatt was shown as both proprietor and occupier

Fig. WO4 Memorial to Richard Winniatt in Woolhope church

of the land at Bent Orchards. At the time of the Tithe Map of 1843 he was farming a surprising 180 acres in 42 different fields, an acreage which also included around 20 acres of woodland. There were no hops but one seven-acre field was designated 'old hop yard' and there were around 50 acres of orchard indicating the importance of cider as a crop at this time. In the census of 1851 Mary Winniatt aged 46, Richard Winniatt's widow, was farming only 75 acres. She was employing two farm labourers and was assisted by her son who had been born in Woolhope.

The land ownership then passed from the Winniatts, initially to William Holmes, a large farmer of Pool End, Pixley. From around 1855 Alfred Hart was the tenant farming 130 acres at Bent Orchards. In the 1861 census he appears with his wife, Annie, and five small children. There is no record of any labourer being employed apart from John Scaffel, aged only 13 who was living in and described as a carter's boy. From soon after the 1861 census until sometime in the 1870s John Hawkins was listed as the farm tenant.

In the latter half of the 19th and early 20th century Bent Orchards was farmed by bailiffs. In 1881, Richard Wooding, a farm bailiff aged 54 from Radnor, was living there with his wife, Ann, and they were still there in 1891. In 1901 William Biggs aged

45, described as a farm foreman but fulfilling the same role as a bailiff, was living on the farm with Annie, his wife, and their three sons: William aged 18 described as a wagoner, and Thomas and Henry aged 14 and 13 described as 'boys on farm'. In 1910 the farm of 122 acres was owned by a Mr Birchley of Colwall. Land valuation records then noted that Bent Orchards had been sold to a Mr Gibbons of Bridge Farm, Allensmore and that a Mr Birch owned 25 acres of Bent Orchards woods. In 1926 it was sold to Tom and Mabel Cryer. Unusually the Cryers were originally from Somerset, not Herefordshire.

Bent Orchards in the Second World War

With the death of her husband just a year and a half before the outbreak of the Second World War and with a lack of labour, the war period must indeed have been a very hard time for Mrs Cryer and her two daughters Mollie and Betty. The condition of the farm buildings and house was fair but the drainage, ditches and fences were judged to be in a poor condition. The official evaluator for the National Farm Survey of 1941–1943 commented "a widow and two daughters farming this holding and trying their best to improve". Bent Orchards was predominantly a pasture farm with 97 of the farm's 120 acres either permanent grass or grass for mowing. In contrast to the importance of orchards at the time of the Tithe Map 80 years before, only 10 acres was orchard leaving a very small acreage of arable of which six and a half acres were beans for stock feeding.

The cattle seemed to be mainly for milk or calf-rearing as of the total herd of 32 there were 14 cows and heifers either in milk or expecting to calf and 10 calves under one year old. The remaining eight were bullocks and heifers of one to two years old. There was a flock of 68 sheep of which 32 were ewes. It would seem that the Cryers were intending to enlarge this flock as 10 of the ewe lambs were to be kept rather than sold. There was a modest flock of 82 poultry, including 50 pullets under six months and 20 ducks. The only pig was between two and five months old, so presumably was kept to supply the household needs. To maintain this farm Mrs Cryer and her daughters had three farm horses and were assisted by one full-time farmworker. There was no tractor.

In 1943 Mollie married Raymond Davies. Betty never married but, like her mother Mabel, continued to help with the farm throughout most of her lifetime.

Bent Orchards after the Second World War

Bent Orchards had always been a mixed farm but in the early post-Second World War period, as with many of the farms in Woolhope, there was an expansion of

Fig. WO5 Cryer/Davies family in the 1950s (back row left to right : Betty Cryer, Raymond and Mollie Davies, front row: Mabel Cryer, John and Lilian Davies) [29]

Fig. WO6 Betty Cryer with suckling calves [29]

dairying encouraged by that reliable and significant Milk Marketing Board monthly cheque. In the late 1940s, well before there was public electricity in Woolhope, the Cryers invested in a new dairy complete with a milking machine and private electricity supply to run it. The cows all had names. Lilian Moss (née Davies), Raymond and Mollie's daughter, recalls Violet and that tiresome cow, Millie: of Millie's five calves four died and the fifth was only saved through the services of the vet.

Dairying remained important. John and Susan Davies kept on with dairy shorthorns and their daughters Jennifer, Rosemary and Hazel enjoyed giving the newborn heifers their names. In the 1970s the farm changed from shorthorns to British Friesians.

Raymond Davies died in 1976 but Mabel Cryer died only in 1985 at the great age of 96. Raymond and Mollie Davies's son, John, and his wife, Susan, continued to farm Bent Orchards with assistance also from Betty Cryer. Betty died in 2001 and Mollie in 2006.

During the foot-and-mouth epidemic of 2001 there was a local case in Woolhope. The rigorous regulations imposed on all the local farmers prevented Bent Orchards for some time from selling their milk. The decision was made to replace dairying with beef cattle and sheep, although Bent Orchards remained a largely pastoral farm. John died in 2015. In late 2016 the farmhouse and much of the land was sold to another Woolhope farmer.

Canwood Farm

Canwood, house, 1¼ m. N. of the church, has been altered and perhaps heightened early in the 18th century[30]

Nestled below the Silurian limestone ridge, Canwood Farm lies close to the border with Mordiford parish. Records in the Hereford Cathedral Archive show that for well over 250 years Canwood was one of the larger farms of Woolhope, including in addition to its farmland some 50 acres of valuable coppice.

Throughout most of its long history Canwood was a mixed farm with an emphasis on pastoral, at least in the last part of the 19th century and most of the 20th century. Members of the Dale family have farmed and lived at Canwood since 1943 and although most of the farmland was sold in 2012, Stephen Dale realised a long-held dream when Canwood Gallery, a distinguished not-for-profit art gallery and 10-acre contemporary sculpture park, was opened to the public in 2016. His daughter, Helen Dale, assists him, the third generation of the Dale family to be associated with Canwood.

Fig. WO7 Canwood farmhouse

History of Canwood Farm

Like most of the farms in Woolhope, the freehold was with the Dean and Chapter of Hereford Cathedral. From 1667 until 1753 the Gregory family were the principal copyholders.[31] In a document in the Hereford Cathedral Archive dated April 1719 the copyholder was Thomas Gregory and the undertenant who farmed the land was Thomas Tombe. The total acreage was given as 250.[32] Although not specified in this early document, from the late 18th-century onwards, and probably earlier, Canwood comprised a farm of around 200 acres and, separately, the valuable coppice woodland of 50 acres.

In 1753 Thomas Foley took over the existing lease of William Gregory for Canwood Farm and the Foley family of Stoke Edith were the principal copyholders from this time until Lady Emily Foley purchased the freehold of the farm and the 50 acres of valuable woodland in 1862.

Throughout the first half of the 18th century Canwood was normally leased for a nominal period of 21 years for an annual rent of £10 per year. A capital sum or 'fine' was imposed twice during this period: once on renewal and once about seven years later. On each occasion throughout the period this fine was usually £13.

In contrast in the latter half of the 18th century and the first quarter of the 19th century much higher fines were imposed, though the annual rent remained at £10 until 1839 where there was a moderate increase to £13 per annum. In 1767 the fine was £40, in 1774 £63 12s, in 1788 £90. (Throughout this period the 50-acre woodland remained with the Dean and Chapter.) The onset of the Napoleonic Wars was reflected in a much sharper increase to £162 in 1796 and £180 in 1803. The land tax records of 1793 give the honourable Edward Foley as the copyhold owner and the tenant as Mr Pritchard. He was paying a moderate £2 in land tax. The *Hereford Journal* of 17 May 1798 notes the death of Mr Pritchard at the considerable age of 74 so he could have been farming at Canwood for much of the second half of the 18th century. Canwood was probably growing hops in the 18th century. A trapdoor on the first floor of the early 18th-century barn is still visible. It would have been opened and a hop pocket positioned underneath. Traditionally a small boy would have been lowered into the hop pocket to trample down the dried hops.

From the early 1800s the Foley family seem to have had the copyhold of the 50-acre coppice as well as the farmland. In 1838 Edward Foley paid a fine of £403 6s 8p. This lease appears to have been a transfer to Edward Foley of a lease previously granted in 1834 to three nominees, including Lord Montagu William Graham, Lady Emily Foley's brother. A valuation of the 1850s identifies the farmland (196 acres containing just over 15 acres of coppice) separately from the 50 acres of woodland, which were retained by the Foley estate rather than being rented out.

Throughout most of the middle years of the 19th century Canwood was farmed by the Badham family. In the 1851 census William Badham aged 61 and born in Mordiford some two miles away was recorded as farming 160 acres at Canwood. Despite the size of the farm he only employed two labourers, which suggests that he was not farming very intensively, possibly because of his age. He was the brother of John Badham of Perton Court, Stoke Edith, also part of the Stoke Edith estate. Hannah, William Badham's wife, had been born in Upton Bishop, some nine miles away. Also living at Canwood were their two unmarried daughters, Elizabeth aged 21 and Hannah 16, and a son, Thomas, aged 14, who was working on the farm. One of the two labourers listed, Charles Edwards aged 14, was living with the family in the farmhouse. William Badham had probably been farming at Canwood since at least 1831 as all his children had been born in Woolhope. The 1861 census records again show the Badham family to be at Canwood: William and Hannah's daughters, Elizabeth and Hannah are still living at home as is their son, Thomas. There is only one living-in servant, George Duff, described as a carter's boy and aged just 11.

The later 19th century in contrast saw a rapid turnover in tenants. In 1881 James Apperley aged 58 with his wife, Rebecca aged 55, were farming 100 acres at Canwood. Living in the household were their three sons, John aged 21 a wheelwright, George 16 farmer's son, Alfred 13 a scholar and a daughter Alice aged 11, as well as James's widowed mother aged 92. The 1891 census shows Charles Davies aged 26 as the tenant. He had been born in the adjacent parish of Mordiford whilst his wife, Susan, was from Tarrington. In 1901 John Welch aged 41 was the tenant with his wife, Mary, and two small children, Violet five and William seven months. The Welch family appear as living in Woolhope in the 1911 census but John is described as a farm labourer. Life had been very difficult. The census record for 1911 records that of their seven children, two had died.

Possibly at least part of Canwood land, including the hop yards, were farmed by others as the farm itself does not appear in any *Kelly's Directories* for Woolhope from 1913–1937. In 1931 Canwood was purchased by Horace Lewes. At this time it was in a very run-down state. Horace remained there until 1943.

Canwood Farm in the Second World War

The National Farm Survey of 1941–1943 was only carried out for Woolhope in March 1943. At that time the farm of 203 acres was owned and occupied by Horace Lewes. He was in poor health and Canwood Farm was given a B grading owing to this and to the shortage of labour. The farm buildings and house were in a good state of repair but the roads, drainage, ditches and fences were only in a fair state. Nevertheless Mr Lewis had instituted some improvements during his time. The comments on the survey report that "many acres covered with thorns now cleared". As part of the war effort five acres of grassland had been planted up with oats in 1940 and a further nine and a half acres of wheat and oats in 1941. The land was described as heavy red sandstone.

The annual Agricultural Census of June 1941 shows that 33 acres of the land was just rough grazing. However Canwood was a significant hop farm with 35 acres of statutory hops. In contrast there were only four acres of orchard. Compared with most farms in Woolhope, a fair proportion of acreage was already given over to arable, including potatoes, turnips and mangolds as well as corn. Only 70 acres, almost one-third of the total acreage, was down to permanent grass. There was a herd of 44 cattle of which 30 were beef animals over one year old. Lambs were an important enterprise with a large flock of 249 sheep including 139 lambs about to be sold. There were 143 poultry but no pigs. To run this farm there were three farm horses and a further three unbroken horses. There were five full-time workers of whom four were men. In addition there were 14 part-time workers, all female (presumably mainly for the hops but additional to hop pickers). There was no tractor.

Canwood Farm after the Second World War

Ellis and Olive Dale purchased Canwood about the time their son Stephen was born in 1943. Ellis Dale was from a farming family from Llanwarne, but the considerable sum needed for the purchase probably came from Olive's father who is thought to have made money in Australia. In the post-war period the Dales ran Canwood as a mixed farm but with some emphasis on livestock.

Stephen and his brother, Robert, took over all but 80 acres of Canwood from their parents around 1973. To satisfy the requirements of the latter 20th century an additional farm, Home Farm, Much Dewchurch, was purchased. Ellis and his daughter, Jenny Jackson, continued to run the remaining 80 acres as mainly a livestock enterprise. Farming can be enjoyable and reminiscing about this period, Jenny considered these among the happiest and most fulfilling years of her life. The 80 acres were then merged into the joint farming enterprise.

Stephen and Robert made what at the time was a radical decision to convert the two farms entirely to arable, removing the hedges and purchasing the most modern and best harvesters. This was a highly profitable strategy in the last quarter of the 20th century. In the second decade of the 21st century Stephen and Robert retired and apart from 10 acres the farmland was sold in 2012.

Developments since 2012 have seen a metamorphosis and more of a beginning rather than the end of Canwood's long history. Stephen Dale has always been a pioneer. Most unusually for a Herefordshire farmer he is passionate about, and remarkably knowledgeable on, modern sculpture and art. In the 1970s he was diagnosed as suffering from leukaemia, at that time considered incurable, and spent months at St Bartholomew's Hospital in London as part of their research programme into the disease. He was one of the first patients to be successfully treated. In leisure moments he visited the Tate Gallery where he developed a passion for sculpture and modern art. Over the years he has come to know many of the artists and has himself answered the question: "Why should not a rural county like Herefordshire have a world-class art gallery?" The entrance to Canwood Gallery is free and any profits are donated to Bart's Charity. The original cow house is now a gallery while still maintaining all its original structures, including that little trapdoor where small boys in the 18th century were lowered down to trample the hops in the hop pockets. The art is also exhibited in a remarkable and specially designed new building.

Fig. WO8 The old cow house at Canwood during its conversion into a gallery

The gallery's exhibitions include works by painters and sculptors of international repute from all over the world as well as local artists. Around the 10 acres are fine examples of modern sculpture. In the distance can be seen one of Canwood Farm's former 'hundred acre fields' with an ancient oak tree still in place. Canwood lives on.

Court Farm

> The Court, house, on the N. side of the road, 320 yards E. of the church, was built early in the 18th century. The walls are of brick with a band-course between the storeys. The windows have solid frames with a mullion and transom.[30]

Court Farm, as its title suggests, looks back to the time when this was the location for the court of the medieval manor. On the Tithe Map and the early Ordnance Survey maps there is evidence of a moated site but this has now been ploughed out. Like most of the other farms in Woolhope parish the freehold was with the Dean and Chapter of Hereford Cathedral. It remained so until the and early 20th century.

Fig. WO9 Court Farm sunflowers and sheep [33]

The present farmhouse dates back to 1727 and is lived in by Elaine and Mike Pudge and their family. Court Farm is well known in Herefordshire for 'Pudge's Lamb' reared on the farm's traditionally managed rich grassland and on sale from the farm and in the local Farmers' Markets, as well as being on the menu of the well-esteemed local country pubs.

History of Court Farm

During the early part of the 18th century it appears that the Gregory family, who had purchased much of the copyhold of Woolhope and also the entitlement to the major part of the tithes of the parish known as the 'Great Tithes', was responsible for Court Farm. (The tithes were the annual payment due to the church by all farmers each year. The ecclesiastical authorities sometimes farmed them out to individuals.) In an extant letter in the Hereford Cathedral Archive34 dating from 1728, Mr Gregory of Wessington Court, the main copyholder, complains at the very heavy expense of building a new house. Together with the repairs to the outbuildings it had cost £150. The farm had been let to James Colcomb for £38 but he and his son had left it two years previously. Mr Gregory had however agreed with Mr Richard Winniat that when the lease was renewed Mr Winniat would take over the farm. The value of the tithes was £82 but Mr Gregory was allowed to keep only £62 of this. "It is customary to provide a dinner at the alehouse for those that came to pay their tithes. £3 10s to be allowed for this."

In a letter of 1768 the then copyhold tenant, Richard Hodges, was asking a Richard Moore of Hereford to plead with the Dean and Chapter to provide timber to enable him to repair the building, arguing that on the whole farm there is "not a tree fit for repair or even a plough bote". In 1776 the farm was let to a Carey Thomas at only £6 per year. According to Mr Hodges the annual rent could have been £45 were it not for the fact that the periodic fine payable to the Dean and Chapter was due shortly.35

The land tax records of the late 18th century do not go into the complexities of the copyhold rights of the Dean and Chapter of Hereford Cathedral. In 1793 the Reverend Hodges was shown as the copyhold proprietor of Court Farm and Stone House, and the recipient for the tithes. The tenant was listed as a Mr Howells. He was paying £4 for the land tax for Court Farm, £3 8s for the Great Tithes and a mere 2s 11d for Stone House.

Throughout much of the 19th century Court Farm was associated with the Williams family. In 1841 the tenant was James Williams aged 25. *Kelly's Directory* of 1858 lists James Williams as the tenant of Court Farm. However the family do not seem to have always lived in the house. In 1861 James Williams, a farmer, his wife, Ann, two sons, James 17 and Henry 15, niece, Mary Winniatt aged 10 (but described as a dairy maid) and one living in farmworker, were living in the School House. They were back at Court Farm in 1871. The cathedral records show that in 1873 James Williams was paying £92 to rent 112 acres. He was the tenant to the main copyholder who was Friedrich Stallard. The last record for James Williams is in the 1891 census. This shows James Williams as the farmer of 105 acres employing one farm worker. He was 69 and his wife, Ann, 62. Significantly there were five other people with the surname Williams listed as 'visitors' indicating perhaps the difficulties of this time. James's brother, William, aged 79 was described as a farm labourer, Ann Williams aged 15 a general servant, Fanny Williams aged 28 a farmer's wife, Eleanor Williams aged two and Herbert Williams aged one. However the census does not appear to be accurate. The Hereford Cathedral Archive records show that in 1889 Henry Williams had taken over the lease from James Williams. At this time of the Great Agricultural Depression the rent had to be reduced. From February 1889 it was £70 per year payable half yearly. In addition Henry was permitted a rebate of £10 each year for five years to be spent on manure.

In 1901 the census records George Powell aged 19 a farmer and his brother, Thomas, aged 21, a farmer's son as living in Court Farm. Shortly afterwards there was another change as in 1902 Walter Morgan was farming Court Farm and was still there in 1910 at the time of the rate evaluation when he was renting the land from Jane Hayes of Wessington Court. The acreage was given as 112 and the annual valuation at £90.

In 1911 the tenancy was taken by Dansey Watkins aged 30, the son of John Watkins of Croose Farm. The locally well-known Watkins family had first come to Woolhope in 1888 and three other members of the Watkins family were also farming other Woolhope farms, Park Farm, Wessington Court and Croose Farm around this period. The farm and buildings were in need of extensive repairs and the total cost of these repairs came to £56. The details provide a good picture of the farm buildings functional at this time which were suitable for a truly diversified farm. There was a stable, a loose box, a cow place under the granary, a small cattle shed, barn, wain house, piggery, potato house and engine shed. The rent had gone up to £100 per year but Dansey was also permitted a rebate of £10 per year for five years towards the cost of fertilisers. In 1926 the farm house and buildings were subject to further repairs.

Court Farm in the Second World War

The National Farm Survey of 1941–1943 and the annual Agricultural Census of June 1941 show that Mr Dansey Watkins was a tenant and farming 110 acres. Like the other farms in Woolhope, Court Farm was pastoral and mixed. The 12 acres of oats and seven of wheat were partly a response to the war effort. He also grew one acre of beans and one acre of potatoes. The rest of the farm, 89 acres, was either permanent grass or grass for mowing. Mr Watkins also had access to 40 acres of rough pasture. Of a herd of 55 cattle 23 were cows in milk or else in calf and 19 were calves under one year old. The remainder were cattle one to two years old. The 113 sheep consisted of a permanent flock of 57 ewes and two rams. The remainder were the lambs which were shortly to be sold. Mr Watkins reared pigs on a small scale with two breeding sows and 10 pigs over five months old. Mr Watkins had 30 chickens, all over six months old. He had one carthorse and was employing only one full-time worker: a larger number of farmworkers would be expected at the time for a farm of this size.

Court Farm after the Second World War

Dansey Watkins had experienced the two World Wars as well as the difficult times of the interwar period. Influenced perhaps by the particular difficulties of farming before the Second World War, he did not wish his son, David, to take up farming. Dansey's wife, Elizabeth, died in 1946 and Dansey died in 1947. Despite his father's wishes, David and his wife, Ailsa, farmed Court Farm until ill health forced David to give up farming in 1964. Court Farm, by this time enlarged to 200 acres, was sold to Geoffrey Pudge who came from a long-established East Herefordshire farming family. Sadly Geoffrey died when his son, Mike, was merely three years old and the farm belongs to Elaine's father, Roger Parker. The Pudges rent part of it for the sheep and the remainder is farmed by Mr Parker. In addition to work with Court Farm's flock of Suffolk cross ewes, Mike works as a contractor and Elaine promotes and sells Court Farm lamb throughout the locality, including the Farmers' Markets at Woolhope, Eaton Bishop, Fownhope, Skenfrith and Bosbury. Also for sale in season from the farm are other seasonal crops, including the sunflowers shown in the photograph.

Overbury Farm

Fig. WO10 Overbury Farm: the right-hand section may well have incorporated part of a medieval building

Overbury, house and cider-house, 625 yards N.N.W. of the church. The House has modern additions on the N. and W. The Cider-house, N. of the house, is weather-boarded.[30]

Overbury Farm land probably formed part of the medieval manor of Overbury. Although much altered over the years, the mainly 17th century farmhouse contains some timbers which are thought to be medieval and recently a mysterious staircase was revealed hidden behind a wall.

The farm has been owned and farmed by the Williams family since 1938 when Percy Williams moved from a rented farm near Weobley which was so infested with rabbits that exorbitant sums had to be spent on fencing to keep them out.

History of Overbury Farm

Surviving land tax records of the 18th century suggest that the farm was approximately the same size as recorded from the mid-19th century onwards with acreage of around 100 acres. In 1752 the principal copyholder was Cope Gregory and £2 0s 6d land tax was paid for Overbury, but unfortunately the records do not give the name of the farmer. In 1793 the copyhold owner was Mr Barrett and Mr Ballard the occupier. He was paying £2 14s land tax. In 1797 Mr Hullett was the copyholder.

From 1841, the year of the Tithe Map as well as the first detailed national census, a clearer picture of the farmers at Overbury can be obtained. According to the Tithe Map records, Overbury was owned in 1841 by William Mailes and farmed by Richard Mailes. The Tithe Map also records William Mailes as owning The Hyde. There were 97 acres divided into 28 different fields. There were no hops grown, but one of the fields of just over four acres was described as 'old hop yard'. There were around nine acres of orchard. The Mailes were a family long associated with Woolhope but it appears that Richard Mailes was not living in Overbury in 1841. The 1841 census shows a John Bray aged 46 to be the farmer and living at Overbury with his two daughters, Elizabeth and Mary Ann, and two live-in farm servants, Richard Turner aged 28 and Joseph Bayliss aged 15.

Richard Mailes was subject to a scandal in 1844 for attacking his estranged wife. For this he was bound over to keep the peace for 12 months for the exceptionally high sum of £20 on his own surety and obliged to find another surety for the same sum.

Overbury seems to have had a succession of tenant farmers in the last half of the 19th century. In 1855 an advertisement for the sale of oak trees on the farm lists the tenant farmer as a Mr Phillips. In the census of 1861 James Cole aged 31 was farming 97 acres and employing a man and a boy. Mr Cole's father-in-law, a retired farmer, was also living at Overbury. *Kelly's Directory* in 1867 lists James Cole as the farmer and he appears again in the 1871 census listed with his wife, Eliza, and five children ranging from 13 years to only 10 months old. In 1881 the farmer of 110 acres was William Slade, unmarried, living with his sister, Esther, and one farmworker. In 1891 it was Alfred Hodges aged 47, his wife, Mary, aged 38 and their five children at Overbury. The Mailes family may then have sold Overbury at around this time as the census of 1901 shows William Bendall aged 59 from Somerset was the farmer. His wife had been born at Holme Lacy. Most unusually, their unmarried daughter, Mary, aged 38, was described as a manageress in a hotel. At the time of the land valuation of 1910 William Bendall owned the farm and 95 acres, together with sporting rights for a further 13 acres of woodland. Thomas Price rented the farm and 95 acres, and he was still farming Overbury in 1917.

Kelly's Directory for the years 1927 and 1937 show Albert Williams as the farmer. He was not, however, related to Percy Williams, who purchased Overbury in 1938.

The Williams family actually took possession of Overbury at Candlemas 1939. As well as Percy, his wife, Mary, and their son, Norman, the household also included one farmworker, Ted Gurney, who moved from Weobley and remained as part of the household for the rest of his life. Norman recalls that he grew up with Ted.

Overbury Farm in the Second World War

At the time of the 1941 census Overbury was recorded as having 98 acres. The area under arable had recently been increased to just over 20% of the total acreage. There were 11 acres under cereals (four acres under wheat, three acres given over to oats and four to mixed corn), a further seven and a half acres were under root crops including the required one acre of potatoes and more surprisingly four acres of sugar beet. There were 13 acres of orchard but this still left most of the acreage under permanent grass or grass for mowing. The farm was also entitled to 10 acres of rough grazing. There were 32 cattle. Of these 18 were dairy cows either in milk or in calf, and there were five bullocks and three heifers over one year old, five calves and a bull. A flock of 129 sheep included 50 ewes, with most of the remainder lambs not yet sold. There was a breeding sow with her 10 piglets and 398 poultry, a large flock for the period. The farm had three farm horses but only two male farmworkers; one full-time and one part-time. Mr Williams was given an A rating. The farmhouse, farm buildings and drainage, ditches, and hedges were all described as being in a fair condition. Four and a half acres had been ploughed up for oats for the 1940 harvest with a further four and a half acres for the 1941 harvest.

The milk round was important. Norman Williams's early memories were of delivering milk to the neighbourhood before going to school. During the latter part of the Second World War Norman recalled the farm also had prisoners of war to assist with the work. The three Italian prisoners of war were not a success. "Father, as he was leaving for Hereford market, found the first asleep in a wheelbarrow, the second did not understand work, the third one was allergic to dust". However Overbury then had a German prisoner of war from a farming background in the Bockum area known as John who lived in the farmhouse with them. The Williams family kept in touch with him for many years after the war and visited him in Germany.

Overbury Farm after the Second World War

During the early post-Second World War period milk was an important source of income as indeed was the case for many other smaller Herefordshire farms. To generate further income the family had a stall in the Butter Market in Hereford and the milk was also sold to the Milk Marketing Board. Originally Percy and his wife, Mary, had to do all the milking by hand but in 1952, even before mains electricity was available in Woolhope, the Williams bought a generator and their first milking machine.

In 1976 when the Milk Marketing Board introduced minimum purchases Overbury ceased producing milk in favour of suckling calves. They then kept about 16 or 17 cows for the calves and also had a flock of around 100 ewes. The farm benefited from Percy Williams's skill in purchasing animals and Norman Williams recalls that his father "was a market man, especially with sheep and spent much of his time at Hereford market". Hereford market was particularly important at this time: "There were steers on a Thursday, Fridays was heifers. Prior to selling heifers on Friday you had barren cows."

Most of the perimeter of the farm adjoined Wessington Court land and hedging was a constant occupation. Norman Williams recalls that he was engaged in this task in 1952 when a lady came to bring them tea and inform them that King George VI had died. The soil is not easy to work "some of it is white clay, so heavy one could make pots out of it" yet Percy Williams planted cider orchards – "Father planted quite a lot of trees" – and the farm made its own cider right up till 1976.

Overbury is now run by Norman's son, Andrew, and his wife, Tracey, the third generation of the Williams family to farm Overbury. It continues to be a mixed farm but with an increasing emphasis on sheep and beef cattle.

Park Farm

Fig. WO11 Park Farm sheep with the 17th-century farmhouse in the background

> ***Park Farm***, house and outbuildings, nearly 1½ m. N.N.E. of the church. The House is stone-built and of two storeys with a basement. It dates possibly from late in the 17th century, but is not all of one date. There is an old Cattle-shed, S.E. of the house, and adjoining it an open shed of five bays.[30]

Graham Watkins is the fourth generation of his family to farm this fine farm which is nestled on the slopes of the Woolhope Dome. His great-grandfather Gwilliam Watkins, whose family originally came from Radnorshire, moved here in 1898. Many earlier generations of farming families have also loved and worked this land.

Remarkably Park Farm has achieved the transformation to the 21st century whilst still retaining nearly all the fields and indeed in quite a number of cases the actual field names listed in the Tithe Map of 1845 of over 170 years earlier. Thus Cockwood remains the same, as does Big Field, and Orchard. Fishpool is now simply called Pool whilst the field that was numbered 1178 on the 1845 Tithe Map is now Little Field. Interestingly Common Field which retains the same name was not originally common land in the usual sense of the word but land used for the overnight pasturing of animals passing through Woolhope on their way to markets either locally in Ledbury or else further afield.

History of Park Farm

It is not easy to trace the names of earlier farmers. However the name of Park Farm itself gives a hint of an earlier existence as the area surrounding the farm was originally Devereux Park. From relatively early medieval times the Ravenhill family were important tenants of the Woolhope manor and it may well be that that Park Farm is close to, or on, the site of their principal messuage, Raven Hall. A branch of the Ravenhill family remained important landowners in Woolhope in the 18th century. It seems probable though that the principal copyholders from fairly early in the 18th century were the Foley family of Stoke Edith. The 1752 land tax records show Thomas Foley Esq. to be the copyhold owner of Devereux Park and the land tax payable to be £3 3s. The tenant's name is not given. Nor is it given in the later land tax records. It may well be that Park Farm was farmed directly by the Foley estate during the later 18th century and early 19th century. Even the land tax records of 1830 do not not list a tenant for 'Debereux farm'.

In the 1841 census the tenant farmer is Richard Roberts aged 62, his wife, Mary, 56 and a large family of four sons and two daughters ranging in age from 30 to nine. The only indoor farm worker was a boy, Thomas Poole aged 11. From at least 1851 when he first appears in the census until his death in 1884 Anthony Godsall was the tenant of Park Farm. He was a descendant of the 18th century Godsalls of Showle Court, Yarkhill. His first wife, Catherine, died young and he married his second wife, Ann née Pitt, in 1865. They had no children. In 1851 he was employing four men and a boy and farming 140 acres. In 1861 he continued to farm 140 acres, employing four men and a boy. Three of these were living in: James Hill a carter, Thomas Harris a groom and cowman aged 19, and James Prosser 14 a cowman's boy. His niece, Susanna, aged 28 was his housekeeper. In 1881 he was farming 160 acres. The household comprised his wife, Ann, a niece, Elizabeth Pitt aged 24 and three male farm servants who had originally been listed as wagoner, cowman and carter's boy in the 1861 census. Presumably when the 1881 census said he was employing one labourer this was in addition to these three living-in employees. In 1891 William Turner was listed as the tenant with Elizabeth, his wife aged 336 and a six-year-old daughter.

Gwilliam Watkins took over the tenancy of Park Farm in 1898 and the Watkins family have been at Park Farm since then. Gwilliam's brother, John, was already farming Croose Farm in Woolhope and John's son, Dansey, later took over the tenancy of Court Farm in 1911 (see above). Unlike most of the other local farmers the Watkins were originally nonconformists and Gwilliam played a leading role in the Baptist Chapel at Checkley. According to the 1910 nationwide valuation of rateable values, Park Farm at this time comprised 147 acres, valued at £59 10s per year. In the 1911 census Gwilliam and his wife, Elizabeth's two daughters, Elizabeth Mary aged 21 and Annie 18, were described as workers with Elizabeth Mary specifically described as dairy worker so presumably the mixed farm included the production of cheese and butter. Another tenant, Jane Cox, farmed a further 24 acres which were listed as part of Park Farm and the landowner, Paul Foley, kept Park Farm Plantation of 20 acres.

At the great Foley sale of 1919/1920 Park Farm comprised only 114 acres. Gwilliam Watkin's younger son, Benjamin, took over the farm around 1931.

Park Farm in the Second World War

The National Farm Survey of 1941–1943 and the annual Agricultural Census of June 1941 show that Park Farm was farmed by Benjamin Watkins. The farm was largely pastoral. Of the 153 acres only nine acres were under cereals (of which six were oats), and there were three acres of root crops, including the usual one acre of potatoes. There was a small orchard of four acres and the rest of the land was either permanent pasture or pasture for mowing. Suckler calves appear to have been a significant source of income as of the total of 39 cattle, 19 were calves under one year old compared with 15 cows and heifers either in milk or in calf and five other bullocks and heifers. There was a significant flock of 139 sheep of which 64 were the breeding ewes and most of the remainder were lambs yet to be sold. The farm had two breeding sows and 11 piglets. There was a flock of 182 chickens, mostly over six months old. There were three farm horses and the farm employed one full-time male farmworker.

Park Farm after the Second World War

In the 1960s Benjamin's son, David, and his wife, Jean, joined the faming enterprise and their four sons, Graham, Bryan, Keith and Philip were born at Park Farm. Benjamin died in 1977. The Watkins recognised that the acreage farmed needed to be increased in order to operate Park Farm more effectively and purchased part of the Green Hill Farm land. At the beginning of the 21st century David Watkins used to say "whereas in the 1940s one lamb would pay for three weeks wages now three lambs are needed for just one week's wage". Until around the year 2000 Park Farm employed one farm worker but since then all the work has been done within the family. The Watkins have recently made a further purchase of land, so that currently they own around 180 acres and rent some 70 more, bringing the farm to around 250 acres.

David Watkins died in 2004. Park Farm is now run by Graham and his wife, Susan. It remains a pastoral farm, traditional for much of Woolhope. Until July 2015 the farm maintained a milk herd of some 70 British Friesians but this has now been converted into a suckler beef herd. Following the age-old tradition, the cows continue to have names. The farm also has a flock of about 200 ewes. Much of the fodder for the animals is grown on the farm, including hay, but concentrates do need to be bought in.

The Hyde

Fig. WO12 The Hyde in 196436

Hyde House, 1 m. S.E. of the church, has a projecting wing on the N.E. side.[30]

The Hereford Cathedral Archive contains records of the copyhold leases of The Hyde right back to 1629 until the freehold was sold in 1865.37 There are also early references to a medieval messuage. Although the acreage attached to the farm has differed over time it has been one of the larger farms in Woolhope throughout its history. Compared with the other Woolhope farms described, the soil is good, mostly red sandstone rather than limestone.

This historic farm has seen remarkable transformations in the past 50 years since it was sold by Mr A.H. Thompson in 1964. Since 1984 it has been the home of John and Mary Windham. The 297-acre farm supports a major sheep enterprise of around 700 ewes. It is registered under the higher-level stewardship scheme as part of which there has been considerable replanting of woodland and a successful coppicing rotation instituted.

Fig. WO13 View from The Hyde in 1964[36]

History of The Hyde

There was a farmhouse on or near the site of the present one far back in medieval times. An early document in the Hereford Cathedral Archive refers to a messuage called le Hyde in the possession of John Hethe, also called John Hyde, and Joan, his wife, late wife of John Skegge. In another somewhat later document Robert Ware and Siabel his wife were specified as the copyhold tenants of The Hyde.

The Hereford Cathedral Archive contains a record of The Hyde from 1629–1865.37 In 1698 the copyhold of The Hyde as well as other farms in Woolhope was leased to William Gregory. Following his death in 1705 The Hyde was leased between 1705 and 1718 to his widow and afterwards to his granddaughter, Elizabeth. The copyhold between 1718 and 1738 was leased to Thomas Traunter and after his death to his widow, Margaret.

In addition to a modest annual rent copyhold farmers paid a significant periodic capital sum ('a fine'). Astonishingly the annual rent for The Hyde remained at 54s 10d from 1663 to 1820. The Hyde was also required to provide 100 bushels of charcoal a year or to pay £6 per year in lieu throughout this long period to the Dean and Chapter, an indication of the importance of charcoal as the main fuel in Herefordshire and its consequent value as a source of income.

Although the annual rent remained unchanged during this long period the same was not true of the fine, the periodic capital charge that was charged every six to eight years. Between 1677 and 1766 it oscillated, but was never lower than £20 or higher than £28. In the review of 1776 the fine was £76 or two and a half times its previous level and these rises continued with sharper increases at the time of the Napoleonic Wars. In 1807 the fine was £200 and in 1820 it was £600. The sum was not always mentioned in the succeeding years but it was never as high as during the first two decades of the 19th century again. It was £105 in 1836 and £182 in 1853.

Long association with the Mailes family 1738–1847

For over 110 years the copyhold of The Hyde was associated with generations of the Mailes family. The Hereford Cathedral Archive shows that from May 1738 until May 1759 the copyhold lease was held by William Mailes. From 1759 it was held by Richard Mailes. In 1780 William Mailes both owned the copyhold and farmed The Hyde. He was paying £5 5s 11d land tax showing that The Hyde was a large farm of over 100 acres. In 1807 the former lease was surrendered and the new lease drawn up for John Mailes MD.

In 1828 following the death of John Mailes, his son, William Mailes, took over the lease. In the same year, following a dispute on boundaries, a large plan in parchment was drawn up. The farm of 119 acres was divided into 99 different strips, partly in common fields. In addition the farm had two entitlements to woodland (six acres and two roods in Glowson Wood and four acres one rood in Haugh Wood).

The common fields had evocative names. The Hyde was entitled to 11 pieces of land in Winter Land, six in Bali Rough, four in Hall Meadow, eight in Breadless, six in Flowerland and four in Barn Croft.

In 1836 it was Peter Mailes who took over the lease. At the time of the Tithe Map in 1844 William Mailes was the copyhold owner and The Hyde had 208 acres divided into 34 different fields, including the strips in the common fields. There were around 32 acres of orchard. Only one field of two acres three perches was given up to hops.

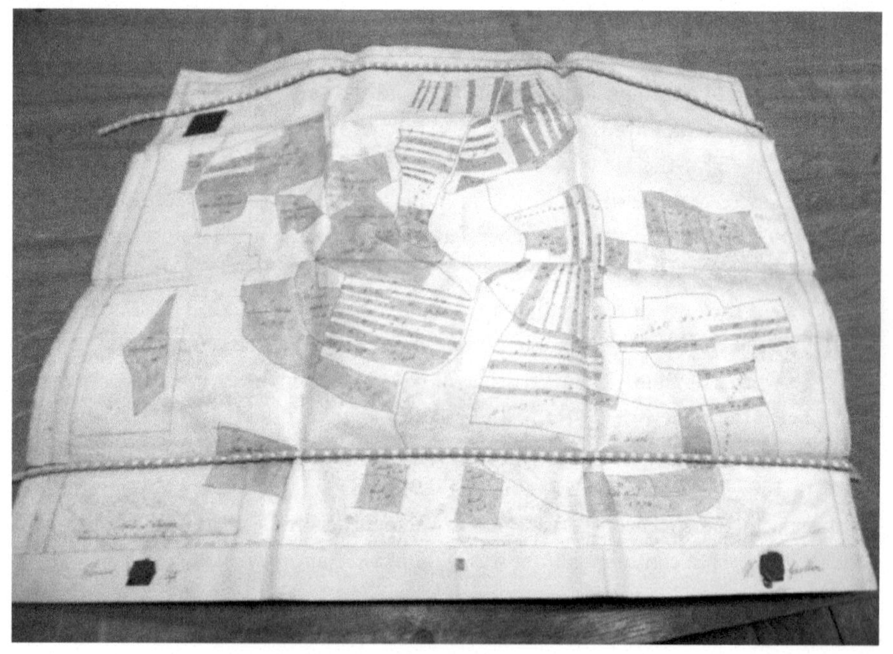

Fig. WO14 Map of The Hyde at the time of the boundary dispute in 1828 [37]

However in 1847 Peter Mailes purchased the lease to the Crown Inn, Woolhope and surrendered the lease of The Hyde to Benjamin Hooke of Norton, Worcestershire. Following Benjamin Hooke's death, the lease was held by his widow. Finally in July 1865 the freehold of The Hyde was purchased by William Freeman and Benjamin Bartram for the substantial sum of £2,400.

Latter 19th century lived in by tenant farmers

From at least 1841 until after the Second World War The Hyde was farmed by tenant farmers. In the 1841 and 1851 censuses, Francis Slade is recorded as farming The Hyde. In 1851 he was aged 37 and his wife, Sarah (née Mailes), 34. Both had been born in Woolhope and Sarah was obviously a member of the Mailes family. Francis was farming 150 acres and employing five labourers. The Slades had a young son and two daughters. There were two house servants living in as well as two male farm labourers aged 22 and 18 and surprisingly one female farm labourer.

However, the Slades must have left the farm by March 1861 as an advertisement in the *Hereford Journal* of 25 December 1860 describes The Hyde as:

a highly valuable and productive estate ... containing about 200 acres and consists of arable, pasture and hop land ... The Rent to be the same as that paid by the present Tenant or at that which, on the valuation of two proper persons, shall be fixed as a fair Rent. Possession was to be given in February 1861.

In 1861 the census shows Ann Field, a widow, as the farmer. She was only farming 108 acres, but was nevertheless employing eight men and a boy. The acreage was even lower in 1871 when the census shows Joseph Till from Totworth, Gloucestershire only farming 87 acres.

There was a disaster waiting. By October 1872 Mr Till seems to have gone bankrupt. The *Worcester Journal* of 2 November 1872 advertised the sale as "under Distress for Rent" of all Joseph Till's livestock, farm and household goods for Friday 8 November. For sale was about 100 bushels of wheat as well as "TWO RICKS OF HAY... ALSO RICKS OF PEAS, BEANS AND STRAW". With the exception of the wheat most of this was probably animal feed destined for Mr Till's livestock. Inevitably for a Herefordshire farm there were also cider casks but the numbers were not given. There is no reference to hops.

However there was a most unexpected development covered by the *Worcester Journal*, the *Worcester Chronicle* and the *Gloucestershire Journal*. The livestock "7 MILCH COWS, 5 HEIFERS IN CALF, 6 REARING CALVES and a BROWN HALF BRED MARE" had been spirited away on 24 October and the auctioneers demanded their return.

Arrival of the Thompson family

In 1888 Mr John Alfred Thompson, an estate agent, rented The Hyde. According to the 1910 valuation the owner was Mrs Clough, 7 Cambridge Park, Redland, Bristol who also owned Sapness Farm and woodlands. Mr Thompson farmed on a substantial scale. He was a hop grower and played a major part in Herefordshire life. He became an Alderman of Herefordshire Council and was also a JP. He was for some years president of the Herefordshire branch of the National Farmers' Union. In 1908 there were calls for his resignation when he refused to countenance the demonstration of hop growers which took place in London on 16 May 1908 to protest against the imports of hops.

One of John Alfred Thompson's daughters, Mildred, married Philip Davies of Claston Farm, Dormington around 1920 so there is a strong connection with this other important Hereford farm, and another of his daughters by an earlier marriage,

Joan, married Mr Powell of Hall Court, Kinnerton. John Alfred Thompson died in the 1920s and was succeeded by his son, Alfred Thompson, who played a similarly important role in both farming and social life in Herefordshire.

The Hyde in the Second World War

The Hyde was not only the largest farm in Woolhope but also the most diversified. Unusually it was still a tenanted farm. Alfred Thompson was paying £446 for renting the 362 acres. The farmhouse and buildings were in a fair state as were the fences but the ditches, drainage and farm cottages were in a good state. He was given an A grading. The owner of both The Hyde and Sapness Farm in the National Farm Survey of 1941–1943 was J. W. B. Clough Esq, presumably a descendant of the original Mrs Clough – his address was in Bristol. The annual Agricultural Census of June 1941 records Mr Thompson's farm as having a statutory 25 acres of hops. Unusually 12 acres were under soft fruit and the farm had no orchards. The acreage under arable was much higher than that for most other farms but included nine and a half acres of approved crops ploughed up in 1940 and nine acres in 1941 as part of the CWAEC war effort. There were 45 acres under cereals as well as 21 acres under beans which were intended for stock feed. The production of potatoes, critical for food supplies in the war, was labour intensive and prone to fail. Most farms limited the acreage to one or at most two acres, but Mr Thompson had seven. Equally unusual for this part of the country were five acres of sugar beet. Despite all these different crops, 230 acres, some two-thirds of all the acreage, was still grass, either for mowing or permanent.

Like all the other farms in Woolhope The Hyde had its herd of cattle. At The Hyde they were reared for beef. Of the 76 cattle, 49 were one to two years old, 22 were calves under a year and only six were cows in milk or in calf. Also like all the other farms in Woolhope described here, the farm had sheep. Of a flock of 223 sheep, 93 were breeding ewes and nearly all the rest of the flock were lambs not yet sold. The Hyde was the only farm in Woolhope which was a significant producer of pigs, with 15 sows either in pig or kept for breeding. In total there were 147 pigs on the farm. By the standards of the day The Hyde was also an exceptionally large poultry producer with 2,500 birds.

These were not normal poultry for sale to the public but farm stocks for the important breeds of the time as Alfred Thompson was an accredited poultry breeder. In an advertisement in the Herefordshire Quarterly Agricultural Journal of September 1939 A. H. Thompson could proclaim:

... for quality combined with hardiness the Woolhope strains of R.I. RED, LIGHT SUSSEX, BLACK LEGHORN and B.L. ... R.I.R. are unique. Stock Blood Tested Annually. EGGS, CHICKS, STOCK COCKERELS IN SEASON.

Unlike many of his neighbours, Mr Thompson had tractors. However to add to his other activities Mr Thompson seems to have been keen on breeding farm horses. In addition to the six working horses there were four unbroken ones. To maintain this large farm Alfred Thompson was employing 13 male and two female workers. In addition to The Hyde Alfred Thompson was also farming 106 acres of Sapness Farm land and the smallholding of Sleaves Oak.

The Hyde after the Second World War

Alfred Thompson continued to farm The Hyde until 1964. It remained a mixed farm but was also especially noted for hops and soft fruit. The major event in the parish in 1964 was the purchase by The Hyde of a hop picking machine. This naturally reduced the demand for casual labour. In the same year The Hyde came up for sale.

From 1964 until 1977, prosperous years, especially for large-scale farming, The Hyde was owned by Charles and Jemima Bristow and was farmed as part of a modern major farm consortium. Besides The Hyde, the consortium owned a number of other farms including Upton Court at Upton Bishop as well as three farms in Castle Frome. Unusually the partners were city dwellers and were not from a local Hereford farming background. During this time The Hyde continued to be a major hop producer and the area under soft fruits, which was already considerable, was expanded. Charles Bristow was a founder of Sun Valley chickens and although the birds were reared on different farms there were often 20,000 at The Hyde. The consortium normally had at least 100 pigs although these were not necessarily all at The Hyde. There was also a dairying enterprise although this was not based at The Hyde.

In contrast, from 1977–1984 The Hyde land was transformed by a new owner, Richard Green, from livestock, hops and fruit into an 'efficient' arable farm for the later 20th century. To facilitate the extensive potato production using modern machinery the fields were amalgamated which involved the ripping up of old hedgerows and trees.

In 1984 The Hyde was sold to the present owners, John and Mary Windham. The Windhams have restocked the woodland with local native trees under which are to be found a variety of rich woodland flora including, in addition to wild daffodils and bluebells, the rare Herb-Paris and Greater Butterfly-orchids. An efficient coppice rotation has been established. Under Natural England's scheme for hedgerow restoration and planting, hedgerows have been planted with the appropriate spacing left around them.

Yare Farm

Fig. WO15 Yare Farm: one of the two oldest farms in Woolhope

Yayer Farm, house, nearly 1¼ m. S.E. of the church, was built probably late in the 16th century and is of T-shaped plan with the cross-wing at the S.E. end. There is a 17th-century extension towards the N.W.[30]

Situated by a little isolated country lane this farm must surely have one of the most beautiful of locations in one of most lovely of Herefordshire parishes. It has been owned and farmed by three generations of the Sayce family for a hundred years. The old farmhouse is remarkable. Although naturally altered and enlarged periodically to meet the needs of the different generations, parts of it, including an old cider house, are thought to date back to at least the 16th century.

History of Yare Farm

Although there have been farmers here since the 16th century, records are only available from the 18th century. In 1752 Mr John Drew was paying £1 13s for the 'Yayer farm'. An advertisement of sale from 1789 shows that Yare Farm was freehold rather than the more normal copyhold and had "90 acres and upwards of arable, meadow, and pasture land, with a very fine plantation of apple and pear trees". The reference to apple and pear trees probably indicates the importance of cider especially valuable at this time. The farmhouse and buildings were said to be in a good state of repair. In 1793 Mr Harvett was shown as the occupier for Yare Farm. He was paying £2 4s in land tax. In 1797 Mr Soward, who came from Gloucestershire, was described as the owner and Mr Harvett continued to be the farmer. The land tax for 1830 shows a Mr Edwards to be the owner and Mr Thomas Hill to be the tenant. The census of 1841 shows Thomas Hill to still be the tenant living there with his four sons, John 13, Thomas 10, William 7 and Richard aged 1. There is no reference to his wife and it may well be that she had recently died. The draft to the 1843 Tithe Map lists John Edwards as owner and there is no record of the occupier. In addition to 86 acres of farmland divided into 24 different fields, the farm at that time owned five acres in Yare Wood. Cider continued to be important as no fewer than 24 acres were given up to orchards.

Fig. WO16 17th-century cider house at Yare Farm

There is no further reference to Thomas Hill. The 1851 census though shows a John Hill born in Woolhope and of the same age as Thomas's eldest son living as a farm servant in Lower Buckenhill Farm, Woolhope. This John Hill appears again in the census of 1861 for Woolhope. He is described as a farm labourer, married, and living in the attractively named Rose Cottage. His eldest son aged 3 is called Thomas, possibly after his grandfather.

The census of 1851 shows Abraham Pitt 42 to be living at Yare Farm with his wife, Elizabeth, 40, a son, George, 14, listed as an agricultural labourer and a visitor, Francis Pitt. Abraham had previously been farming in Sutton St Nicholas and his son and wife were born there. The household also contained a female servant, Harriet Roberts, and an agricultural labourer, Abraham Claridge. There was no reference to hops in the Tithe Map but in 1854 Abraham Pitt was one of the signatories to an advertisement in the *Hereford Times* welcoming a new hop market for Hereford.

Abraham Pitt died in 1861 and there is a memorial to him in Woolhope church. His son, George, seems to have been an invalid. At the time of the 1871 census he was living in the adjacent parish of Fownhope and described as a 'retired farmer' though aged only 34. He had a young son also called George aged 8. In 1871 a Mr Powell was farming 87 acres at Yare Farm. In 1881 Joseph Tovey aged 47, unmarried, was farming 100 acres with nine labourers, two of whom were living in the farmhouse. Around 1887, George Pitt, the grandson of Abraham Pitt, was the farmer. George Pitt then aged 38 was still at Yare Farm in 1901. His wife, Ann, had died in 1897 and the household this time comprised his daughter, Eleanor, aged 14 and five younger brothers, Arthur, John, Robert, James and Thomas. He also employed a housekeeper.

Kelly's Directory of 1905 shows George Rowberry as the farmer. He had previously been farming in the adjacent parish of Fownhope. According to *Kelly's Directory* George Rowberry was still at the Yare farm in 1913. At the 1910 land valuation it was farmed by George Rowberry and owned by Charles Rowberry. The census records suggest that Charles Rowberry was the brother of George and living in Fownhope. Charles appears in the 1891 census as a draper and in the 1911 census as a draper and farmer. The land acreage was given as 86 with an annual valuation of £50, or on average 12s 6d an acre, suggesting that it was not considered high quality land. However in addition there were slightly over five acres of woodland and the sporting rights were with the farm. The produce of the woods was valued at £2 10s and the sporting rights at £2 17½s so in total the wood was worth slightly more than 21 shillings per acre. George Rowberry 55 and his wife, Elizabeth, 61 appear in the 1911 census with one indoor farm worker, James Pitt aged 17. He and Elizabeth had only been married for three years. He is still listed as the farmer in *Kelly's Directory* of 1913.

In the 1917 *Kelly's Directory* William Sayce was recorded as farming at Yare Farm and the error was repeated in each edition right up to the Second World War: in fact Mr

Sayce's Christian name was James. As common in Herefordshire there were probably family links with the previous farmer as the maiden name of Charles and George Rowberry's mother, Mary Ann, was Sayce and she had been born in Fownhope.

Yare Farm in the Second World War

The National Farm Survey of 1941–1943 and the annual Agricultural Census of June 1941 show that Yare Farm was 102 acres and the farmer was James Sayce. It was a mixed farm but essentially a pastoral one with over two-thirds of the farm down to permanent grass, either for mowing or for grazing. James Sayce was awarded an A rating. The farmhouse, buildings roads and fences were in a good state of repair but the ditches and drainage were only in a fair condition. The farm had planted four and a half acres of approved crops for the CWAEC requirement for 1941 and another four and a half acres for the 1941 harvest. In consequence, in 1941 the farm had 11 acres of wheat. In addition there were four and three-quarter acres of beans. The acreage down to potatoes was the minimum normal requirement of one acre but there were also three and a half acres down to turnips, swedes and mangolds, with a further four acres of kale – all probably destined for animal feed. Unusual for Woolhope farms were the four acres of vegetables for human consumption. There were seven acres of orchard of which four were traditional orchards with grass underneath the fruit trees and three acres had soft fruit under them. There were 40 cattle of which 16 were either cows in milk or in calf. Of the remaining cattle, 19 were heifers of one to two years old, there was one cow of more than two years old and there were four calves for rearing. The farm had a flock of 75 sheep including the lambs and also had 32 pigs. Poultry was clearly a commercial enterprise with numbers high for the time at 713. The farm was run with the aid of two farm horses plus one unbroken farm horse and two full-time male workers.

Yare Farm after the Second World War

The Sayce family still retains copies of the annual farm statements required in the early post-Second World War period which give glimpses of the changing farm activities. The statement of 1947 shows the farm operating in a very similar fashion to that of 1941 and lists the names of the two carthorses: Stout aged 10 (no doubt 18 hands or so) and Bouncy aged eight. There was a herd of 35 cattle, exclusively dairy. There was a flock of sheep, much the same size as the 1941 flock with 24 ewes, 33 lambs and 17 shearlings, and 12 pigs. The number of poultry was larger than in 1941 with 850 fowls and chickens as well as a few ducks, turkeys and guinea fowls.

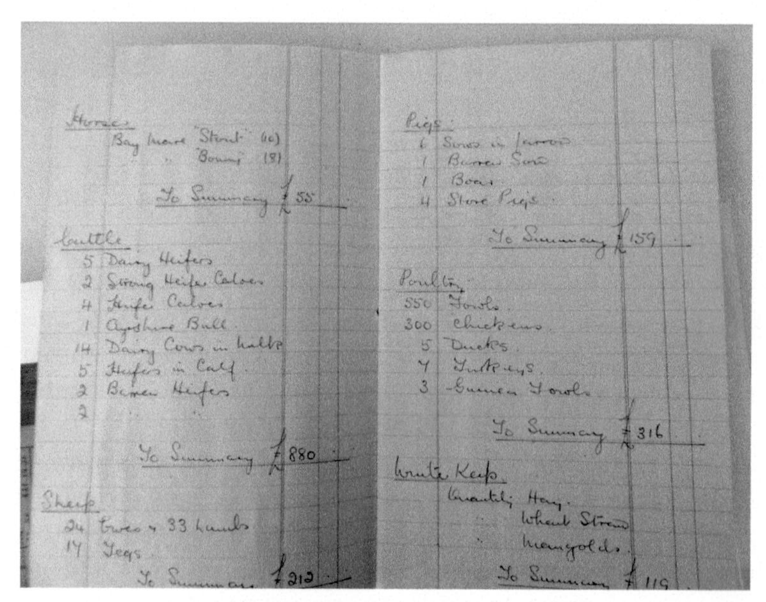
Horses
Bay Mare "Stout" (10)
" "Bonny" (18)
To Summary £55

Cattle
5 Dairy Heifers
2 Strong Heifer Calves
4 Heifer Calves
1 Ayrshire Bull
14 Dairy Cows in milk
5 Heifers in Calf
2 Barren Heifers
2 " "
To Summary £880

Sheep
24 Ewes & 33 Lambs
14 Tegs
To Summary £212

Pigs
6 Sows in farrow
1 Barren Sow
1 Boar
4 Store Pigs
To Summary £159

Poultry
550 Fowls
300 Chickens
5 Ducks
7 Turkeys
3 Guinea Fowls
To Summary £316

Winter Keep
Quantity Hay
" Wheat Straw
" Mangolds
To Summary £119

Fig. WO17 Livestock on Yare Farm in 1947 [38]

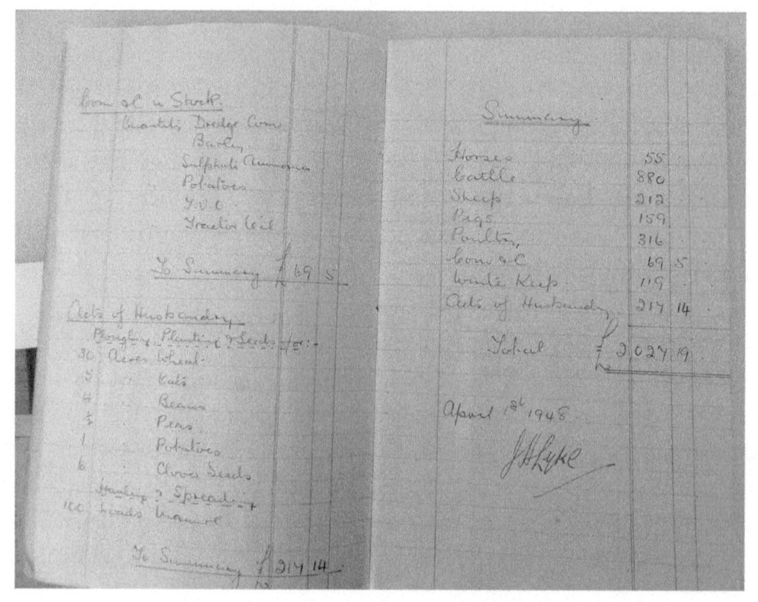
Corn etc in Stock
Quantity Dredge Corn
" Barley
" Sulphate Ammonia
" Potatoes
" T.V.O.
" Tractor Oil
To Summary £69 5

Acts of Husbandry
Ploughing, Planting & Seeds etc:-
30 Acres Wheat
5 " Oats
4 " Beans
½ " Peas
1 " Potatoes
6 " Clover Seeds
Hauling & Spreading
100 Loads Manure
To Summary £214 14

Summary

	£	s
Horses	55	
Cattle	880	
Sheep	212	
Pigs	159	
Poultry	316	
Corn etc	69	5
Winter Keep	119	
Acts of Husbandry	214	14
Total	£2,024	19

April 1st 1948

Fig. WO18 The official return for Yare Farm in 1948 [38]

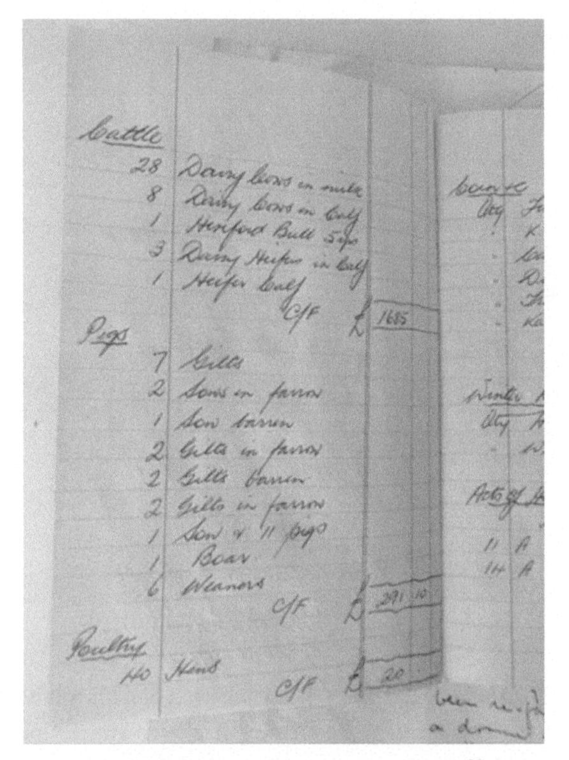

Cattle
28 Dairy Cows in milk
8 Dairy Cows in Calf
1 Hereford Bull 5yrs
3 Dairy Heifers in Calf
1 Heifer Calf
C/F £ 1685

Pigs
7 Gilts
2 Sows in farrow
1 Sow barren
2 Gilts in farrow
2 Gilts barren
2 Gilts in farrow
1 Sow & 11 pigs
1 Boar
6 Weaners
C/F £ 291 10

Poultry
40 Hens
C/F £ 20

Fig. WO19 Livestock on Yare Farm in 1962 [38]

Farm records for 1947 and 1948 show that the farm had succeeded in increasing the arable under cultivation compared with 1941, but Yare Farm remained mixed with an important milking herd as well as pigs and sheep.

James died in 1949. The Yare was then farmed jointly by James's two sons, David and Henry, their wives and, until she died in 1962, their widowed mother, Frances. By 1962 changes were under way. This was the time of the Milk Marketing Board and that reliable cheque for the milk. The size of the dairy herd had increased to 41 giving much-welcomed revenue. By this time at last Woolhope had electricity and the cows were no longer milked by hand. The much loved carthorses had gone, replaced by tractors and other machinery and, no doubt, an item for the cost of diesel. The farm still employed two farm labourers at this time, one of whom used to bicycle over from Putley.

During the latter part of the 20th century around an extra 30 acres was purchased to meet modern needs. David and Henry Sayce ceased to trade in 1989.

Fig. WO20 Yare farm cattle 2015

The farm is now run by David's son, Duncan Sayce, and his mother, Barbara. From the beginning of the 21st century the farming has been entirely pastoral. The farm concentrates on suckler calves using a pedigree Hereford bull on Friesian-Hereford cross cows. It also overwinters some 1,500 sheep from the farms in the Welsh hills. To facilitate this some land is rented from Sapness Farm, Woolhope.

Notes

[1] The National Archives, National Farm Survey of England and Wales 1941–1943: Pixley MAF 32/21/161.

[2] By kind permission of Edward Thompson.

[3] 'Pixley', in *An Inventory of the Historical Monuments in Herefordshire*, Volume 2, East (London, 1932), pp. 153–155.

[4] Robinson, Rev., Charles J. (1872). *A History of the Mansions and Manors of Herefordshire*. Longman and Co. p. 234.

[5] By kind permission of Edward Thompson.

[6] www.pixleyberries.co.uk/

[6] The National Archives, National Farm Survey of England and Wales 1941–1943: Aylton MAF 32/2/146.

[7] 'Aylton' in *An Inventory of the Historical Monuments in Herefordshire*, Volume 2, East (London, 1932), pp. 8–9.

[8] By kind permission of Penelope Cunningham.

[9] Ian and Rebecca Jones most generously provided the author with the research documentation they commissioned for their successful application for DEFRA Higher Level Stewardship funding for the remarkable early 16th-century barn, including the document *Aylton Court Farm Landscape and Historical Analysis* prepared by PJM Associates Ltd. of Much Marcle. Extensive use has been made of this documentation in the discussion of the history below.

[10] The detailed deeds of Court Farm were extensively transcribed by PJM Associates Ltd: Herefordshire Archive Service (HAS) G37/11/6.

[11] PJM Associates Ltd. *Aylton Court Farm Landscape and Historical Analysis* pp. 12–16.

[12] Herefordshire Archive Service (HAS) G 2/111/54.

[13] Herefordshire Archive Service (HAS) G 37/11/6.

[14] Herefordshire Archive Service (HAS) P 59/1.

[15] PJM Associates Ltd. *op. cit.*

[16] The National Archives, National Farm Survey of England and Wales 1941–1943: Little Marcle MAF 32/15/85.

[17] 'Little Marcle', in *An Inventory of the Historical Monuments in Herefordshire*, Volume 2, East (London, 1932), p. 127.

[18] Herefordshire Archive Service (HAS) AA 59/50/7/1.

[19] *Ledbury Guardian* 3 July 1915, researched by Jenny Harrison.

[20] Reeves, Theodora C. (November 1974). *The Powell, Stedman, Sparkman Family History*. By kind permission of David Powell. pp. 46–47.

[21] By kind permission of Anne Blandford.

[22] Tonkin, Jim. (1965). *Transactions of the Woolhope Naturalists' Field Club*, Volume XXXVIII: II. p. 162.

[23] Reeves, Theodora C. (November 1974). *op. cit.* pp. 75–78.

[24] By kind permission of Melissa Hawker.

[25] Duncumb, John. (1804). *Collections Towards the History and Antiquities of the County of Hereford*, Volume 1. E. G. Wright.

[26] Robinson, Rev., Charles J. *op. cit.* p. 198.

[27] The National Archives, National Farm Survey of England and Wales 1941–1943: Woolhope MAF 32/27/167.

[28] Hereford Cathedral Archive (HCA) 3883/25.

[29] By kind permission of Susan Davies and Lillian Moss.

[30] 'Woolhope' in An Inventory of the Historical Monuments in Herefordshire, Volume 2, East (London, 1932), pp. 220–223.

[31] Hereford Cathedral Archive (HCA) 3886/2–14.

[32] Hereford Cathedral Archive (HCA) 3494.

[33] By kind permission of Alison Wilcox (née Pudge).

[34] Hereford Cathedral Archive (HCA) 5065/2.

[35] Hereford Cathedral Archive (HCA) 5065 (1728 correspondence: 5065/2; 1768 correspondence: 5065/3; 1776 correspondence: 5065/4).

[36] By kind permission of John and Mary Windham.

[37] Hereford Cathedral Archive (HCA) 3777.

[38] By kind permission of Barbara Sayce.

EPILOGUE: THE WAY FORWARD

The farms as well as the farming families of East Herefordshire have withstood so much. What is their future? Are they like other aspects of modern life 'an endangered species' destined for extinction with just a few very large agribusiness farms remaining or are there brighter, more varied prospects? It is true that quite a number of farms have succumbed to the radically different world of the late 20th and early 21st century but a number still exist and a few, like Stone House Farm in Withington, Walsopthorne Farm in Ashperton, and Overbury Farm and Yare Farm in Woolhope, with acreages which have changed little since the beginning of the 18th century.

The farms and the families have absorbed remarkable changes. The 18th century with its appalling communications, its simple tools and oxen for ploughing, was indeed a very different world. In contrast the mid-19th-century farmers of the early railway but post-Corn Law era would have had little difficulty in recognising their East Herefordshire farms a century later at the start of the Second World War. The farmers were still the important members of the community generating the majority of rural income and providing most of rural employment. The farm horses and those dedicated farmworkers without which the farms could not have functioned were there. The acreage and the fields were probably much the same. Farming activities would have improved, but would have not been greatly altered. The farms would still have been mixed although with much less arable. That 'modern' threshing machine of which the 19th-century farmer had been so proud was not much changed a century later. The bigger farms would have instituted improvements in the hop yards but the hops were still dried in hop kilns and picked by hand. On most farms cider was still made for the farmworkers and, quite probably, crushed on the same stone as in the 19th century. The pedigree Hereford cattle would have looked in good fettle, the result of continued improved breeding in the latter half of the 19th century when the farmers were already showing their Herefords at Agricultural and Ploughing Societies. Milking would still have been done by hand as almost all the farms had no electricity. Mid-19th-century farmers would have been surprised that many of the farms were owned rather than tenanted, but would have sympathised with the struggle the owners were having in paying their mortgages.

What a contrast though if mid-19th-century farmers had moved on 60 years to the early decades of the 21st century and the machine age. They would have been surprised that the farm buildings had been replaced by new constructions capable of housing those huge machines. They would have difficulty in comprehending that the simple farm cottages which used to house their labourers were now transformed into expensive dwellings owned by prosperous inhabitants with no contact with farming but with apparently considerable influence over local affairs. They would have been astonished to discover that some of the largest and most prestigious farms of East Herefordshire which had such an important role in the community in their time, and indeed for centuries before then – Yarkhill Court, Dormington Court, Aylton Court and Court Farm in Aylton, Brook Farm and Little Marcle Court in Little Marcle – are now no longer farmhouses. They would have been similarly surprised at the demise of some of the small yeoman farms, such as Bent Orchards, Hazel Court, Weston Corner Farm and Lower House Farm, which were farmed by families they would have respected and known. They would have been profoundly shocked at the near absence of hop yards but heartened to know there had been some revival in the growing of hops.

In contrast to the bitterness their parents had felt at the abolition of the Corn Laws in 1846, they would no doubt have been delighted that for over 70 years the government 'had come to its senses' and supported farming. They would have had considerable difficulty though in understanding the complexities of this assistance apparently decided by a club of European countries containing the UK and 27 others called the European Commission or EC. They might well have asked why the majority of the assistance in 2018 was a payment simply dependent on hectarage, a European measurement for land used instead of acreage. Would this not then go mainly to the largest landowners in the country? They might have been surprised when told than at EC negotiations it was the UK plus one other country that insisted that there should be no upward limitation on such payments. If they had attended the Big Apple celebrations at Putley and Much Marcle parishes they would have been taken aback to be told that the Herefordshire orchards producing artisanal cider so appreciated by consumers received no per hectarage payment at all. Why the discrimination against the smaller farmer?

The nature of the 'cross compliance regulations' that farmers have to follow to obtain support would have totally baffled them. They would also not have understood the regulation requiring each animal to be tagged immediately after birth. They never liked paperwork anyway and the requirement to put all information on something called the Internet (apparently a modern type of telegraph) would have been beyond them.

They could not but have noticed a change in the landscape – many fewer hedges and often larger fields. They would have been told there were fewer birds, flowers and fauna. (They had not appreciated some species of birds and had, indeed, employed the young children of farmworkers to keep them off the crops.) There were no poppies in wheat fields and there seemed to be fewer primroses, wild daffodils, and cowslips. There were many fewer stoats and weasels. They would have been surprised that part of the government assistance was intended for 'environmental purposes' to encourage the reversal of this situation.

They would have been told that East Herefordshire agricultural land had for some years been priced so high that it was near impossible for farmers to purchase land for their sons or their daughters. It was being bought not by the local landowners but by companies, both British and foreign, as well as by town dwellers for taxation and investment purposes. They would have been puzzled as to the reasons why the government, despite their avowed support of agriculture, appeared content with this.

They would have found that the main topic of conversation was something called Brexit. The UK was intending to leave the alliance of 28 countries called the EU. It will result in a total change in the British government support for agriculture which was at present a compromise agreed by the different European member states. The government would be 'free' to give whatever support it wanted to farmers.

This, they would be told, could create a make or break situation for farming in East Herefordshire as elsewhere in the United Kingdom. Some East Herefordshire farmers were worried they would not be able to employ farmworkers from Eastern Europe who at present provided the main labour force for their soft fruit cultivation and harvests. European countries provide important markets for many agricultural products, including blackcurrant juice. These markets are especially important for the livestock industry with many of each season's lambs exported to France and other European countries, duty-free and without restrictions. All this might change with the EU and other countries imposing a tax on British produce or limiting it. They would have been told about possible future trade deals with the US as well as the Commonwealth (as the former Empire was now called). These might help some British industries but such countries had large farming sectors who would surely expect easier access to the British market.

Forecasts of the future usually turn out to be wrong. It is to be hoped that, as so often in the past, problems eventually are overcome and the East Herefordshire families continue for yet more generations to occupy the farms and cultivate the land in this most beautiful of counties.

Selected Bibliography

Books

Bick, David (1994). *The Hereford and Gloucester Canal.* The Oakwood Press.

Box, Sidney. (1950). *The Good Old Days: Then and Now.* Reliance Printing Works Halesowen, Worcs.

Cooke, W. H. (1882). *Collections Towards the History and Antiquities of the County of Hereford. In Continuation of Duncumb's History.* Volume 3. John Murray.

Cooper, Janet. (2013). *The Victoria History of Herefordshire: Eastnor.* Institute of Historical Research.

Cordle, Celia. (2011). *Out of the Hay and into the Hops.* University of Hertfordshire Press.

Currie, Jean Ila. (2009). *Three Centuries of a Herefordshire Village.* Owlstone Press.

Davies, Peter. (2007). *A Herefordshire Tale: Claston, Hops and the Davies Family.* Peter Davies.

Defoe, D. (1927). *A Tour Through England and Wales,* Volume 2. J. M. Dent & Sons Ltd.

Duckham, Thomas. (1858). *Eyton's Herd Book of Hereford Cattle,* Volume 3. Hereford: William Phillips.

Duncumb, John. (1804). *Collections Towards the History and Antiquities of the County of Hereford,* Volume 1. E. G. Wright.

Duncumb, John. (1812). *Collections Towards the History and Antiquities of the County of Hereford,* Volume 2 Part 1. E. G. Wright.

Duncumb, John. (1813). *General Review of the Agriculture of the County of Herefordshire.* London: printed for Sherwood, Neely and Jones.

Eyton, T. C. (1846) *The Herd Book of Hereford Cattle,* Volume 1. Longman and Co.

Eyton, T. C. (1853) *The Herd Book of Hereford Cattle,* Volume 2. Longman and Co.

Fiennes, Celia. (1947). *The Journeys of Celia Fiennes.* Ed. Morris, Christopher. The Cresset Press.

Finnegan, Oliver & Glover, Catherine (Eds.). (2014). *British Farm Surveys, 1941 to 1943: Reports and Statistical Analysis.* List and Index Society.

Garrard, George. (1800). *A Description of the Different Varieties of Oxen, Common in the British Isles.* London: J. Smeeton.

Garrard, T. W. (1898). *Transactions of the Herefordshire Agricultural Society 1797–1809.* Herefordshire Agricultural Society. Herefordshire Archive Service (HAR) AF 57/14/12.

Gayer, A. D., Rostow, W. W., Schwartz, A. J. (1953). *The Growth and Fluctuation of the British Economy, 1790–1850*, Volume 1. Oxford.

Grundy, J., Paske, H., Walker, P. (2007). *A Pocketful of Hops*. Bromyard & District Local History Society.

Hancock, W. K. & Gowing, M. M. (Eds.). (1949). *British War Economy*. H. M. Stationery Office.

Heath-Agnew, E. (1983). *A History of Hereford Cattle and Their Breeders*. Duckworth.

Herefordshire Federation of Women's Institutes (1989). *The Herefordshire Village Book*. Countryside Books.

Herefordshire Federation of Women's Institutes (1993). *Herefordshire Within Living Memory*. Countryside Books.

Hillaby, Joe. (2003). *St Katherine's Hospital, Ledbury c.1230–1540*. Logaston Press.

Hillaby, Joe & Hillaby, Caroline. (2013). *The Palgrave Dictionary of Medieval Anglo-Jewish History*. Palgrave Macmillan.

Holderness, B. A. (1985) *British Agriculture Since 1945*. Manchester University Press.

Kain, Roger J. P. & Oliver, Richard R. (1995). *The Tithe Maps of England and Wales*. Cambridge University Press.

Kelly's Directories of Herefordshire (1858–1941). Kelly's Directories Ltd.

Laws, Bill. (2016). *Herefordshire's Home Front in the First World War*. Logaston Press.

Macdonald, James, & Sinclair, James. (1909). *History of Hereford Cattle*. London: Vinton & Company Ltd.

Marshall, William. (1796). *The Rural Economy of Gloucestershire; Including its Dairy: Together with the Dairy Management of North Wiltshire; and the Management of Orchards and Fruit Liquor, in Herefordshire*, Volume II. London: Printed for G. Nicol, etc.

Martin, J. F. (2000). *The Development of Modern Agriculture: British Farming Since 1931*. Palgrave Macmillan.

Morris, John. (Ed.). (1985). *Domesday Book: Herefordshire*. Philiimore & Co. Ltd.

Murray, K. A. H. (1955). *Agriculture (History of the Second World War Series)*. HMSO and Longmans, Green & Co.

Orwin, Christabel S, & Whetham, Edith H. (1964) *History of British Agriculture 1846–1914*. Longman.

Perry, P. J. (1974). *British Farming in the Great Depression 1870–1914*. David & Charles.

Philips, John. (2001) *Cyder: A Poem in Two Books*. Eds. Goodridge, John & Pellicer, J. C. The Cyder Press.

Prosser, Doris M. (August 1991). *Times of Change*. Doris Prosser.

Robinson, Rev., Charles J. (1872). *A History of the Mansions and Manors of Herefordshire.* Longman and Co.

Short, Brian. (2014). *The Battle of the Fields.* Boydell Press.

Simpson, Helen J. (1997). *The Day the Trains Came.* Gracewing.

Skidelsky, Robert. (2014). *Britain Since 1900 – A Success Story?* Vintage.

The Duke of Montrose. (1952). *My Ditty Box.* Jonathan Cape.

Trumpet and District Agricultural Society. (2007). *In the Wake of the Plough.* Trumpet and District Agricultural Society.

Watkins, Rev., Morgan G. (1902). *Collections Towards the History and Antiquities of the County of Hereford. In Continuation of Duncumb's History: Hundred of Radlow.* Hereford: Jakeman & Carver.

Whetham, Edith H. (1952) *British Farming 1939–1949.* Thomas Nelson.

Whetham, Edith H. (1978) *The Agrarian History of England and Wales 1914–1939,* Volume VIII. Cambridge University Press.

White, Paul & Ray, Keith, Ed. (2011). *The Frome Valley Herefordshire: Archaeology, Landscape Change and Conservation.* Herefordshire Archaeology.

Wilt, Alan F. (2001) *Food for War: Agriculture and Rearmament in Britain before the Second World War.* Oxford University Press.

Woods, Abigail. (2013). *A Manufactured Plague: The History of Foot-and-Mouth Disease in Britain.* Routledge.

Articles and pamphlets

Barnes, Christopher. (2007). *Pure Nostalgia.* Christopher Barnes.

Bolton, Paul & Baker, Carl. (January 2016). *Agriculture: Historical Statistics.* House of Commons Briefing paper SN03339.

Bowers J. K. (1985). *British Agricultural Policy Since the Second World War.* Agricultural History Review.

Department for Environment, Food and Rural Affairs. (1989–2017). *Agriculture in the United Kingdom.* Annual Reports 1988–2017. DEFRA.

Empson, John. *The History of the Milk Marketing Board, 1933–1994.* International Journal of Dairy Technology Volume 51.

Grundy, Joan E. (2002). *The Hereford bull: his contribution to New World and domestic beef supplies.* Agricultural History Review.

Jones, E. L. (1961). Agricultural Conditions and Changes in Herefordshire 1660–1815 *Transactions of the Woolhope Naturalists' Field Club,* Volume XXXVII: I. pp. 32–55.

O'Donnell, Jean. (9 February 2010). *Hereford's Markets, Past, Present and Future.* Herefordshire & Wye Valley Life.

Parker, W. K. (1979). Wheat Supplies and Prices in Herefordshire 1793–1815. *Transactions of the Woolhope Naturalists' Field Club*, Volume XLIII: I. pp. 44–53.

Report from the Select Committee on Hop Duties; Together with the Proceedings of the Committee, Minutes of Evidence and Appendix. (1857). The House of Commons.

Return of acres of hops grown in each parish, 1829–1835, quantity grown and duty paid (1839). Parliamentary papers, Volume XLVI. p. 519.

"The Hop Industry." *Times* [London, England] 18 May 1908: 8. The Times Digital Archive. Web. 7 Oct. 2017.

The Parliamentary Gazetteer of England and Wales. (1843). London: A. Fullarton and Co.

Tonkin, Jim. (1965). *Transactions of the Woolhope Naturalists' Field Club*, Volume XXXVIII: II. p. 162.

Whiteman, Anne & Clapinson, Mary (Eds.). (1986). *The Compton Census of 1676: A Critical Edition.* British Academy.

Documents

Cherry, Iain Gordon, Cherry, Gordon & Rogers, A. W. (1996). *Rural Change and Planning: England and Wales in the Twentieth Century.* Taylor & Francis.

Hereford Cathedral Archive (HCA)

Farm records from Tarrington, Withington and Woolhope as footnoted.

Herefordshire Archive Service (HAS)

Correspondence, sales catologues, farm documents, wills and inventories as footnoted.

Hill, Berkeley. (2000). *Farm Incomes, Wealth and Agricultural Policy.* Routledge.

National Farmers' Union Herefordshire Branch Annual Reports (North and South Herefordshire reports 1909–1916; Amalgamated branches 1917–1919 BA 49 180–189).

PJM Associates Ltd. *Aylton Court Farm Landscape and Historical Analysis.*

Reeves, Theodora C. (1972). *History of Little Marcle and Preston Parishes.* Gloucestershire Archives B146/36709G.

Reeves, Theodora C. (November 1974). *The Powell, Stedman, Sparkman Family History.* By kind permission of David Powell.

Royal Commission on the Historical Monuments of England. (1932). *An Inventory of the Historical Monuments in Herefordshire*, Volume 2, East. London.
The farmers and millers guide at the markets, etc. 1853. The *Hereford Journal.*

The National Archives

National Farm Survey of England and Wales 1941–1943: Aylton MAF32/2/146; Ashperton MAF 32/1/145; Dormington 32/7/124; Felton MAF32/9/19; Little Marcle MAF 32/15/85; Lugwardine 32/16/112; Pixley MAF 32/21/161; Stoke Edith MAF 32/23/121; Tarrington MAF32/24/166; Weston Beggard MAF 32/26/128; Withington MAF 32/27/129; Woolhope MAF 32/27/167; Yarkhill MAF32/27/168.
Herefordshire War Agricultural Committee (WAEC) documents: Herefordshire Reconstitution WAEC MAAF 39/346; MAF 80/1058 Minutes Farm Survey Subcommittee; MAF 80 /1059 Minutes Farm Survey Subcommittee; MAF 80/1085 Herefordshire Machinery Subcommittee.
Herefordshire Parish Summaries 1877 MAF 68/528.

Websites

National

www.ancestry.co.uk
www.bbc.co.uk/history/british/
www.britishnewspaperarchive.co.uk
www.nationalarchives.gov.uk
www.theguardian.com
www.thetimes.co.uk/archive
www.ukcensusonline.com
www.visionofbritain.org.uk

Local

www.bigapple.org.uk/
www.british-history.ac.uk/rchme/heref/vol2
www.canwoodgallery.com/
www.herefordcathedral.org/library-and-archives
www.herefordcattle.org
www.herefordshire.gov.uk/archives
www.herefordshire.gov.uk/downloads/file/11924/draft_neighbourhood_development_plan_july_2017

www.herefordshirehistory.org.uk/archive/herefordshire-images/herefordshire-railways/the-building-of-the-hereford-and-worcester-railway
www.jusapples.co.uk
www.pixleyberries.co.uk
www.thehopshires.co.uk/index.php/hop-growing-in-the-hopshires/
www.trumpetanddistrictagriculturalsociety.co.uk
www.yarkhillfieldtofork.co.uk

General Index

A

Agricultural Act 1920 60

Agricultural Act 1937 65

Agricultural Act 1947 74, 78

Agricultural Census June 1941 64, 68, 69, 70, 129, 149, 154, 214, 217, 223, 232, 244, 256, 263, 267, 289, 306, 314, 318, 325, 331, 339, 350, 355, 362, 368, 373

Agricultural Marketing Act 1931 64

Agricultural Marketing Act 1933 64

Aldersend Farm 234, 241, 252

Anthrax 290

Association for the Protection of Agriculture 37

Ast Wood 120, 294, 314, 316, 333, 335

Awnells Farm 64, 108, 109

Aylton Court 6, 11, 13, 32, 69, 70, 73, 80, 90, 93, 106, 107, 180, 294, 295, 296, 297, 298, 299, 323, 327, 380

B

Baregains Farm 11, 109, 127, 132, 134, 310, 311, 312, 313, 314

Bartestree 81, 211, 212, 213, 214, 234, 235

Beans Butts 71, 106, 110, 231, 270, 276, 297, 339, 340, 342

Bent Orchards 72, 80, 93, 94, 105, 128, 339, 343, 344, 345, 347

Big Apple 97, 140, 301, 380

Bishop of Hereford land 3, 5, 6, 312

Board of Agriculture 21, 56

Bovine Spongiform Encephalopathy (BSE) 88, 90

Brook Farm 309, 310, 314, 315, 316, 317, 318, 319, 321, 330, 331, 333

Bulmers cider 52, 61, 97

Butter Market 40, 222, 359

C

Canwood Farm 2, 72, 85, 93, 137, 339, 347, 348, 350, 351, 352

Claston Farm 5, 13, 50, 52, 59, 65, 70, 73, 80, 81, 83, 85, 86, 90, 101, 106, 110, 132, 134, 156, 213, 228, 229, 230, 231, 232, 236, 237, 238, 241

Corn Laws 27, 28, 36, 37, 96, 286, 380
Corn Production Acts (Repeal) 1921 60
County Council Agricultural Executive Committee 67
County War Agricultural Executive Committee (CWAEC) 56, 57, 67, 68, 71, 103, 149, 160, 233, 368
Court Farm Aylton 6, 11, 13, 26, 93, 282, 294, 295, 296, 300, 301, 302, 303, 304, 305, 306, 307, 308
Court Farm Woolhope 56, 106, 352, 353, 354, 355, 356
Cross Keys Inn 34, 116
Crown and Anchor 116
Crown Inn 116

D

Dean and Chapter of Hereford Cathedral land 2, 144, 162, 338, 348, 349, 354
Dormington Court 5, 24, 32, 36, 52, 57, 59, 83, 87, 90, 103, 111, 113, 119, 138, 189, 204, 228, 229, 234, 235, 236, 237, 238, 239, 240, 241, 380

E

Eastnor estate sale 1916 58, 289, 318, 321, 324, 331
Eastwood Farm 67, 69, 70, 71, 74, 81, 93, 104, 107, 166, 213, 214, 234, 246, 249, 253, 254, 256, 257, 258, 259
Egg Marketing Board 78
Enclosure Act of 1798 186
English Hop Growers Association 62

F

Farmers' Aid Women's Society 57
Felton Court 7, 32, 33, 43, 83, 96, 104, 128, 129, 134, 139, 147, 163, 168, 169, 170, 171, 172, 173, 174, 175, 217
Field to Fork Festival 203, 208
Foley sale 1919/1920 59, 181, 182, 189, 195, 229, 247
Foot-and-mouth epidemics 61, 80, 94, 201, 334, 347
Freetown 5, 43, 51, 59, 63, 71, 79, 80, 97, 104, 110, 189, 190, 244, 252, 263, 264, 265, 266, 267, 268
Frome River 9, 35, 44, 227

G

Garford Farm 5, 43, 50, 51, 57, 59, 71, 95, 104, 138, 187, 188, 189, 190, 191, 195, 203, 204, 207, 239, 252, 265, 266
Gloucester to Hereford canal 35, 144, 262
Green Farm 7, 168, 170

H

Hall Court 108, 109, 137, 273, 317, 368
Hawkbrand Hops 292
Hazel Court 3, 64, 70, 80, 128, 253, 255, 257, 258, 259, 260, 380
Herd Book of Hereford Cattle 32
Hereford Cathedral Dean and Chapter 3, 53
Hereford Cattle Society 99, 104
Hereford Farmers Club 33, 36
Hereford Herd Book Society 63, 88
Herefordshire Agricultural Society 22, 27, 33, 37, 118, 147, 153
Herefordshire Agricultural Workers' Union 53
Herefordshire Domesday Book (HDB) 294, 302
Hop Marketing Board 63, 64, 78, 81, 208, 290, 291
Hynett Farm 70, 80, 96, 107, 127, 128, 129, 134, 137, 159, 160, 214, 215, 216, 217, 218

K

Knapp Farm 282, 285, 288, 289

L

Laddin Farm 5, 13, 58, 71, 72, 108, 130, 132, 310, 318, 319, 320, 321, 324, 331
Ledbury Agricultural Society 33, 34, 135, 140
Lillands 5, 58, 59, 81, 87, 90, 97, 105, 106, 127, 129, 310, 321, 322, 323, 324, 325, 326, 327, 330
Little Malvern Priory 280, 284 294
Little Marcle Court 5, 33, 42, 43, 51, 58, 59, 62, 71, 90, 127, 131, 132, 134, 310, 314, 317, 319, 321, 323, 324, 328, 329, 330, 331, 332, 380
Little Tarrington Farm 252, 253, 267
Livestock Market 44
Local Government Acts 1888, 1894 135, 154

Local Government Board orders 1884, 1885 244
Longworth Manor 213
Lower House Farm 71, 80, 89, 107, 109, 120, 129, 140, 310, 314, 326, 332, 333, 334, 380
Lugg Meadows 212, 221, 223
Lugg River 9, 158

M
Mainstone Court 281, 282, 299
Milk Marketing Board 64, 78, 80, 89, 224, 347, 359
Monksbury Court 82, 83, 169, 187, 194, 261
Moorend Farm 5, 30, 51, 55, 59, 64, 70, 80, 82, 83, 106, 128, 178, 179, 181, 182, 183, 184, 221, 222, 231, 289, 297

N
National Farm Survey of 1941–1943 64, 68, 70, 149, 183, 190, 198, 200, 207, 228, 232, 240, 244, 252, 256, 262, 267, 277, 282, 289, 298, 308, 314, 318, 321, 325, 331, 334, 339, 345, 350, 355, 362, 373
New Court 3, 7, 163, 168, 170, 213

O
Old Court 3, 70, 80, 90, 128, 135, 137, 213, 214, 219, 220, 221, 223, 224, 225
Overbury Farm 72, 80, 105, 110, 356, 357, 358, 359, 379

P
Park Farm 2, 59, 72, 80, 89, 106, 107, 339, 355, 360, 361, 362, 363
Parliamentary Enclosure Act 1798 25
Perton Court 5, 59, 63, 67, 70, 74, 79, 86, 90, 104, 166, 244, 245, 246, 247, 248, 249, 250, 256, 297, 349
Pixley Berries 292
Pixley Court 30, 32, 33, 52, 58, 59, 62, 64, 71, 73, 78, 87, 98, 105, 106, 107, 121, 122, 131, 134, 139, 156, 180, 203, 282, 283, 284, 285, 286, 287, 288, 289, 290, 291, 292, 294, 297, 299
Pomona Farm 62, 234, 236, 241
Potato Marketing Board 78
Pridewood 262
Priors Court 103, 228, 230, 235, 240, 284, 285, 288, 293, 294, 295

Progressive Verticillium Wilt (PVW) 86, 208, 234
Public Money Drainage Act 1846 40

R
Railway Crewe–Hereford–Newport 39, 130, 131
Railway Hereford–Worcester–Birmingham 40, 131
Reform Acts 1832, 1867, 1884 135
Rosemaund Farm 168, 174
Royal Agricultural Society of England (RASE) 32, 52, 62, 79, 194, 232, 247, 248, 266, 268

S
St Guthlac's Priory 7, 144, 167, 228
St Katherine's Hospital 3, 178, 198, 200, 310
Showle Court 5, 15, 17, 32, 43, 49, 52, 59, 70, 72, 89, 104, 107, 110, 114, 131, 136, 138, 153, 158, 186, 187, 189, 192, 193, 194, 195, 196, 197, 244, 266, 361
Stone House Farm 2, 27, 32, 33, 42, 43, 55, 58, 71, 81, 104, 105, 109, 111, 114, 118, 119, 127, 130, 144, 145, 146, 148, 149, 153, 239, 379

T
Tarrington Arms (formerly Foley Arms) 116, 251
The Grove Farm 3, 30, 70, 71, 94, 189, 198, 199, 200, 201, 202
The Hyde 69, 109, 232, 363, 364, 365, 366, 367, 368, 369
Three Counties Show 138, 140, 356
Thinghill Court 7, 17, 22, 27, 32, 33, 36, 42, 43, 52, 61, 69, 71, 83, 84, 87, 89, 98, 101, 105, 111, 118, 130, 135, 144, 148, 151, 152, 153, 154, 155, 156, 164, 165, 194, 203, 208, 239, 266, 292
Thinghill Grange 152, 153, 154
Tipsgrove 281, 282
Trumpet and District Agricultural Society 139, 140, 218
Trumpet Inn 116, 281, 286
Tuston Farm 262
Tyrell's Frith 310, 313

W
Walsopthorne Farm 6, 7, 11, 17, 18, 30, 42, 43, 51, 59, 71, 87, 101, 106, 110, 262, 264, 269, 270, 271, 274, 276, 278, 281, 297, 342, 379

Weston Corner Farm 3, 70, 90, 107, 130, 134, 145, 156, 157, 158, 159, 380
Westons cider 52, 61, 97, 335
Wheat Act 1932 65
Withington Court 3, 7, 50, 52, 71, 74, 104, 114, 126, 129, 144, 153, 161, 162, 163, 164, 165, 166, 168, 170, 249
Withington Ploughing Society 33, 34, 135, 147
Women's Land Army 58, 73
Woolhope Naturalists' Field Club 24
Wye River 9, 227

Y

Yare Farm 2, 26, 69, 80, 82, 105, 110, 134, 339, 370, 371, 372, 373, 374, 375, 376, 379
Yarkhill Court 5, 18, 59, 61, 69, 93, 107, 111, 114, 118, 135, 138, 187, 188, 189, 190, 194, 202, 203, 204, 205, 206, 207, 208, 239, 380

Names Index (selected)

A
Albert HRH Prince Consort 42, 147
Apperley family (Stone House Farm) 147
Apperley James (1828–1901) 147, 148
Apperley John Havard Apperley (1723–1812) 27, 118, 147
Apperley William (d. 1726) 130, 147
Apperley William (1684–1766) 147
Apperley William Havard (d. 1851) 33, 43, 118, 148
Apperley James and Rebecca (Canwood Farm) 350
Atwood Caroline 230, 231
Atwood James 220
Atwood William 230

B
Badham John (b. 1829) 247, 297
Badham John (d. 1864) and Sarah 247
Badham William and Hannah 349
Ball John 64, 308
Ballard William 40, 148, 195
Barnes Bill 197
Barnes Caleb 220
Barnes Christopher 196
Barnes Mr (of Putley) 158
Barnes Robert 196
Barnes Tom 70, 196
Barrett family 329, 331, 332
Baylis George (d. 1777) 285
Baylis George (d. 1818) 285
Baylis John 33, 285
Bayliss Charles Reginald 182
Bayliss Clement 55, 178, 182
Bayliss Eliza Jane 55, 128, 182, 183
Bayliss Harry 184
Bayliss Keith and Marie 178

Bayliss Reg 64, 82, 83, 184
Bayliss Reginald (d. 1915) 55, 182
Bendall William 358
Biggs William 344
Bird John 195, 196
Bishop Jonathan (Freetown) 265
Bishop John (Aylton Court and Court Farm Aylton) 296, 305
Blades family 297
Blandford Anthony 201
Blandford Godfrey and Pat 321
Blandford Tim and Ann 321
Blonder Tania 160
Bodenham family 5, 188, 202, 329, 330
Bodenham Sir Roger 188, 203
Bosley family 313
Bosley Benjamin 313
Bosley John 313
Bosley Thomas 83, 120, 129, 333
Bowcott Leslie 83, 169
Bowcott Thomas (18th century) (Felton) 104, 173
Bowcott Thomas (1847–1910) 104
Bowcott Thomas (1879–1947) and Annette (Felton Court) 104, 163, 173, 174, 217
Bowcott Thomas Ernest (1909–1975) (Felton Court) 104, 169, 174
Box Sidney 53
Bradstock Margaret 264
Bradstock Mrs P. E. 57
Bradstock Percy 43, 57, 61, 63, 71, 79, 138, 189, 252, 265, 268
Bradstock Richard 104, 264, 268
Bradstock Thomas 43
Bradstock Tom 79, 137, 138, 268
Bradstock Tony 104, 268
Bray G. H. 57, 103, 138, 240
Bray Mrs G.H. 57
Brewer Mrs 89, 89, 334
Bristow Charles and Jemima 369
Broome family 163

Burden family 213
Butcher George 215

C
Chase William 96, 319
Clarke Mark and Elizabeth 163
Clay Tom and Harvey 192, 193
Coates Robert (18th century) 238
Cocks family 4, 5, 6 (see also Somers)
Cocks Charles (later Baron Somers) (1725–1826) 4, 5, 315
Cole James and Eliza 357
Colley Edward 334
Colley Mathew Edward 334
Cooke George and Ann 135, 221
Cooke Percy 90, 221
Cornewall Catherine (née Hanbury) 310
Cornewall General 71
Cornewall Velters 5, 310, 330
Court W. J. 200
Cowell John 321
Criketot family 271
Croft Noel 62
Croft Sir Herbert 213
Cryer Betty, Mabel and Mollie 105, 343, 345, 346
Cryer Tom 105, 345

D
Dale Ellis and Olive 351
Dale Helen 347
Dale Robert 351
Dale Stephen 137, 347, 351
Dallimore John 121, 122, 316, 333
Dallimore John (son) 333
Davies Barnaby (d. 1829) (Coldmore Farm) 106
Davies David (Bent Orchards) 105
Davies Edward (Walsopthorne Farm) 100, 106, 270

Davies Eliza (née Shale) 106
Davies Frederick Pope 298, 299
Davies Harvey (Walsopthorne Farm) 270
Davies Herbert (Walsopthorne Farm) 106, 276, 277
Davies John (d. 1849) (Pixley Court) 32, 121, 122, 286
Davies John and Susan (Bent Orchards) 105, 347
Davies John Charles (d. 1932) 103, 289
Davies Joseph and Elizabeth (Withington Court) 129, 163
Davies Mildred (d. 1984) (Claston Farm) 65, 232, 367
Davies Pam (d. 2017) (Claston Farm) 107
Davies Peter (d. 2017) (Claston Farm) 13, 65, 81, 86, 87, 90, 107, 229, 232, 233, 234, 235, 236, 241
Davies Peter and Phyllis (Court Farm Aylton) 73, 298, 299
Davies Philip (d. 1977) (Claston Farm) 65, 229, 232, 233, 234, 235, 236
Davies Philip (d. 1988) (Claston Farm) 229, 235, 236
Davies Raymond (Aylton Court) 298
Davies Raymond (Bent Orchards) 345, 346, 347
Davies Thomas Edward 62, 289, 342
Davies Thomas (Claston Farm) 106, 132, 132, 229, 231, 289, 297, 342
Davies Walter Thomas 231, 342
Davies William Henry (1860–1943) (Hillend Farm and Claston Farm) 50, 51, 106, 229, 232
Davies William (b. 2016) (Walsopthorne Farm) 278
Davies Winifred 67
Davison Angus 98
Day family 208
De Broye family (medieval) 294, 302
Deem family (late 17th century) 146
Defoe Daniel 10, 13
Dent Dean 79, 104
Dent H. C. 67, 71, 74, 104, 213, 248, 166
Dent H. J. 59, 63, 74, 79, 104, 247, 166
Dent John and Elizabeth 74, 104, 162, 165
Dent Oscar William Robert 74, 249
Dobbs George and Sarah 333
Dobbs Joseph 320
Dobbs Samuel and Elizabeth 130, 132, 150, 320

Dobbs Thomas and Hannah 320
Drew John (d. 1741) 15, 16, 17, 18, 28, 314, 315, 370
Drew John (d. 1728) 314, 315
Drew William and Lydia 6, 315
Duncumb John 21, 22, 23, 24, 25, 35, 144, 162, 163, 167

E
Edwards John 371
Edwards Richard and Clare 104, 170, 175
Edwards Robert and Joy 104, 169, 174
Elliot Joseph 164
Evans Mr BSc 67
Evans William and Clara 173
Eyton Mr 32, 42

F
Farley family 126, 127, 331
Farley Roger 6, 7, 11, 17, 271, 272
Farmer William 129, 164, 165
Field William 126
Fiennes Celia 1, 8
Foley family 4, 6, 8, 25, 40, 41, 43, 177, 256, 243, 348, 349
Foley Edward (18th century) 25, 349
Foley Edward (d. 1844) 36, 118, 121, 349
Foley Lady Emily (d. 1900) 40, 41, 113, 122–125, 133, 135, 255, 265, 348
Foley Paul (d. 1698) 5, 8, 9
Foley Paul (d. 1928) 59, 60, 138, 265
Foley Thomas 5

G
Garrard George 26
George William 172
Gibbs family 215
Gibbs Geoffrey and Donna 218
Glossop Francis 153
Glossop Francis H. Newland 153

Glossop Rev. 154
Godiva Lady 2, 338
Godsall Anthony (Monksbury Court) 194
Godsall Anthony (Park Farm) 107, 361
Godsall Charles Harold (Moor Court Stretton Grandison) 107, 159
Godsall Elizabeth (18th century) 254, 255, 256
Godsall Elizabeth (b. 1846?) (Eastwood Farm) 254, 255, 259
Godsall Ernest (Eastwood Farm) 254
Godsall James (1780–1835) (Weston Corner Farm) 158
Godsall John (d. 1886) (Weston Corner Farm) 107, 130, 134, 150, 158
Godsall John (d. 1912) (Weston Corner Farm) 107, 134, 159, 216
Godsall Joseph (Weston Corner Farm) 160
Godsall Thomas (1779–1855) (Eastwood Farm) 254, 255
Godsall Thomas William (1827–1873) (Eastwood Farm) 254, 255
Godsall Walter (d. 1705) 15, 17, 18, 107, 114, 193
Godsall William (Underhill Farm) 107, 159
Goode Matthew 32, 33, 43, 134, 147, 171, 172
Green Richard 369
Gregory family 348, 353
Gregory Mr (18th century) 8, 353
Gregory William 348, 364
Griffiths H. R. 79, 252
Griffiths T. (d. 1799) 7, 163, 168, 170
Griffiths William 252

H
Hall George 50, 188, 189
Hall Henry Scott 52, 239, 240
Hall John (b. 1750) 188
Hall John (b. 1777) 188
Hammond family 6
Hammond John 323
Hammond Thomas 295
Hanbury Thomas and William 5, 330
Hankins family (16th–18th centuries) 6, 303, 304, 305
Hankins John and Elizabeth 305

Harley family 303
Harrison J. 318
Harrison J. T. 93, 203, 318, 319
Hart Alfred and Annie 344
Hartland John 323
Harvett Mr 370
Hatton Brian 53, 212
Hawkins James 152, 155
Hawkins John 155
Hawkins Paul 105, 156
Hawkins Sandra 155
Hawkins Sheila 152, 155
Hawkins Stuart 83, 152, 155
Hawkins Thomas 71, 105, 152, 154, 155
Hess H. Daniel 162, 165
Hewer John 32
Hewer William 32
Hill Thomas 371
Hill Thomas (of Blaenavon) 163, 168
Holder William 342
Holland Thomas 33, 330
Homes William 344
Hooke Benjamin 366
Hooper family 340
Hooper Anne 341
Hooper James 341
Hooper Richard 341
Hopton family 3, 256, 262
Hopton Rev. John 43

I
Innes Frederick and Ann 275

J
Jeffcock Captain W. P. 321, 324, 331
Jenkins Miss O. 67

Jones Ian and Rebecca 301, 307, 308
Jones Mr (18th century) (Old Court) 219

L
Leake J. M. 149, 150
Leake Rachel 105, 127, 146, 151
Legeyt John and Elizabeth 163
Leigh Michael and Gilla 202, 208
Lewes Horace 350
Lewis Edward 103
Lilly John 7, 163, 168, 170
Lingen family 4
Lingen Sir Henry 4
Lloyd John 317

M
Mailes family 365
Mailes John MD 365
Mailes Peter 365
Mailes Richard 357
Mailes Richard and William (18th century) 365
Mailes William (19th century) 357, 365
Marshall William 9, 12, 13, 15, 16, 17
Mason C. 36
Mason John 33
Mason John and Mary 306
Meredith Owen 70, 249
Miles William 296
Milner Lord 56
Moore family (Thinghill Court) 7, 152
Moore Harry (Shucknall Court) 103
Morris Annette 129
Morris Marie 128, 172
Morris Mary 129
Morris Stephen 128, 172
Myers family 163

N
Nellist Ann 137, 139, 218
Nellist Tom 139, 218
Newton Thomas 230
Nutt William and Abigail 159, 323

O
Oliver Robert and Penny 332, 335

P
Parker James and Helen 187, 191
Parker Trevor 191
Philipps family (Walsopthorne Farm and Putley Court) 6
Philipps Hugh 6, 7, 271, 272
Philips family (Withington Court) 162
Philips John (author of Cyder) 1, 11, 162
Philips Robert (d. 1760) 162
Philips Stephen (d. 1754) 42, 162
Phillipps John (Hynett Farm) 216
Pitt Abraham, Elizabeth and George 134, 372
Pitt John 265
Pitt Stephen 43, 264, 273, 274
Pitt Thomas 71, 264, 265
Pitt William and Emma 274
Pope Daniel 131, 134, 288
Powell Alice (d. 1908) (née Sparkman) 317
Powell David (Awnells Farm) 108, 317
Powell Henry (d. 1770s) (Laddin Farm) 320
Powell James John Stedman (Hall Court) 109
Powell Joan (Hall Court) 109, 137
Powell John (d. 1758) (Laddin Farm) 320
Powell John (d. 1908) 109, 317
Powell John and William (Hynett Farm) 216
Powell Richard (late 17th–early 18th centuries) (Laddin Farm) 320
Powell Rupert 64, 109
Powell Thomas and son John (late 18th century) (Much Marcle) 114, 115

Poyner John 79
Preece John and Charlotte 220
Price Editha 127, 128, 216, 160
Price Jack and Hilda (Hynett Farm) 137, 217, 218
Price Reuben (Hynett Farm) 160, 169, 216
Price Thomas (Overbury Farm) 358
Pritchard Elizabeth 179
Pritchard James Morris 30, 178, 179
Pritchard Mr (18th century) (Canwood Farm) 349
Pritchard William (18th century) (Old Court) 220
Prosser Doris 128, 219, 221, 222, 223, 224
Prosser William 342
Prothero David 103
Pudge Geoffrey 356
Pudge Mike and Elaine 354, 356

R
Racster William 33, 36, 71, 118, 150, 153, 164
Ravenhill family 3, 258, 281, 361
Ravenhill Thomas (d. 1748) 258
Reed family 213
Riley John 52, 61, 259
Roberts Mr 307
Roberts Richard and Mary 361
Rogers family 339
Rowberry George 372
Rudge Charles 334
Russell family (Aylton Court) 307

S
Samuel Marion and Desmond 311
Saville C. 67
Sayce family 105, 379
Sayce David and Henry 375
Sayce Duncan and Barbara 376
Sayce James (also known as William) 372, 373

Shale Jane and James 296, 306
Shaw Henry 307
Sirrell Jonathan 246
Sirrell Samuel (1738–1786) 264
Sirrell Thomas 34, 264
Skey Captain 307
Skinner family (17th and early 18th centuries) (Pixley) 282, 285
Skittery David 327
Skittery Graham 322
Skittery James 105, 322, 327
Skittery Jane 97, 127, 322, 327
Skittery Michael 105, 322, 327
Skittery Lesley 322, 327
Skittery W. M. (called Martin) 64, 325
Skittery William Mathias 105, 323
Skittery William Ward 105, 322, 324
Smith Albert (The Grove Farm) 189, 200
Smith Ann (The Grove Farm) 128, 199, 200
Smith John (The Grove Farm) 199
Smith John (Thinghill Court) 105, 135, 152, 153, 154
Smith Thomas (The Grove Farm) 199, 200
Somers 1st Earl (1760–1841) 4, 120, 121
Somers 2nd Earl (1788–1852) 36
Somers 3rd Earl (1819–1883) 42, 43, 133
South Charles 323, 324
Sparkman Ann 134
Sparkman John 43, 134, 316, 330
Stedman Harry 190
Stedman Harry Shelley 190
Stedman Harry T. 205, 206
Stedman Raymond 206
Stephens Albert 53, 313
Stephens William and Mary 53, 313

T

Taylor H. W. 52, 104, 189, 194, 266

Taylor John (1835–1866) (Claston Farm) 231
Taylor William (Showle Court) 32, 43, 49, 130, 131, 153, 194, 266
Taylor William (Thinghill Court) 266
Thomas Derek 236, 237
Thomas William 28, 316
Thompson A. H. 364
Thompson Alfred 368
Thompson Denys 291
Thompson Edward (d. 1942) 64, 284, 289, 290
Thompson Edward 98, 105, 283, 290
Thompson J. A. 367
Till Joseph 367
Tombe Thomas 248
Tomkins Benjamin (1745–1815) 153
Tremayn B. 93, 308
Tristam J. 314
Turner William 361

V
Vevers John (1750–1835) 194, 204
Vevers John (1811–1877) 118, 204, 205
Vevers John Edward (1851–1906) 205
Vevers Margaret (née Godsall) 204
Vevers Thomas 239
Vevers William (1782–1858) 32, 33, 36, 119, 239
Victoria HM the Queen 43, 147

W
Walker Mr and Mrs 80, 89
Wallwyn Shepheard (1750s) 238
Wallwyn Shepheard (1790s) 5, 238
Walwyn family 213, 219, 244, 302, 303
Walwyn Edward 114, 115
Warnecombe family (16th century) 6, 303
Watkins Benjamin 362
Watkins Dansey 57, 106, 355

Watkins David (Court Farm Woolhope) 355
Watkins David (Park Farm) 93
Watkins David and Jean 362, 364
Watkins Graham 106, 360, 362
Watkins Gwilliam 106, 361
Watkins John 106, 355
Welsh John and Mary 350
Weynan Jones Jack 103
White Thomas 296
White Thomas 32, 296
Williams Andrew and Tracey (Overbury Farm) 359
Williams Dennis, Gwyneth and Mark (Hazel Court) 128, 259, 260
Williams family (The Grove Farm) 168, 198, 201, 202
Williams family (Overbury Farm) 105
Williams Norman (Overbury Farm) 259
Williams Percy (Overbury Farm) 357
Williams Glyn and Richard (Claston land) 236
Williams Henry (Court Farm Woolhope) 51, 152, 354
Williams James, Ann and family (Court Farm Woolhope) 354
Williams Jonathan and Mary Ann (Court Farm Aylton) 307
Williams Henry Williams (Thinghill Court) 22, 27, 118, 152, 153
Williams Reginald (Baregains Farm) 314
Williams Sidney Archer (Hazel Court) 64, 259
Windham John and Mary 364
Winniatt family 343, 344, 354
Wooding Richard and Ann 344
Woodyatt George 333
Wulviva Lady 2, 338

Y

Yapp Arthur Aaron 297
Yeomans family 149
Yeomans Haywood (1892–1917) 55, 148
Yeomans Honor 1,48, 149
Yeomans Jane 148, 149
Yeomans John (d. 1812?) 43, 153

Yeomans John (d. 1920) 43, 55, 148, 149
Yeomans Rebecca 55, 148
Yeomans Walter (1897–1917) 148, 149